Mass Spectrometry for Lipidomics

Methods and Applications

Edited by Michal Holčapek and Kim Ekroos

Volume 1

AF753045

WILEY-VCH

Editors

Dr. Michal Holčapek
University of Pardubice
Faculty of Chemical Technology
Studentská 573
53210 Pardubice
Czech Republic

Dr. Kim Ekroos
Lipidomics Consulting Ltd.
Irisviksvägen 31D
02230 Espoo
Finland

Cover Design: Wiley
Cover Images: © Kateryna Kon/Shutterstock; Courtesy of Michaela Chocholoušková

All books published by **WILEY-VCH** are carefully produced. Nevertheless, authors, editors, and publisher do not warrant the information contained in these books, including this book, to be free of errors. Readers are advised to keep in mind that statements, data, illustrations, procedural details or other items may inadvertently be inaccurate.

Library of Congress Card No.: applied for

British Library Cataloguing-in-Publication Data
A catalogue record for this book is available from the British Library.

Bibliographic information published by the Deutsche Nationalbibliothek
The Deutsche Nationalbibliothek lists this publication in the Deutsche Nationalbibliografie; detailed bibliographic data are available on the Internet at <http://dnb.d-nb.de>.

© 2023 Wiley-VCH GmbH, Boschstraße 12, 69469 Weinheim, Germany

All rights reserved (including those of translation into other languages). No part of this book may be reproduced in any form – by photoprinting, microfilm, or any other means – nor transmitted or translated into a machine language without written permission from the publishers. Registered names, trademarks, etc. used in this book, even when not specifically marked as such, are not to be considered unprotected by law.

Print ISBN: 978-3-527-35221-0
ePDF ISBN: 978-3-527-83649-9
ePub ISBN: 978-3-527-83650-5
oBook ISBN: 978-3-527-83651-2

Typesetting Straive, Chennai, India

Contents

Preface

The field of lipidomics has undergone an enormous growth in recent years, which can be illustrated by the number of published articles and other bibliometric parameters. This highlights the renewed interest in lipids, now driven by the enthusiasm to explore the world of lipidomes and how these, among others, impact health and disease. The excitement is enormous, prompting many newcomers to enter the field. However, training and education in lipidomics are still scarce or even lacking. A successful lipidomics study requires appropriate expertise in all aspects of the lipidomic workflow, covering experimental design, sample preparation, analytical measurement using mass spectrometry techniques, data processing, and finally correct reporting of lipidomic results. The large discrepancy in know-how and lipidomics assessments causes confusion in the field that is also mirrored in the literature. Recently, the International Lipidomics Society was established to fill this gap and to unite researchers around the world interested in all aspects of lipidomics research and collectively start creating urgently needed textbook chapters in lipidomics. This situation prompted us to start working on this book project, where we have assembled the content covering three sections: analytical methodologies in lipidomics, lipidomic analysis according to lipid categories and classes, and finally lipidomic applications. We invited leading experts for particular topics, and, after more than a year of tedious work, we are proud to present the result.

We believe that this book can serve as a valuable tool and resource for anyone interested in lipidomics, from beginners to field leaders, because everyone should be able to find something new in these 27 chapters. The methodological section describes the most common methods used in lipidomic analysis, such as the preanalytical phase, sample preparation, shotgun mass spectrometry, coupling with chromatography, mass spectrometry imaging, ion mobility, advanced tools for structural characterization, approaches for the right identification and quantitation, and finally bioinformatics, software, and databases. The second section is prepared from a different view, targeting selected lipid categories and classes and then sorting convenient methods for their analysis. We believe that this point of view is important for researchers looking for the best method for their lipids of interest. Finally, we present an application section to illustrate a wide range of lipidomics, which covers, for example, clinical diagnostics, biobanking, nutritional aspects, plant science, fluxomics, multiomics, cell biology, microbial lipidomics, and research on serious diseases, such as cancer, Alzheimer's disease, and aging. We hope that these chapters provide an interesting inspiration for new possible applications of lipidomics.

We greatly appreciate the great effort and the extensive time invested by all authors in the preparation of their chapters. Last but not least, we appreciate the support of the publisher in compiling this up-to-date book on lipidomic analysis. We hope that you enjoy reading and that the book will be an everyday companion rather than a dust-covered item on the bookshelf.

Michal Holčapek and Kim Ekroos
Pardubice and Esbo
31 July 2022

1

Introduction to Lipidomics

Harald C. Köfeler[1], *Kim Ekroos*[2], *and Michal Holčapek*[3]

[1] *Medical University Graz, Center for Medical Research, Stiftingtalstrasse 24, 8010, Graz, Austria*
[2] *Lipidomics Consulting, Esbo, Finland*
[3] *University of Pardubice, Faculty of Chemical Technology, Department of Analytical Chemistry, Pardubice, Czech Republic*

1.1 Preface

We are entering a new era in lipidomic analysis. Technology advances in conjunction with community-wide collaboration efforts have prompted new ways to investigate the world of lipids. These developments have revoked interest in lipids, creating new opportunities to study lipids in different biological and biomedical settings in the hope of improving health and disease. Today, technologies allow us to dive deep into the lipid content and dissect the lipid makeup in detail, providing quantitative numbers of hundreds of lipid molecules. Lipid measurements no longer circle just around cholesterol in the context of LDL or HDL, but now the typical target is to determine the comprehensive lipidome of these particles. The new previously unseen lipid details spark curiosity and interest in reactivating research on cellular membranes, signaling cascades, and metabolic networks, among others, to shed new insights into the dysfunctions underlying a disease or a disorder. The objectives are clear. Can lipid details untangle disease biology, provide improved predictive or diagnostic biomarkers, and deliver new therapeutic strategies? However, opportunities extend further beyond, as a detailed lipid fingerprint can be envisioned, serving as a health status map of individuals. Our unique lipid code, which all of us possess, becomes a tool for precision health and medicine, which we are only beginning to explore.

The study of lipids using lipidomics can be rephrased as mass spectrometry (MS)-based lipid analysis. Until now, the field has been living its Wild West era where everything has been allowed. Although this has provided significant development, the downside is that it has resulted in inaccurate and irreproducible research results, preventing science from moving forward. With the establishment of the International Lipidomics Society (ILS), we have taken an active role in further maturing,

Mass Spectrometry for Lipidomics: Methods and Applications, First Edition.
Edited by Michal Holčapek and Kim Ekroos.
© 2023 WILEY-VCH GmbH. Published 2023 by WILEY-VCH GmbH.

harmonizing, and developing the lipidomics field to meet the current and future needs. By connecting the worldwide lipid community and focusing on transparent communication and collaboration, we aim to identify the common language for the entire discipline. Simply, the focus is to guide, educate, collaborate, and provide services to the academic and medical communities, industries, and the public in lipidomics. We have established several interest groups (see https://lipidomicssociety.org/working-groups) with different focuses to accelerate various angles of the field. A central program is briefly described here with the focus on the standardization of lipidomics, where we are preparing a new reporting checklist for any future lipidomics study. This is a true game changer that is needed to unlock the full potential of lipidomics. Now, we can meet the regulatory requirements for use in clinical research and diagnostics and enhance the comparability of data and understanding of the functional roles of specific lipid species. A new order in lipidomics has begun.

1.2 Historical Perspective

Although the determination of individual lipids by MS goes back to the 1970s (e.g. prostaglandins by GC/MS), the term lipidomics was introduced in 2003 by Xianlin Han and Richard Gross, defined as the system-level analysis of lipid species' abundance, biological activities, subcellular localization, and tissue distribution [1]. Lipidomics became possible by the introduction of new technologies in MS, particularly electrospray ionization (ESI), matrix-assisted laser desorption/ionization (MALDI), and Orbitrap instrumentation, resulting in a broader scope of analysis with increased sensitivity and selectivity. Fueled by these technical prerequisites and the concomitant increased biological usability of lipid data, a growing number of scientific groups have joined the field. In parallel, it soon became clear that the fast growing lipidomics field would need some sort of guidance for standards. In the early new millennium, LIPID MAPS was funded by NIH as a huge "glue grant" that included multiple labs in the United States. The most important achievement of the LIPID MAPS consortium was a comprehensive classification scheme of lipids into eight categories subdivided into dozens of lipid classes and subclasses [2, 3]. Based on this classification scheme, the LIPID MAPS Structure Database (LMSD) became the most important and comprehensive international lipid database containing 46 843 lipid structures as of December 2021, 24 815 of them experimentally proven and curated, and 22 028 of them generated *in silico* [4]. In parallel, a large-scale European grant LipidomicNET was awarded by the European Union and started to develop annotation rules for lipids detected by MS [5]. These rules culminated in the slogan: "Only annotate what is experimentally proven." According to this motto, a shorthand nomenclature for lipids was designed, where it is possible to simply infer the degree of annotation certainty by the nomenclature level used. In 2020, the shorthand notation for lipidomic data got a major overhaul, and now, e.g. also includes oxidized lipids and sphingolipids beyond ceramides and sphingomyelins [3]. The whole shorthand nomenclature project was performed according to the lipid categories developed by LIPID MAPS [2]. In the direct legacy of the shorthand nomenclature project, the Lipidomics Standards Initiative (LSI) was established in 2018 by Gerhard Liebisch and Kim Ekroos together with an informal group of lipidomics scientists who care for the development of standards in lipidomics (Figure 1.1). In 2019, the LSI led to the foundation of the ILS, in which the LSI constitutes one of the most important interest groups. Besides LSI, ILS hosts seven additional interest groups (applied bioinformatics, clinical lipidomics, global networking, instrumental and methodology development, lipid function, lipid ontology, reference materials, and biological reference ranges) and coordinates their activities. Some of the aforementioned interest groups and their activities will serve as a structure template for this chapter. Other community-wide standardization endeavors of the past decade worth mentioning are ring trials. Between 2014 and 2017, a ring trial organized by John A. Bowden at the National Institute of Standards and Technology (NIST) occurred [6]. The aim of this ring trial was limited to an interlaboratory lipidomics precision comparison on NIST Standard Reference Material (SRM)-1950, a reference plasma collected by NIST, because the true quantitative values of lipids in this biological material were unknown, and thus, it was impossible to determine the accuracy of the experimentally determined values. Furthermore, several community-wide position papers recently clearly defined the necessity and demand for standardization in lipidomics, including further steps to be taken toward achieving this goal [7–9].

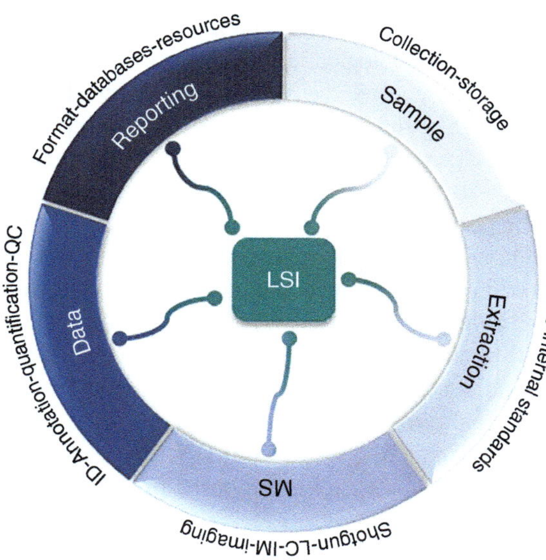

Figure 1.1 The Lipidomics Standards Initiative (LSI) and its various fields of action within the lipidomics workflow, ranging from sample collection to data analysis.

1.3 Sampling and Preanalytics

"*Without a community-wide consensus on best practices for the prevention of lipid degradation and transformations through sample collection and analysis, it is difficult to assess the quality of lipidomics data and hence trust results*" [10]. Keeping this quote in mind, monitoring and documentation of the sampling step in the lipidomics workflow are of utmost importance because whatever is lost at sampling cannot be regained even by the most sophisticated analysis methods. Because of its importance in the workflow for lipidomics analysis, the LSI dedicates a separate chapter on this topic in its lipidomics guidelines (manuscript in preparation). Although stability is not as critical as when, e.g. handling RNA, there are nevertheless two big stability issues to be specifically considered when working with lipids: hydrolysis and oxidation [10, 11]. While hydrolysis affects esterified fatty acids, lipid peroxidation can occur at the methylene groups spacing two adjacent double bonds, e.g. C11 in linoleic acid. Both mechanisms may result in extensive fragmentation, truncation, and modification of lipids [12]. In contrast to lipid peroxidation, which is, in the context of sample stability, primarily a nonenzymatic chemical reaction, the threat of lipid hydrolysis also arises from enzymatic reactions catalyzed by lipases in the sample matrix. Thus, the most important measure to be taken against sample degradation is a short storage time and keeping the samples at as low temperatures as possible if storage of samples is needed. Sample workup immediately after collection is recommended because this would at least eliminate any enzymatic degradation, or, if this is not possible, the addition of methanol before freezing, to precipitate enzymes, and therefore minimize biological degradation processes. When already extracted samples are stored in organic solvents, a neutral pH avoids the hydrolysis of fatty acids, and the coverage of the extracts by an inert gas, such as nitrogen or argon, aids in preventing lipid peroxidation. Nevertheless, it is highly recommended to store samples at least at −80 °C for not too long periods. All listed recommendations and issues have to be particularly emphasized when working with lipids such as oxidized phospholipids or lysophospholipids, which are inherent degradation products of other lipids and occur only in small amounts. In such a case, only the slightest degradation could already immensely distort the results. Finally, above all, the most important point stipulated in the lipidomics guidelines is the proper documentation of preanalytics in a comprehensive way, which then even allows retrospectively evaluating the quality of the final data. In summary, the lipidomics community represented by LSI and ILS is well aware of the above-mentioned points, and recommendation guidelines for standardization of preanalytics are close to publishing.

1.4 Reference Materials and Biological Reference Ranges

The first concerted approach toward the determination of reference ranges in biological samples was undertaken by the LIPID MAPS consortium in 2010. In two consecutive publications, they quantitatively determined the lipidome of human plasma [13] and mouse macrophages [14] in great detail. From a technical perspective, it is worth mentioning that these were the first harmonized interlaboratory approaches in which each contributing laboratory was responsible for one lipid category; for example, glycerolipids were determined in Denver (Murphy group), sphingolipids in Atlanta (Merrill group), fatty acids in San Diego (Dennis group), etc. Thus, the studies were organized as a multisite trial and resulted in the first broad high-quality lipidomic analysis of both biological matrices. The second concerted approach in this field was performed by John A. Bowden from NIST in 2017, but this time, it was designed to be a ring trial using, as the LIPID MAPS trial described above, again NIST SRM-1950, a standardized NIH plasma pool, with 31 international laboratories contributing to this endeavor (Figure 1.2) [6]. As the true values for the 339 lipids analyzed were not known, it was just possible to determine the consensus values for each lipid, including the interlaboratory precision. Furthermore, not every laboratory determined each lipid species but rather contributed whatever was in its quantitative lipidomics portfolio by this time. Figure 1.3 shows the consensus values and the interlaboratory spread of the lipid classes analyzed. The graph clearly shows that certain lipid classes, such as free fatty acids (FFAs) or oxylipins, are analyzed by a handful of laboratories, while others, such as the membrane lipid class phosphatidylcholine (PC), are analyzed by almost every laboratory. Although the spread of quantitative numbers is considerable, most of the mean quantities correlated quite well with the LIPID MAPS study on the same reference material and thus could be considered close to the real values of individual lipids. However, the issue of "real value" in biological reference materials remains untouched in its core and could only be solved by future inclusion of complementary analysis methods with quantitative properties better than ESI, e.g. NMR. The second important point when talking about reference materials are lipid

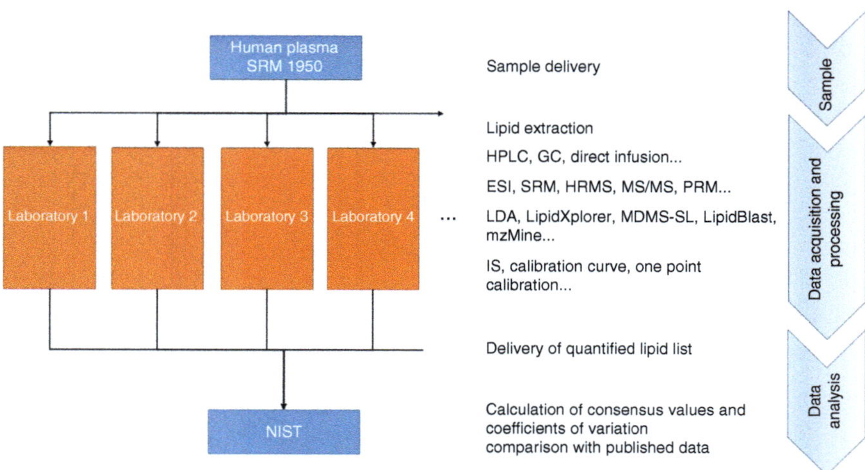

Figure 1.2 HRMS, High Resolution Mass Spectrometry; PRM, Parallel Reaction Monitoring; LDA, Lipid Data Analyzer; MDMS-SL, Multi-Dimensional Mass Spectrometry-based-Shotgun Lipidomics; IS, Internal Standard.

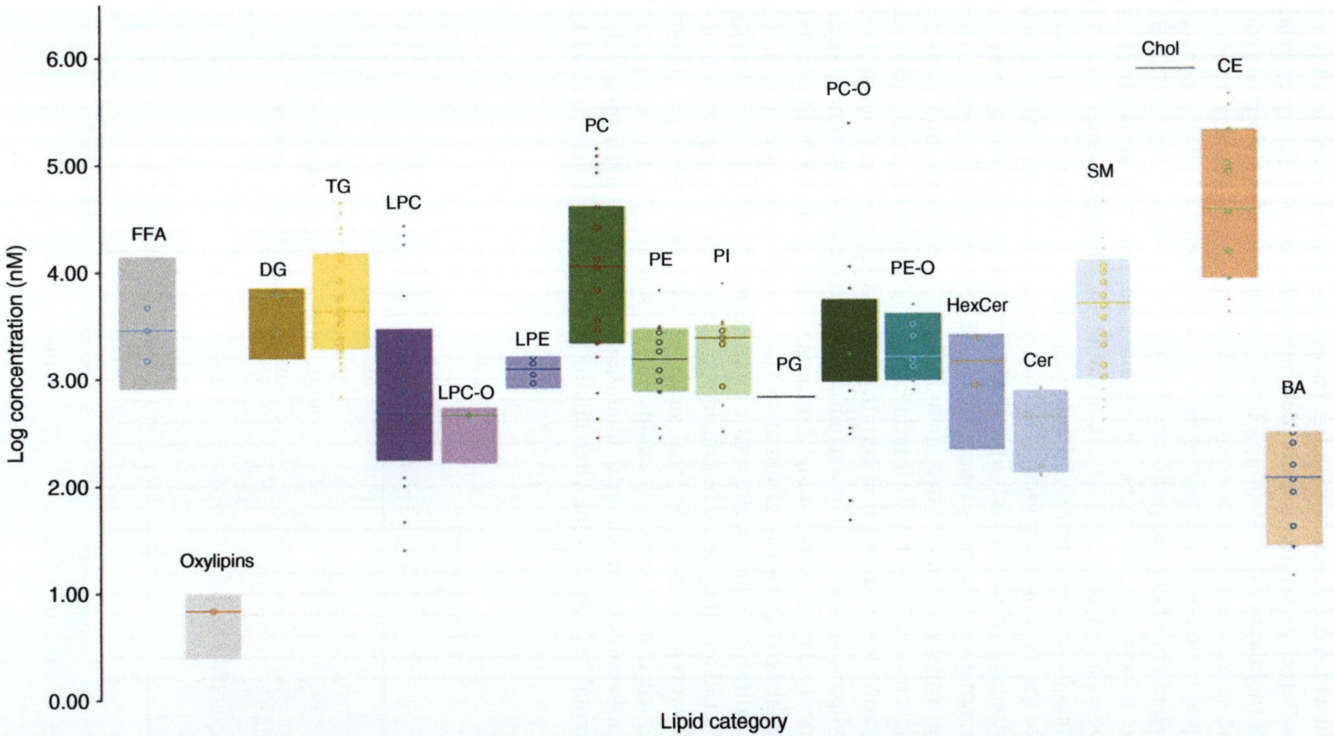

Figure 1.3 Consensus values for individual lipid classes as calculated from the lipidomics ring trial initiated by John A. Bowden (NIST, Gaithersburg, MD, USA). As not every participating laboratory performed the same panel of analysis, not every lipid class has the same number of data points. DG, diacylglycerol; TG, triacylglycerol; LPC, lysophosphatidylethanol; PE, phosphatidylethanol; PI, phosphatidylinositol; PG, phosphatidylglycerol; SM, sphingomyelin; BA, bile acid; CE, cholesterylester.

standard compounds, whether nonlabeled reference standards or stable isotope-labeled internal standards [9]. In this regard, the interest group reference materials and biological reference ranges are the central coordination hub for lipid synthesis companies and also academic groups working on novel concepts for the biotechnological bulk generation of total isotope-labeled lipidomes.

1.5 Clinical Lipidomics

Clinical lipidomics aims at the application of lipidomics to clinical diagnostics. Based on the harmonization study initiated by Bowden et al. [6], a position paper organized by the Wenk group in Singapore together with 16 additional internationally recognized lipidomics laboratories wrapped up the state of the art in the field of lipidomics with regard to clinical applications [7]. The article also lists the most crucial prerequisites that must be met by lipidomics analysis to make an impact in clinical diagnostics. Among these, the most important are reproducibility, accuracy, and precision. While reproducibility and precision are easy to get under control, as long as sufficient resources are invested into quality assurance, accuracy is a factor that still poses a problem in handling. In real-life samples, such as human plasma, the quantity of each individual lipid cannot be known a priori, and thus, it is per definition impossible to calculate the accuracy. This shortcoming is circumvented by taking the consensus values from the Bowden et al. study for NIST SRM-1950 and assuming that the concordant values from 31 laboratories are close to the "true" values [6]. Furthermore, this publication lists the full workflow of lipidomics from preanalytics to data analysis, discussing all relevant steps and a number of key issues for each step of the workflow. The next topic on the agenda of this group of principal investors was an international ring trial that monitored ceramide concentrations in human plasma, performed in 2019 (manuscript in preparation). In this case, the organizers, according to an already published methodology, predetermined the LC/MS methodology. This was in contrast to the previous study conducted by John Bowden, where each laboratory was free to choose its method [6]. Based on these pieces of preliminary work, the Interest Group Clinical Lipidomics led by Michal Holčapek picked up the topic and is currently underway in organizing a lipidomics ring trial that includes 30 academic groups and corporate laboratories, distributed all over the globe. Regarding the methodology, this round robin will neither be completely open like the Bowden et al. study [6], nor will it be restricted to just one predetermined method. It will rather give a choice from four internationally established lipidomics workflows, i.e. lipid class separation, lipid species separation, and shotgun approaches either with low or high resolving power MS. The workflows by themselves try to keep a balance between parameters strictly demanded by the protocol, parameters just recommended, and parameters open to choose freely. In summary, the organizers anticipate that this clinical lipidomics ring trial on SRM-1950 will give a good idea where the lipidomics field stands regarding the clinical application of this methodology.

1.6 Identification and Annotation

The identification of lipids by MS and their subsequent correct annotation are what could be called the core business of lipidomics. The most important issue with respect to the identification of lipids by MS and their further annotation is that the annotation nomenclature used always must reflect the identification status of the individual lipid. During the EU FP7 large-scale grant LipidomicNET (2008–2012), it became evident that the various analytical laboratories involved in this endeavor do use different styles of annotating the same molecular compound, which in turn was detrimental to database generation, where each compound needs one unique ID. The root of this issue is the fact that the overwhelming majority of lipid identification generated by MS never reaches the level at which each molecular detail of a compound, including double-bond positions and double-bond stereochemistry, is known and where the nomenclature designed by the LIPID MAPS consortium could be applied. Although this level of detail could basically be obtained by MS and aligned technologies such as chromatography, the degree of analytical effort required can hardly be justified in an omics setting, where hundreds of lipids need to be identified in each sample. Kim Ekroos already proposed a hierarchy of lipid annotation back in 2011 [15]. Figure 1.4 shows the scheme based on this hierarchy jointly proposed by LipidomicNET and the LIPID MAPS consortium in accordance with the International Lipid Classification and Nomenclature Committee (ILCNC) in 2013 and updated in 2020. The leading figure in this endeavor has been Gerhard Liebisch from Regensburg. This hierarchy correlates the level of structure details

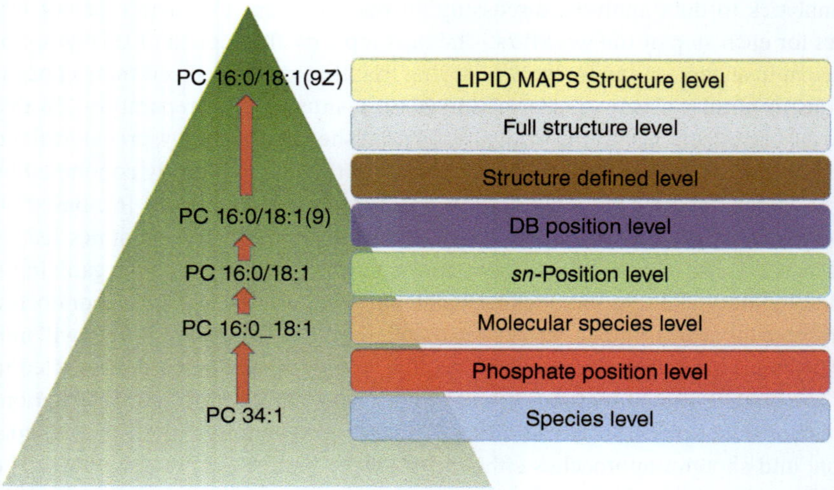

Figure 1.4 The hierarchical lipid shorthand nomenclature pyramid depicted for a phosphatidyl choline species on the left side of the figure integrates with the various levels of this nomenclature on the right-hand side. This example shows that not all annotation levels are applicable for every lipid. In this case, the phosphate position level, structure-defined level, and full structure level are skipped because the lipid does neither have an inositol phosphate group nor any other additional functional group in the fatty acyls.

elucidated by mass spectrometric/chromatographic/ion mobility spectrometric analysis with certain annotation requirements. Because of the high degree of isomerism that inherently arises in many lipid classes because of the variations in fatty acyl composition, each annotation in the nomenclature hierarchy reflects a subset of isomeric lipids, unless the fully defined LIPID MAPS structure level is used. In this case and only in this case, it is possible to pinpoint one unique lipid structure in the LMSD, while the molecular species level in Figure 1.4 leaves the *sn*-positions of the corresponding fatty acyls, their double-bond location, and the double-bond configuration unresolved. Furthermore, each level of depth of structural identification is closely related to certain analytical techniques. While it may be sufficient for annotation at the species level to involve just reversed-phase liquid chromatography and a low-resolution precursor ion scan on the phospholipid head group, further levels of the pyramid will require MS/MS spectra, high mass resolution, and additional advanced techniques such as OzID, chiral chromatography, or ion mobility spectrometry. At the end of the day, it will always come down to a tradeoff between the available resources (manpower, instrument quality, etc.) and the minimum structural depth needed for answering a certain scientific question.

1.7 Quantitation

When identification issues are resolved, the immediately subsequent question usually is about the quantity of individual lipid species or, in some cases, whole lipid classes. Again, the quantitative aspects depend heavily on the scientific questions to be answered. Although in some cases it might be good enough to state that a knockout mouse model accumulates some lipids roughly by a factor of 10, in other cases such as clinical diagnostics, exact molar numbers of highly reliable quality might be required. To deal with such a wide spectrum of quality requirements, LSI recommends protocols for three levels of quantitation. For all the three levels of quantitation, it is necessary to use an internal standard, which has to be a nonendogenous compound added to the sample at the beginning of the lipid extraction process. The reason for the importance of internal standards in lipidomics is the tendency of ESI toward ion suppression effects, which may vastly distort quantitative results. Despite these shortcomings, ESI is still the ionization of choice because it allows coupling with liquid chromatography and has the ability to ionize a large spectrum of various lipids. Ideally, the internal standard should be of the same chemical nature as the target lipid but be separable by its mass, which naturally results in stable isotope-labeled lipids as the premier choice for internal standards. The superiority of stable isotope-labeled internal standards is reflected in Level 1 and Level 2 quantitation, both of which rely on stable isotope-labeled internal standards and can be considered as the gold standard in quantitative lipidomics. Preferably, the internal standard should coionize (coelute in the case of chromatography) with the target lipid compound with known response factors. Alternatively, when no coionizing internal standard is available or the applied internal standard is from another lipid class, Level 3 quantitation has to be used. The development of this standardized three-level system reflects the quality of quantitative data and should thus provide a standardized quality assessment at a glance for journals and readers alike. Further important quantitative aspects are isotopic correction [16] and one-point calibration versus multipoint calibration [17]. These aspects of quantitation are well covered by several publications, and LSI has elaborated rules and recommendations for various procedures concerning isotopic correction and handling of analytical response issues. Finally, normalization of data is eventually the most important aspect in quantitation because without any reference point such as cell number, amount of protein, phosphate content, etc., quantitative data are almost meaningless because of the lack of intersample comparison possibility. This point is even more important because it is typically located at the interface between the analytical chemist responsible for producing lipidomic data and the researchers (biologists, medical doctors, etc.) interested in these data. This in turn means that it is often beyond the direct field of action of the analytical chemist, but the researcher responsible for providing this crucial piece of information is eventually not even aware of its importance and thus simply does not determine any normalization parameter. The most important take-home message in this respect is that the interface communication between different disciplines is often a step in the workflow, which either makes it or breaks it.

1.8 Lipid Ontology

Lipid ontology is an aspect of lipidomics, which starts to draw more and more attention recently, because it directly touches the question of the biological relevance of lipidomic datasets. Lipid Ontology is closely interconnected with data analysis strategies such as multiomics approaches and pathway analysis. Similar to the already existing ontology endeavors, such as Gene Ontology, the main benefit of Lipid Ontology would be the classification of lipids not only because of their chemical and physical properties but also because of their biological context. The biological context should comprise a lipid localization, either at the organ, cellular, or even subcellular level, and a molecular lipid function embedded in certain biological processes. Unlike genes, proteins, or even metabolites, the classification of lipids according to their functionality is sometimes more opaque because membrane lipids cannot be as unambiguously classified by individual biochemical cause–function relations as enzymes, genes, metabolites, etc. The reason is that membrane lipids work in a substantial biophysical network where the change in one cause–function relation could easily be balanced by hundreds of other lipids in the same biophysical network. Despite these particularities of lipids, a proper ontology could foster further biological exploitation of lipidomic datasets. Figure 1.5 shows an example of how such a Lipid Ontology project could be organized and implemented in practice. When receiving annotated datasets in the context of a certain publication, a lipid ontology consortium would need to perform a quality check. This is an essential step because compromised data quality easily produces a large number of

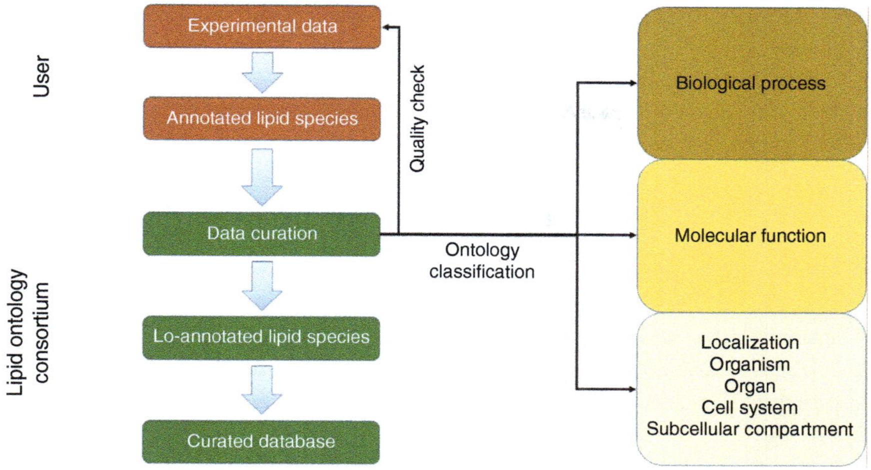

Figure 1.5 Proposal for a Lipid Ontology workflow, which should be governed by a Lipid Ontology Consortium along the lines to the Gene Ontology Consortium. The two most important steps to be performed by this consortium would be a data quality check of each identified lipid followed by its classification according to various ontology terms.

false-positive lipids [18], and in turn false ontology annotations, resulting in lipids classified into biological entities where they do not exist in reality. After a quality check, categorization due to LO terms is performed, and finally, the LO annotated lipids are published in a curated database, where they could eventually be cross-linked to other existing databases (LMSD, Swiss Lipids, etc.).

References

1 Han, X.L. and Gross, R.W. (2003). Global analyses of cellular lipidomes directly from crude extracts of biological samples by ESI mass spectrometry: a bridge to lipidomics. *J. Lipid Res.* 44 (6): 1071–1079.

2 Fahy, E., Subramaniam, S., Brown, H.A. et al. (2005). A comprehensive classification system for lipids. *J. Lipid Res.* 46 (5): 839–861.

3 Liebisch, G., Fahy, E., Aoki, J. et al. (2020). Update on LIPID MAPS classification, nomenclature, and shorthand notation for MS-derived lipid structures. *J. Lipid Res.* 61 (12): 1539–1555.

4 Sud, M., Fahy, E., Cotter, D. et al. (2007). LMSD: LIPID MAPS structure database. *Nucleic Acids Res.* 35 (Database issue): D527–D532.

5 Liebisch, G., Vizcaino, J.A., Kofeler, H. et al. (2013). Shorthand notation for lipid structures derived from mass spectrometry. *J. Lipid Res.* 54 (6): 1523–1530.

6 Bowden, J.A., Heckert, A., Ulmer, C.Z. et al. (2017). Harmonizing lipidomics: NIST interlaboratory comparison exercise for lipidomics using SRM 1950-metabolites in frozen human plasma. *J. Lipid Res.* 58 (12): 2275–2288.

7 Burla, B., Arita, M., Arita, M. et al. (2018). MS-based lipidomics of human blood plasma: a community-initiated position paper to develop accepted guidelines. *J. Lipid Res.* 59 (10): 2001–2017.

8 Liebisch, G., Ahrends, R., Arita, M. et al. (2019). Lipidomics needs more standardization. *Nat. Metabo.* 1 (8): 745–747.

9 Triebl, A., Burla, B., Selvalatchmanan, J. et al. (2020). Shared reference materials harmonize lipidomics across MS-based detection platforms and laboratories. *J. Lipid Res.* 61 (1): 105–115.

10 Ulmer, C.Z., Koelmel, J.P., Jones, C.M. et al. (2021). A review of efforts to improve lipid stability during sample preparation and standardization efforts to ensure accuracy in the reporting of lipid measurements. *Lipids* 56 (1): 3–16.

11 Triebl, A., Hartler, J., Trotzmuller, M., and Köfeler, C.K. (2017). Lipidomics: prospects from a technological perspective. *Biochim. Biophys. Acta* 1862 (8): 740–746.

12 Fruhwirth, G.O., Loidl, A., and Hermetter, A. (2007). Oxidized phospholipids: from molecular properties to disease. *Biochim. Biophys. Acta* 1772 (7): 718–736.

13 Quehenberger, O., Armando, A.M., Brown, A.H. et al. (2010). Lipidomics reveals a remarkable diversity of lipids in human plasma. *J. Lipid Res.* 51 (11): 3299–3305.

14 Dennis, E.A., Deems, R.A., Harkewicz, R. et al. (2010). A mouse macrophage lipidome. *J. Biol. Chem.* 285 (51): 39976–39985.

15 Ekroos, K. (2012). *Lipidomics: Technologies and Applications*, 2012. Wiley-VCH.

16 Kofeler, H.C., Ahrends, R., Baker, E.S. et al. (2021). Recommendations for good practice in MS-based lipidomics. *J. Lipid Res.* 62: 100138.

17 Rampler, E., Abiead, Y.E., Schoeny, H. et al. (2021). Recurrent topics in mass spectrometry-based metabolomics and lipidomics-standardization, coverage, and throughput. *Anal. Chem.* 93 (1): 519–545.

18 Kofeler, H.C., Eichmann, T.O., Ahrends, R. et al. (2021). Quality control requirements for the correct annotation of lipidomics data. *Nat. Commun.* 12 (1): 4771.

Part I

Analytical Methodologies in Lipidomics

2

Preanalytics for Lipidomics Analysis

Gonçalo Vale and Jeffrey G. McDonald

UT Southwestern Medical Center, Center for Human Nutrition and Department of Molecular Genetics, 5323 Harry Hines Blvd., Dallas, TX, 75390, USA

2.1 Safety

Working with biological samples and extracting lipids involves many health and safety hazards. Biological samples may contain one or more infectious pathogens such as HIV, hepatitis C, or prions. Many of the solvents used in lipidomic extractions are both toxic and flammable. When in doubt, the researcher should utilize materials safety data sheets (MSDSs) and other readily available resources for guidance on specific hazards associated with the chemicals used in these methods. Before using any of the methods and techniques described here, a researcher should receive training in (i) the handling of biological samples, (ii) proper storage and use of solvents and preparation of reagents, and (iii) equipment used in these methods. The researcher should also wear the appropriate personal protective equipment (PPE), such as eye protection, gloves, and a lab coat. Long pants and close-toed shoes are also highly recommended.

2.2 Introduction

Preanalytics for lipidomics analysis is defined as everything involved in the planning and acquisition of biological samples, extraction of lipids, and preparation of samples for analysis by chromatography and/or mass spectrometry (MS). This is graphically depicted in Figure 2.1. Some of the steps involved in preanalytics are well known within the community as some protocols used for lipid extractions have been utilized for over 60 years. The other aspects of preanalytics, such as sample origin and sample storage, are frequently overlooked, sometimes leading to challenges in data interpretation and reproducibility. Researchers can use the most modern and sophisticated mass spectrometers, employ the best chromatographic

Mass Spectrometry for Lipidomics: Methods and Applications, First Edition.
Edited by Michal Holčapek and Kim Ekroos.
© 2023 WILEY-VCH GmbH. Published 2023 by WILEY-VCH GmbH.

techniques, and enlist cutting-edge computational techniques to interpret data. However, if the collection, extraction, and processing of samples for lipidomics analysis is not done correctly, all these efforts may be wasted, and the data generated will be of questionable value. The goal of this chapter is to provide general guidance in best practices for all aspects of preanalytics for lipidomics. Additionally, we will introduce and comment on some of the overlooked or misunderstood steps of preanalytics.

2.3 Sample Origin

Lipid analysis can be performed on a variety of different sample types as shown in Figure 2.1. Probably, the most common and familiar sample type is plasma or serum obtained from blood as it is relatively abundant and easy to collect. The concept of lipids in plasma or serum is also familiar as the measurement of cholesterol and triacylglycerols is typically performed as part of an annual physical examination. Lipidomics analysis of plasma or serum from humans and other animal species is routinely performed in a laboratory research setting. The other frequently encountered sample sources are tissues and cultured cells. Common tissue sources include liver, brain, and adipose tissue. Cultured cells originate from a variety of cell types, are grown under various conditions, and often consist of genetically modified cells. Foods and plants are also often measured for lipids; however, it is typically for nutritional content rather than the purpose of basic biological research.

Consistency across the set of samples to be analyzed is critical, regardless of their origin. The larger the sample set, the greater the logistical challenges in maintaining consistency. Samples may be obtained through a variety of sources, such as in-house collection, a research laboratory, a biorepository, or a commercial vendor. Considerations should include using a single source or in lots for supplies used in sample collection, storage, and processing (i.e. tubes, pipette tips, etc.), as well as a well-defined and meticulously followed protocol for aliquoting and sample preparation. Although they appear identical, supplies obtained from different vendors or even differing lots from the same vendor may vary in terms of glass composition,

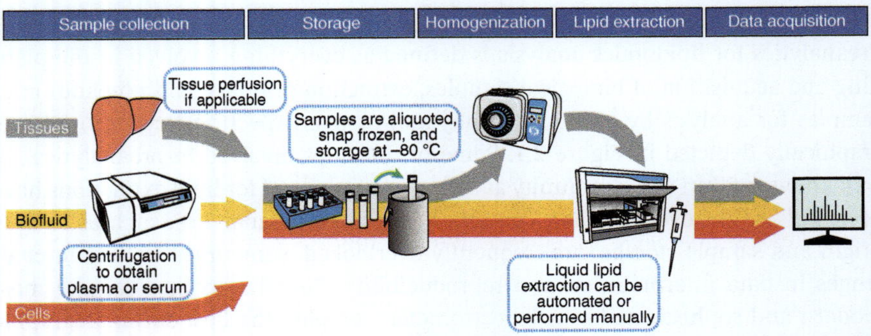

Figure 2.1 Preanalytics for lipidomics analysis.

slip-release agents used in plastic production, cleanliness, and a host of other variables that can impact lipidomics analysis. The need for careful planning and thoughtful execution of studies cannot be overstated. If you are sourcing samples from a biobank, other repository, or have no control over the collection of the samples to be analyzed, it is important to seek as much information as possible regarding all the aspects of the sample collection process. That way you can be informed of any possible confounds in the study design.

When collecting blood-based samples, proper and consistent phlebotomy practices are essential for obtaining quality samples. For any single experiment or a large-scale sample collection program, it is recommended that there is well-advanced planning so that a single source of supplies (preferably with a single lot number) is used for sample collection. It is also recommended, when possible, to limit the number of phlebotomists involved in the collection. Although not always practical because of numerous logistical issues, consistency in collection supplies and practices will reduce experimental variables and lead to better lipid data.

To ensure sample purity, a large bore needle should be used for blood-based sample collection so that red blood cells can pass through the needle with breaking open. The use of smaller gauge needles can lead to varying degrees of hemolysis and has a significant impact on the lipidomics profile because of the contamination from the red blood cells [1]. The use of an 18-gauge needed is preferred; however, it can cause discomfort to the subject during the blood collection. At a minimum, a 21-gauge needle should be used for collection of blood samples. Anything smaller than a 21-gauge needle should not be used [2].

For tissue samples, ensuring sample purity may require perfusion of the tissue sample to remove blood and other fluids present due to peripheral circulation. If the goal of a lipidomics analysis is to understand the lipid profile of a specific tissue type, the tissue should be perfused with either saline or other suitable solutions before processing. Liver and other tissues will require perfusion because of the presence of a significant quantity of blood as a result of peripheral circulation. It is important to perfuse these tissue types before lipid analysis as the lipid profile of the peripheral circulation will confound the lipid profile of the tissue.

2.4 Sample Collection

Lipids in biological matrices are prone to degradation, with oxidation and enzymatic hydrolysis being the two major causes. Both oxidation and enzymatic hydrolysis occur during the sample collection, preparation, and storage processes. Rapid processing and stabilization of samples following collection reduces degradation of lipids and provides more reliable and reproducible lipidomics results.

For a general lipid analysis focused on major lipid classes, lipid oxidation can be negligible. However, lipid oxidation might significantly affect the results of analysis for oxidized lipids, eicosanoids, and polyunsaturated fatty acid (PUFA)-containing species. The rate of lipid oxidation correlates with the presence of double bonds in the lipid species. These double bonds are mostly because of the presence of PUFAs within the lipid structure. The more double bonds present in the lipid species, the faster the rate of autoxidation, and vice versa. To reduce or prevent auto-oxidation, antioxidants are commonly added to the samples during sample preparation and storage. Antioxidants reduce oxidation by either scavenging free radicals, chelating metal ions, or inhibiting enzymatic activity. The most used antioxidants in lipidomics are butylhydroxytoluene (BHT) and citrate. Antioxidants can be included in a lipidomics protocol as a precaution for lipid degradation; however, their use might not be necessary. For this reason, an evaluation of the lipid classes to be analyzed should be performed before initiating sample collection and processing [3, 4].

Degradation of lipids can also occur as a result of enzymatic activity that catalyzes hydrolysis and dehydration reactions in the sample. The enzymatic activity can be reduced using chemical or physical treatments. For example, the presence of the enzyme phospholipase A (PLA) in the sample can catalyze the hydrolysis of phospholipids (PLs), resulting in elevated levels of lysophospholipids and free fatty acids in the sample. The chemical treatment of the sample with phenylmethanesulfonyl fluoride (PMSF) has been shown to inhibit the PLA activity and prevent the hydrolysis of some lipid species [5, 6]. Phospholipase D (PLD) cleaves phospholipids into phosphatidic acid (PA). The use of methanol during the extraction of samples with high PLD content results in the ethylation of methylated lipid species [7]. This phenomenon is frequently observed in the plant lipidomics community because of the presence of high PLD levels in plant seeds. To avoid any PLD-associated enzymatic lipid transformation, a heat treatment in an organic solvent such as isopropanol is applied during sample preparation [8]. The enzymatic activity and lipid oxidation rates have also been shown to decrease when the samples are stored at lower temperatures [5, 9, 10]. For improved lipid stability, the samples should be kept cold during processing and snap-frozen in liquid nitrogen before long-term storage at $\leq -80\,°C$ or lower.

Plasma and serum are two of the most used matrices for lipid analysis [3, 11]; however, studies have shown that plasma and serum lipid profiles obtained from the same blood sample can differ [12, 13]. Although both can be used for lipid analysis, they should be treated as different matrices and should not be considered as interchangeable sample types. Plasma is often preferred as it is considered the closer representative of whole blood properties [3, 14]. It is prepared from the whole blood collected directly in a tube containing an anticoagulant. The anticoagulant ethylenediaminetetraacetic acid (purple top tube; K_2-EDTA) is routinely used in clinical practices and is the most common for general lipidomics analysis of plasma. Other anticoagulants such as heparin and citrate can also be used during blood collection. There is no consensus about the best anticoagulant for lipidomics analysis. Anticoagulants can have an impact on lipid extraction and also MS ionization [3, 15–17]. It is important to (i) use the same anticoagulant through the entire study, (ii) meticulously describe the blood collection and tubes used, and (iii) carefully compare the plasma lipidomics data obtained with different anticoagulants [15, 17, 18].

Contrary to plasma samples, serum is obtained from coagulated blood. The tubes used for the blood collection should be absent of any anticoagulant. When processing the clotted serum samples, it is essential to have a defined clotting time and centrifugation protocol. Following centrifugation, the serum samples can be aliquoted, snap-frozen, and placed into long term storage at ≤−80 °C.

Tissues, on the other hand, may require additional processing steps before storage. For example, liver perfusions are often recommended before storage [19, 20]. Samples can be stored either fresh, hydrophilized, or in a solution following sample preparation or homogenization. It is recommended that airtight glass containers be used to store tissue samples. The storage of samples in organic solvents in plastic containers should be avoided.

Both biofluid and tissue samples should be stored at −80 °C or lower in an environment free of oxygen, peroxides, and metal ions. It has been shown that the samples can be stored at −80 °C for several years without experiencing significant lipid deterioration [21]. However, storage of samples under an atmosphere of nitrogen or argon will reduce the presence of oxygen in the headspace above the sample. For long-term storage of samples in organic solvents, degassing the solvent by sparging or sonication will also reduce the presence of oxygen in the storage vessel. Exposure of the samples to freeze–thaw cycles should be avoided as it can impact lipid stability. Aliquoting of biofluids and tissue before freezing can eliminate unnecessary freeze–thaw cycling of samples. Biofluids require minimal sample preparation and can be easily aliquoted and frozen following collection. Advanced planning, however, may be needed when dealing with aliquoting tissue samples before storage. Often, only small pieces of tissue are needed for lipidomics analysis (<10 mg). If a single, large piece of tissue has been collected and immediately frozen, it will likely have to be thawed to generate subsamples, resulting in decreased sample quality. Furthermore, weighing a thawed tissue sample can be challenging because of the cold storage conditions and subsequent condensation of ambient water in the sample, which may result in an inaccurate weight of the sample. Weighing tissue samples immediately after sample collection will result in higher quality samples and a higher quality lipidomics analysis.

2.5 Tissue Homogenization

While sample preparation of biofluids can be straightforward, the preparation of tissue samples is often more complex. Depending on the nature of the tissue and/or the collection method used, tissue samples may in fact be heterogeneous regarding their lipid profiles. Some portions of the sample might overrepresent certain lipids, while other portions of the sample may be completely devoid of them. Therefore, it is necessary to ensure sample homogeneity before performing lipidomics analysis. Mechanical processes such as grinding, shearing, and beating can be used to disrupt tissue into smaller parts and equally distribute the lipids within the sample (Figure 2.2a).

Lipids exist in tissues in many forms, often as lipids aggregated in storage tissues (fat) or as membrane constituents closely associated with proteins. For lipidomics analysis, it is critical that those lipids present in the sample are accessible for lipid extraction. In addition to breaking up tissue into smaller parts, one or more solvents

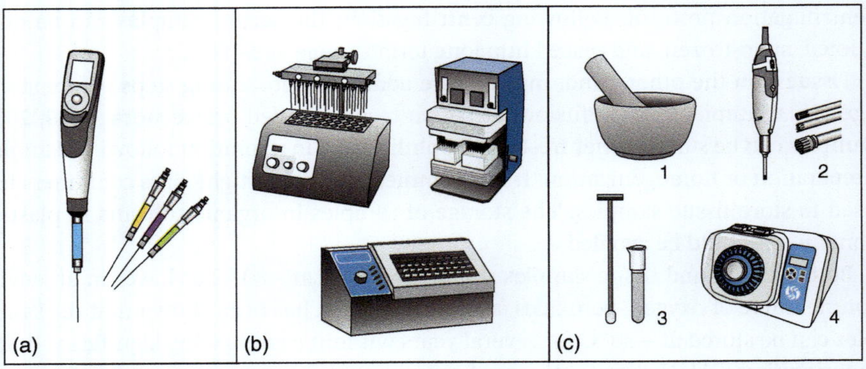

Figure 2.2 Commonly used tools for sample extraction and preparation for lipidomics analysis. eVol automated pipette with glass/stainless steel/Teflon™ syringes suitable for organic solvents (a). Common sample evaporators for drying samples in test tubes and 96-well format (b). Various tools used for tissue homogenization including manual and powered homogenizers (c).

must be used during the homogenization process. The use of a solvent will not only dissolve the lipids present in the tissue but will also overcome their interaction within the tissue matrix (proteins, polysaccharides, etc.). Horing et al. [22] studied the influence of sample concentration, solvent composition, and homogenization technique for lipid analysis in liver tissues. Homogenization was performed in water, methanol, and water:methanol (1 : 1, v/v) using different physical disruption techniques such as grinding tissue in liquid nitrogen and bead-mill-based homogenization techniques. Their data showed that the solvent system used for homogenization did influence the lipid recovery primarily because of the formation of lipid-containing precipitates.

No universal solvent has been identified for use in the extraction and homogenization of all lipids. Depending on the liquid species, tissue homogenization may be performed using aqueous, methanol, or methanol-containing solvents [22–25]. Typically, it is performed using not one but a combination of solvents. The most common solvent combination used in tissue homogenization is chloroform:methanol (2 : 1, v/v). The use of these combined solvents originates from the work of Folch, and Bligh and Dyer, in the late 1950s and has been used in conjunction with both a mortar and pestle and the Potter-Elvehjem apparatus [23, 25]. Another solvent system used in tissue homogenization is dicloromethane:methanol (2 : 1, v/v). Dichloromethane (DCM) has a similar extraction efficiency as chloroform and is preferable to use as it is less toxic and more stable [26]. The dicloromethane:methanol solvent system has been shown to be effective when used in conjunction with a bead-based homogenizer [27].

2.5.1 Mortar and Pestle

The mortar and pestle (Figure 2.2a1) is the most well-known tool for the grinding of tissue samples. It can be used on wet, dry, and even with frozen tissue samples and is a simple, cost-effective way to homogenize a tissue sample. One consideration when using a mortar and pestle is the possible deterioration of lipids in the sample because of the heat generated through friction. To prevent possible deterioration, tissue samples should be frozen before homogenization and/or homogenized on dry ice. A commonly used technique involves the pouring of liquid nitrogen onto the mortar and pestle several minutes before sample homogenization. The frozen or snap-frozen sample is then placed in the mortar and gently ground with the pestle to avoid sample spattering.

The use of a mortar and pestle for the grinding of frozen samples is the best-known technique for tissue homogenization. It is an inexpensive technique, but it requires manual labor and can be very time-consuming. Tissue homogenization is performed on one sample at a time and requires thorough cleaning of the tool between samples in order to prevent cross-contamination of samples. For this reason, it is not often used for tissue homogenization and may not be the best technique for use in high-throughput workflows.

2.5.2 Rotor–Stator

A rotor–stator (Figure 2.2a2) consists of a fast-spinning rotor equipped with a probe that homogenizes samples through the process of mechanical shearing. It is analogous to an immersion blender. Like the blender, it produces a uniform homogenate relatively quickly and can be used to homogenize a variety of sample types and volumes. Mechanical shearing generates heat and should be taken into consideration when homogenizing samples. There are some temperature-sensitive models available that monitor the temperature of the sample and stop when the defined temperature is reached. There are single- and multi-sample rotor–stator homogenizers commercially available. Multi-sample devices allow homogenization of multiple samples at the same time. The rotor–stator probe(s) are then cleaned between samples. Use of a multi-sample rotor–stator allows for simultaneous homogenization and may be more amenable for use in larger sample sets.

2.5.3 Blender

The blender homogenizer is analogous to a kitchen blender in that it disrupts samples by shearing. Tissue samples are placed in a cup containing homogenization media and sheared by the blender's blades. It can be used to process a wide diversity of samples (cells and tissues) in a variety of volumes (1 ml to several liters). Processing times are much shorter than that of the mortar and pestle or a glass homogenizer. High-speed homogenization generates heat, so it is important to consider temperature effects during the shearing process. Some models are temperature sensitive and can be programmed to stop when a certain specific temperature is reached. Blenders are widely available and are easy to clean. Like the mortar and pestle and glass homogenizer, however, the blender can only process a single sample at a time and may not be suitable for use in high-throughput workflows.

2.5.4 Potter-Elvehjem

The Potter-Elvehjem apparatus (Figure 2.2a3 homogenization panel), also known as a glass homogenizer, is similar in principle to the mortar and pestle. It is composed of a glass tube mortar with a tight-fitting pestle and is suitable for use with much smaller amounts of tissue. The tissue sample is placed inside the glass tube mortar and the pestle is lowered, raised, and twisted like a piston to grind the sample. The grinding process is repeated several times until the sample is homogenized. Because of the strong vacuum created inside the glass tube mortar during the pulverization process, the pestle should be removed gently between repetitions. As the Potter-Elvehjem apparatus is glass, it can easily break during use or when cleaning between samples. As with the mortar and pestle, it is a time-consuming process that may not be suitable for high-throughput workflows or larger sample sets.

2.5.5 Bead Mill

Bead-based homogenization (Figure 2.2a4) approaches are advantageous for high-throughput workflows. These systems are very versatile allowing for the processing of a few to several hundred samples per day. The samples are placed in a tube containing homogenization solvent and ceramic or metal beads. The tubes are placed in a bead mill and vigorously agitated for a period a few seconds to several minutes. The bead-agitation process disrupts the cells and homogenizes the tissue sample. The tissue homogenate is then removed from the tube and the tube discarded. There is no need for cleaning or any type of equipment maintenance.

As with grinding, bead-beating generates heat and can cause lipid degradation. Cooling samples before homogenization can minimize any temperature increases. Additionally, some bead mills offer cooling features and or can be programmed to pace the shaking intervals with pauses between cycles to avoid the high-temperature increases. Bead mills that have the most powerful shaking action will require the shortest homogenization cycles and therefore generate the least heat. The biggest disadvantage of the bead-based technique is the cost associated with the bead mill and consumables.

2.6 Liquid–Liquid Extraction (LLE)

The importance of sample preparation before lipidomics analysis is crucial for obtaining quality data. An extremely important step in the analysis is lipid extraction, where the appropriate solvent system is used to (i) effectively extract representative lipids from a sample, and (ii) remove contaminants and interferants, such as non-lipid biomolecules (e.g. peptides, proteins, and sugars) inorganic residues (e.g. salts), and detergents. The presence of these contaminants can lead to ion suppression and matrix effects that interfere with lipid analysis. Ensuring the quality of the lipid extraction step will minimize complex mass spectra and simplify data interpretation.

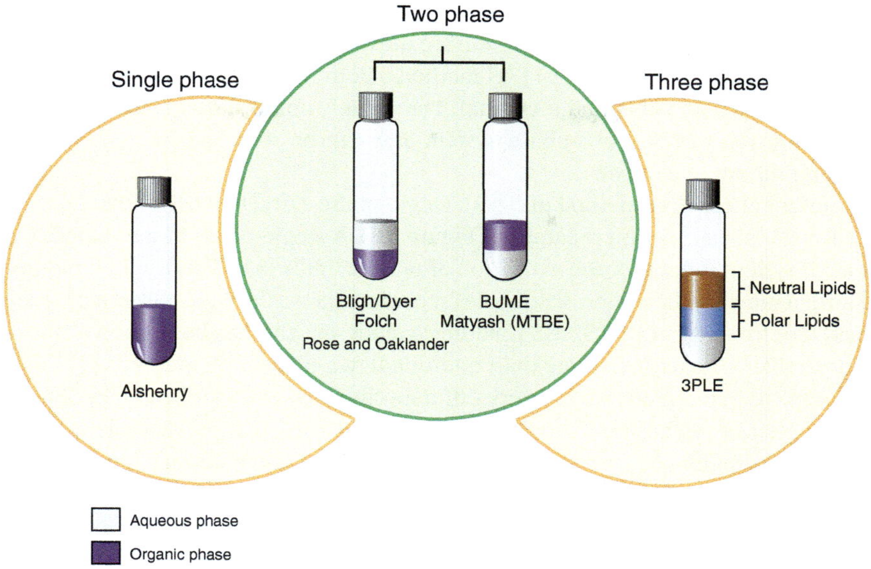

Figure 2.3 Examples of liquid extraction methods for lipids.

Liquid–liquid extraction (LLE) is the partitioning of lipids into an organic phase. The efficiency of the partitioning is dependent on the solvent(s) used in the extraction process. Polar lipids such as phospholipids (PLs) are soluble in more polar solvents such as DCM, chloroform, or alcohols (methanol, ethanol, and isopropanol), whereas nonpolar lipids such as triacylglycerols (TAG) or cholesteryl esters (CEs) are soluble in hydrocarbon solvents such as hexane or iso-octane. To efficiently extract lipids from a sample, it is necessary to use a solvent system that will isolate the representative lipids from the biological matrices.

The most popular solvent systems used for lipid extraction are the Folch [23] and Bligh/Dyer [25] methods. Figure 2.3 shows that these methods are both based on a binary or two-phase system. Lipids are partitioned into the organic phase (chloroform), while proteins, sugars, inorganic residues, and some hydrophilic lipids remain in the water/methanol phase. Both the Folch and Bligh/Dyer methods have been in use for decades and have been proven very effective in extracting a broad range of lipid classes. They are often referred as the gold standard for use in LLE. The potential toxicity and carcinogenicity of chloroform [28, 29], however, has led to modified versions of these methods. In these methods, chloroform has been replaced by DCM, a less toxic alternative with similar extraction efficiency [26, 30]. The only drawback to the chloroform/DCM methods is these solvents have a higher density than both water and methanol. The organic layer will partition to the bottom layer of the two phases. Recovery of the organic layer requires the pipette to cross the aqueous layer containing most of the non-lipid species interferents mentioned above, potentially contaminating the organic layer.

As result, alternative methods have been developed to avoid contamination of the organic layer. Among the most common are the methyl-*tert*-butyl ether (MTBE) [24] and butanol–methanol (BUME) [31] methods. Both MTBE [24] and BUME have a lower density than water and methanol. The organic phase subsequently partitions as the top layer of the two-phase system and can be removed without crossing through the aqueous layer.

Another alternative method utilizes a single-phase extraction (SPE) that does not involve a biphasic solvent separation (Figure 2.3). A single-phase butanol:methanol solvent system is used for the extraction of plasma lipids [32]. This method requires minimal sample preparation, is suitable for use in large-scale liquid chromatography-mass spectrometry (LC-MS)/MS lipidomics analyses, and has been shown to be a comparable or better technique than traditional two-phase LLE methods [33].

Complete lipid extraction of every different lipid class cannot be achieved using any single LLE technique. The extraction method used will be dependent on the matrix, the lipidomics workflow (targeted, untargeted, fatty acid profile, etc.), and the subsequent MS technique used for downstream analysis of the sample. Although a single-phase, as compared to a two-phase, method may be advantageous for use in LC-MS/MS analysis, it is not when using direct-fusion techniques. The resulting high presence of inorganic residues in the sample will lead to chemical noise and convoluted MS spectra, resulting in complex data interpretation.

A more recent novel technique uses a three-phase liquid extraction (3PLE) composed of two organic phases (upper and middle phases) and a single aqueous phase (bottom) [27]. This tri-phasic system (Figure 2.3) not only extracts lipids from the sample, but it also separates the lipids by polarity; neutral lipids (glycerolipids and cholesteryl esters) partition to the upper organic phase and polar lipids (glycerophospholipids and sphingolipids) partition into the middle organic phase. Separating lipids between two organic phases results in less complex lipid extracts and decreases ion suppression and background noise, resulting in increased sensitivity and better data quality when used in MS-based techniques. The most frequently used LLE methods are summarized in Table 2.1.

2.6.1 Folch Method

The Folch LLE method is one of the oldest and most popular methods for extracting lipids from biological samples. It is often considered as one of the gold standard LLE methods for lipidomics and has been exhaustively tested in different biological matrices and compared to other LLE techniques [24, 33, 34]. "*Chloroform, methanol, and water are mixed in a separatory funnel in the proportions 8 : 4 : 3 by volume. When the mixture is allowed to stand, a biphasic system is obtained*" [23]. The method involves homogenization of a sample in a chloroform – methanol mixture where water is then added to wash the extracts. This solvent mixture results in a biphasic layer where the aqueous phase (upper) will contain non-lipids and the organic phase (bottom) will contain most lipids. In his original manuscript, Folch reported a loss of 0.3–0.6% of the tissue lipids to the aqueous phase. This loss of lipids to the aqueous phase could have been significantly reduced if he had used a salt solution

Table 2.1 Summary of liquid extraction methods commonly used in lipidomics.

Method	Solvent system	Matrix	Phases	OP[a]	Example	References
Folch	Chloroform:methanol:water (8 : 4 : 3) (v/v/v); room temperature	Tissues and fluids	Two	Down	Tissues (1 g) are homogenized in $CHCl_3$:MeOH (2 : 1, (v/v)) mixture to a final dilution 20-fold the volume of the tissue sample (1 g tissue diluted to 20 ml). The extract is mixed with 0.2 its volume of water and allowed to separate into two-phases either by standing or by centrifugation	[1]
Bligh/Dyer	Chloroform:methanol:water (2 : 2 : 1.8) (v/v/v); room temperature	Tissues and fluids	Two	Down	Tissues (100 g) are firstly homogenized in a blender with 100 ml of $CHCl_3$ and 200 ml of MeOH (1 : 2, v/v). Then, 100 ml of chloroform and 100 ml of water are added with a mixing step between additions. After filtration, the mixture is left to separate into two phases	[2]
Rose and Oaklander	Chloroform:isopropanol:water (7 : 11 : 1), room temperature	Red blood cells	Two	down	1 ml of water is added to 1 ml of red blood cells. After vortexing, 11 ml of IPA is added. The solution is mixed and 7 ml of $CHCl_3$ is added. The mixture is centrifuged, and the organic phase is collected	[3]
(Matyash) MTBE	MTBE:methanol:water (10 : 3 : 2.5) (v/v/v), room temperature	Tissues and fluids	Two	Up	1.5 ml of MeOH was added to 200 μl of sample and the solution was vortexed. Then, 5 ml of MTBE was added, and after the mixture was shaken at room temperature for 1 h, 1.25 ml of water was added. The mixture was centrifuged, and the organic phase was collected	[4]

(Continued)

Table 2.1 (Continued)

Method	Solvent system	Matrix	Phases	OP[a]	Example	References
BUME	(Butanol:methanol [3 : 1]):(heptane:ethyl acetate [3 : 1]):(1% acetic acid) (1 : 1 : 1) (v/v/v), room temperature	Plasma and tissues	Two	Up	To 1–75 μl of plasma, 300 μl of butanol:MeOH(3 : 1, v/v) is added. The solution is mixed, and 150 μl of heptane:etyl acetate (3 : 1, v/v) is added. After mixing, 300 μl of 1% acetic acid is added to the solution which is mixed again. The mixture is left to stand to separate in two phases and the organic contact is removed	[5]
Alshehry	Butanol:methanol (1 : 1) (v/v), sonication, and centrifugation at 20 °C	Plasma	One	N/A	To 10 μl of plasma, 100 μl of butanol:MeOH (1 : 1, v/v) was added. The mixture was vortex, sonicated, and centrifuged at 20 °C. The supernatant was removed from the tube	[6]
3PLE	Hexane:methyl acetate:acetonitrile:water (4 : 4 : 3 : 4) (v/v/v), room temperature	Tissues and fluids	Three	Up and mid	To a tube containing the samples, 1 ml of hexane, 1 ml of methyl acetate, 0.75 ml of acetonitrile, and 1 ml of water were added. The mixture was vortexed and centrifuged resulting in a three-phase system. The upper and middle layers were collected to different tubes	[7]

[a] OP, Organic phase.

instead of water during extraction. The presence of salts would have altered the lipid distribution by shifting the acidic lipids from the aqueous phase to the organic phase [23]. Although the presence of salts would have increased the efficiency in lipid extraction, it would have potentially resulted in trace amounts of sodium chloride in the sample, which may be detrimental for some MS techniques such as direct infusion. Before the use of the Folch extraction method, one should determine if using water or salt solution is more prudent. Additionally, to increase the lipid recovery from the sample, one might also have to perform multiple extractions. Typically, lipids are almost completely extracted from the sample following two or three extractions.

2.6.2 Bligh and Dyer (BD) Method

Along with the Folch method, the Bligh and Dyer (BD) method [25] is also considered one of the gold standards for LLE extraction and has been extensively used in lipid analysis by the scientific community. Originally developed to be a rapid and economical technique for extracting lipids from frozen fish (wet tissue), it has become one of the oldest and most popular methods for extracting lipids from biological samples. It was developed as an alternative to the recently published Folch method [23], which had the disadvantage of using *"large and inconvenient volumes of solvent"* [25]. First, tissues are homogenized in a mixture of chloroform and methanol at such proportions to form a single-phase system, without the addition of water. Further dilutions of the sample in chloroform and water result in a two-phase system where the organic layer (bottom) contains the lipids. The resulting homogenate is filtered, and the organic phase is removed. The filtrate is re-homogenized in chloroform, and the process is repeated to ensure a higher lipid recovery. The two organic phases are then combined. *"Many alterations of the procedure are permissible, but it is imperative that the volumes of chloroform, methanol, and water, before and after dilution, be kept in the proportions 1 : 2 : 0.8 and 2 : 2 : 1.8, respectively"* [25]. This second extraction step recovered only 6% of the total lipids in the sample. When using this method, it is up to the user if this additional extraction step is necessary for downstream analysis.

2.6.3 Modified Folch and Bligh/Dyer (BD) Methods

Many modifications have been made to the original published Folch and BD methods. One of the most common is the extraction of lipids using DCM instead of chloroform [26, 27, 30]. The use of chloroform in LLE has frequently been scrutinized because of its toxicity environmental impact and instability with propensity to form phosgene. Classified as a probable human carcinogen, chloroform has been banned from products and its use is restricted in several countries [29, 30]. DCM is less toxic than chloroform and has been shown to yield comparable results when used in place of chloroform in Folch and BD lipid extraction methods [4, 26, 30]. For this reason, DCM has become an acceptable alternative to chloroform and is routinely used by laboratories in LLE. Another common modification made to the Folch and BD methods is a change in solvent ratios. The slight changes in solvent ratios are directly related to the nature of the samples or are made in order to simplify sample preparation. Any modification made to either of these traditional LLE methods should be carefully evaluated and vetted before use in lipidomics analysis.

2.6.4 Rose and Oaklander (RO) Method

The Rose and Oaklander (RO) method was developed specifically for the extraction of lipids from red blood cells [35]. The Folch method had been determined to be unsuitable for use with this type of matrix as the resulting extracts were contaminated with heme pigment and denatured proteins. Additionally, cholesterol recovery was low using the Folch method on red blood cells. The Rose and Oaklander method employs the addition of 1 ml water to 1 ml of erythrocytes, vortexing of the solution, followed by incubation at room temperature (≈20 °C) for 15 minutes. Isopropanol is slowly added over the course of one hour with occasional mixing, followed by the addition of chloroform. The mixture is then vortexed and centrifuged, and the organic phase (bottom) was collected. By replacing methanol with isopropanol, Rose and Oaklander demonstrated that there was a significant decrease of the heme residues in the organic phase and an increase in cholesterol and phospholipids yield.

2.6.5 Matyash or Methyl-*tert*-Butyl Ether (MTBE) Method

The Matyash or the MTBE extraction method has several advantages to the classic two-phase chlorinated solvent systems. Besides being a less toxic solvent, MTBE has a lower density compared to water resulting in the lipid-containing organic phase partitioning in the upper layer. This simplifies sample handling as there is no need to cross the non-lipid-rich aqueous solution to collect the organic fraction and reduces the possibility of contaminating the sample with salts, proteins, or other residues. Moreover, the partitioning of lipids in the upper layer lends itself for use of the method in high-throughput workflows by simplifying fraction collection when using automated processing systems. Samples are first vortexed with MeOH, with MTBE added later to the mixture. Following a one-hour incubation in a shaker, water is added to the solution in order to induce phase separation. The organic phase containing the lipids (upper) is then collected. The method has been proven to be efficient in the extraction of lipids from a variety of different matrices (cells, tissues, and fluids) and to have similar or better lipid recoveries when compared to both the Folch and BD methods. The authors recommend a re-extraction of the aqueous phase to increase the lipid yield.

2.6.6 BUME Method

The butanol:methanol (BUME) method is another alternative to two-phase chlorinated solvent systems and is specifically designed to automate workflows for high-throughput lipid analysis [31]. In this method, the sample is initially mixed with butanol:methanol (3 : 1, v/v) to form a one-phase extraction. Heptane:ethyl acetate (3 : 1, v/v) and 1% acetic acid are then added to induce two-phase separation. Lipids are then collected from the upper organic phase. Originally, the BUME method was designed for lipid profiling of plasma samples and showed extraction yields comparable to the Folch method. Modifications have since been made to the method in order to extract lipids from other types of biological samples. In most cases, the modifications consist of the replacement of the acetic acid solution with a salt solution [36].

2.6.7 Alshehry Method

The Alshehry method is a single-phase method for plasma lipid extraction suitable for high-throughput LC-MS/MS lipidomics analysis [32]. The advantage of this method is its speed and simplicity, allowing the recovery of major lipid classes with minimal extraction steps. Plasma samples are mixed with 1-butanol:methanol (1 : 1, v/v), vortexed briefly, and sonicated for one hour at 20 °C. The solution is centrifuged, and the supernatant is recovered for downstream analysis. The method has been shown to efficiently extract all major lipid classes (including sterols, glycerolipids, glycerophospholipids, and sphingolipids) [32]. One limitation of the Alshehry method is that both lipids and non-lipid components are present in the same phase. There is reduced capability for removing salts and non-lipid contaminants from the sample extract. For this reason, this method is not suitable for direct-fusion techniques. The authors have demonstrated success by modifying the analytical methods to accommodate for the presence of these salts and other aqueous components in the sample extracts [32].

2.6.8 Three-Phase Lipid Extraction (3PLE)

The 3PLE method extracts and separates lipids by polarity in a single LLE [27]. The 3PLE is a three-phase system composed of one aqueous and two organic phases. The upper organic phase is enriched in neutral lipids, the middle organic phase contains the major glycerophospholipids, and the lower aqueous phase contains the non-lipid and inorganic residues. The method has been to be effective at extracting lipids in plasma, brain, liver, and white adipose tissue and produce lipid yields comparable to the BD method. In this method, hexane, methyl acetate, acetonitrile, and water are added to the sample (4 : 4 : 3 : 4 [v/v]). The solution is vortexed and then centrifuged to separate the sample into the three phases. The upper and middle organic phases can then be collected and analyzed separately.

Separation of the lipid content into two distinctive organic phases results in less complex lipid extracts. By decreasing ion suppression, the method increases the number of lipids that can be identified by direct-infusion techniques. It is also an advantageous method to use with LC-MS-based techniques in that it decreases the background noise in MS spectra and separates out high abundant lipid species (such as glycerolipids) from lesser abundant species. As a result, a larger sample injection can be used to measure the less abundant lipid species. By separating lipids by polarity before the hydrolysis process, it is also possible to differentiate between the polar and neutral fatty acid content. Therefore, 3PLE can also be used in the analysis of fatty acids.

Regardless of the method chosen to extract lipids from samples, it is important to consider the role of temperature both from a practical and physical aspect. Lipids have a tremendous range of solubilities. Temperature plays a significant role in lipid solubility and solvent miscibility and can influence multi-phasic systems such as those described here. Once samples are mixed with organic solvents, all enzymatic activity should cease. The cold temperatures typically used to slow or stop the biological activity are no longer needed. If labile lipids are the focus of the analysis, it may still be necessary to continue the extraction at under cold temperature conditions. Many lipids, however, are stable at room temperature for a period of hours or even days. As a result, one might consider performing extractions at room temperature for simplicity and convenience. The difficulty comes with the centrifugation steps of the extraction process. It is common in laboratories focused on biological research to have centrifuges with refrigeration. Samples placed in the centrifuge are incubated at 4 °C. The transfer of extracts from room temperature to 4 °C and back may result in inconsistent solubility of lipids and poor-quality phase separation. One alternative would be to equilibrate the centrifuge to room temperature before performing the extractions. Depending on the length of time needed for the equilibration, this approach may create logistical challenges and require longer time to process samples. It is recommended that the researchers have a dedicated centrifuge that is maintained at room temperature.

In some lipidomics experiments, it is necessary to employ a chemical hydrolysis to aid in isolating specific lipid classes, modifying lipid classes, or simplifying the overall composition of the lipid extract. Hydrolysis is used to convert steryl esters into a homogeneous pool of free sterols and oxysterols, to eliminate glycerol and phospholipids from samples used in sphingolipid analysis, and to isolate ether-linked glycero lipids. Typically, a base hydrolysis procedure is utilized. The sample is placed in a screw-cap test tube containing KOH in methanol and incubated at 80 °C for one hour. At this temperature, the base will solubilize the lipids and allow for hydrolysis of the ester bonds. Alternatively, an acid hydrolysis procedure (1 M HCL in methanol) can be used in order to selectively remove ether-linked alkyl groups from the lipids. Although not part of a general lipid extraction, chemical hydrolysis can be a very useful, when needed.

2.7 Resuspension and Solubilization

The final step in preanalytics for lipidomics analysis is resuspension of the final sample in a solvent suitable for the desired chromatographic and mass spectral analysis. Because of the range of solubilities across the lipidome, great attention must be given to this step. The fundamental challenge is identifying a suitable solvent that fully solubilize the lipids and is also compatible with the chromatography and MS protocols. For example, in hydrophilic interaction and reverse-phase chromatography techniques, the starting conditions include a mobile phase containing water. Ideally, the sample could be reconstituted in the mobile phase; however, many lipids are not soluble in aqueous solvents. If an aqueous environment is required, sonication and gentle heating of the sample might encourage solubilization of the lipids. An alternative approach would be to first dissolve the sample in a small volume of a strong organic solvent (chloroform, DCM, isopropanol, etc.) to ensure complete solubilization of the lipids before reconstitution of the sample in the mobile phase. For normal phase and infusion-based analyses, the solvents appropriate for MS are generally well suited for dissolving lipid samples. Sonication and gentle heat are still encouraged, however, to ensure maximum recovery.

In addition to general solubility issues pertaining to the solubilization of lipidomic extracts, the possibility of chemical adhesion to the vials used in extract storage merits some discussion. Some lipids are notorious for their adhesion to glass, especially general inexpensive borosilicate laboratory glass. In fact, phosphate-containing lipids such as phosphatidic acid, sphingomyelins, and sphingosine-1-phosphate can be challenging to resolubilize solely because of their propensity to adhere to glass. There are several possibilities to mitigate this issue depending on the lipid class: (i) incubate overnight on the bench top, (ii) using extended time interval, the extract is sonicated, (iii) use acid modifiers in your solvents during resolubilization, (iv) use silinated glass vials or inserts to prevent adhesion, and/or (v) use plastic vials of inserts when appropriate.

2.8 Automation

Extraction and isolation of lipids from biological and other samples has traditionally been a manual process involving test tubes, Pasteur pipettes, and analytical glass pipettes (Figure 2.2b). Solvents and samples are transferred and aliquoted by hand, as are lipid-containing fractions from a multi-phase extraction. Over the past decade, interest in lipidomics profiling of large cohorts (500–5000 samples) has led the community to begin adopting and implementing automation in lipidomics workflows. Automation generally refers to automated pipetting systems or liquid-handling robots as shown in Figure 2.4. This technology has been in place for decades but was geared mostly toward aqueous-based systems in industrial labs. Over the past 5–10 years, multiple labs around the world have begun implementing automation as an effective approach for lipidomic processes using strong organic solvents. This includes implementation of automation in the authors' laboratory.

Automation is generally bifurcated into workflows that use test tubes and workflows that use a 96-well plate format. The 96-well format is also commonly referred to as "SBS format," an abbreviation for the Society for Biomolecular Screening. Modern liquid-handling robots can be configured with 8 or 12 channels, each channel representing an individual pipette. With the appropriate racks, either configuration can readily handle the solvent volumes typically used in lipid extractions (1–5 ml). The 8 or 12 channel design is flexible in that the individual channels can

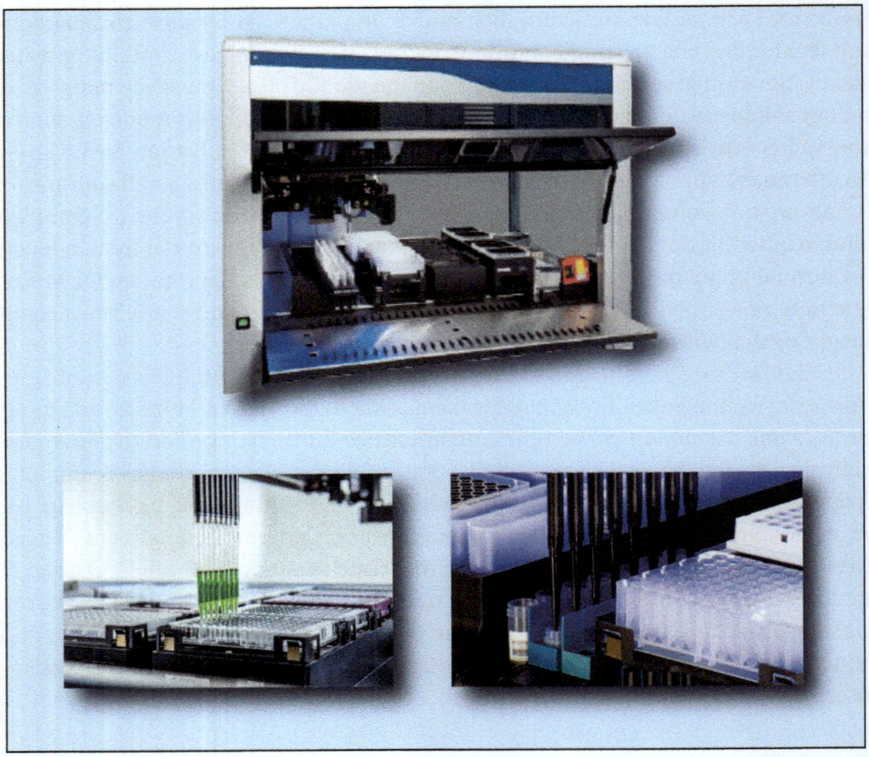

Figure 2.4 Liquid-handling automation. Source: Hamilton Company.

be configured independently of one another. The platform can be adapted to accommodate many different test tube and vial sizes and configurations. The platform allows for visual verification of the programmed processes, allowing the operator to confirm that the method is correctly being executed before implementation. The alternative to the multi-channel (8 or 12) configuration is a 96-well head that is only capable of dealing with the SBS-plate format. The 96-well head configuration allows large numbers of samples to be processed daily and for extended periods of time. For example, a researcher would have the capability to analyze 200 samples per day, several days per week, for over a year. The 96-well head configuration is quicker in that it can execute each step on 96 samples at a time versus the 8 or 12 channel configurations described above. While the 96-well format is more efficient for large sample sets, it is a less flexible system. If less than 96 samples are to be processed, most systems lack the flexibility in loading less than 96 tips at a time or executing the steps for less than 96 samples. Although automation technology is ever evolving, the authors are unaware of a commercially available system that allows for the changing out of head configurations without extensive mechanical effort and recalibration.

While liquid-handling robotic platforms can automate almost all steps of a lipidomic extraction, there is a clear cost/benefit threshold. Automating centrifugation, sample drying, SPE, and other tasks is possible but can be prohibitively expensive and is generally reserved for large pharmaceutical companies or biotechnology operations. Most of those who use these robotic platforms utilize them as advanced pipetting systems to merely transfer and manipulate samples and solvents in an automated manner. For example, they may choose to utilize the system to transfer aliquots of plasma into sample tubes, add appropriate solvents to sample tubes, remove and transfer the organic phases to new tubes, and/or load samples and solvents into SPE plates. All other activities performed during sample extraction, such as centrifugation, positive-pressure SPE, and sample drying, are typically done by bringing the samples out of the robot, or "off the deck" Figure 2.2c illustrates examples of this equipment.

The resistance to transitioning to liquid-handling robots has largely been driven by the initial investment costs; however, the issues surrounding the pipetting of volatile organic solvents using plastic, air-displaced pipette technology have also been a factor. The use of plastic tips in preanalytics is not optimal. The potential for background contaminants being added to the sample by using plastic tips is of concern. Polypropylene is the most often used, solvent-resistant polymer in consumable lab plasticware [37]. In many cases, the most leachable plasticizers are those added to make polypropylene clear. Perhaps, to reduce the amount of leachable material in the plastic, the pipette tips manufactured for use with liquid-handling robots are not clear and are often black in color as can be seen in Figure 2.4. Some plastic pipette tips have proven to be exceptionally clean and contribute little to no background to the sample. However, lot-to-lot variation in the manufacturing process can result in variation in the amount of background signal observed with the same type of tips (see the commentary on plastics in Section 2.9 for further discussion).

Other plastics used during the extraction process are solvent reservoirs or "troughs" that contain the stock solution(s) used in the various extraction steps shown in Figure 2.4. Like pipette tips, these containers are traditionally produced from plastic, and therefore, leaching of plasticizers into the stock solution(s) is possible. Recently, some liquid-handling robot manufacturers have started producing troughs suitable for use with organic solvents that are made from materials other than plastic. Custom glass troughs can be purchased for use with organic solvents; however, they are expensive and have the potential to break with extensive use. Alternatively, metal troughs can be purchased from some vendors that are similar in cost to glass troughs but last indefinitely. Some researchers have developed a hybrid solution. They purchase inexpensive, disposable plastic troughs and line them with Teflon or polytetrafluoroethylene (PTFE) plastic bags. This approach has proven to be a very cost-effective solution that does not require custom glass or special machining.

Another concern related to transitioning to an automated liquid-handling platform is the handling of organic solvents in an open laboratory environment. In addition to being toxic, many organic solvents, such as hexane and MTBE, are very volatile and odiferous. Safe handling of organic solvents requires proper ventilation and the use of a chemical fume hood. The large size of most robots, however, prevents them from being placed within a hood. Some manufacturers have designed their robots to be self-enclosed. The top panel can then be modified to adopt an exhaust line that vents solvent fumes out of the laboratory. Although not a formal or proper chemical fume hood, this small modification makes liquid-handling robots usable in an open lab environment. An example of this enclosed configuration is shown in Figure 2.4.

The physical act of pipetting organic solvents can also be a challenge when using liquid handlers. Many liquid-handling robots use air-displaced pipette technology; a certain volume of air (headspace) is present between the sample and the pipette piston. This air cushion allows for expansion of volatile solvent vapors and can result in solvent being pushed out, or dripped, from the pipette tip. Air-displaced liquid-handling robots have been successfully implemented in multiple lipidomics labs and used in sample preparation. Improved engineering has led to the development of robots that can accurately and routinely transfer organic solvents with little or no dripping. Using pressure sensors, some robots can identify when solvents are about to drip and correct for the increased vapor pressure. Other liquid-handling robots use liquid-displaced pipettes rather than the air displacement ones. Liquid displacement pipetting involves priming the lines to the pipettes with water to minimize the headspace available for solvent vapors to expand. While effective, this approach to pipetting volatile solvents comes with increased engineering, complexity, and cost.

Despite the challenges faced with using liquid-handling robots to pipette volatile organic solvents, many labs in the field have successfully adopted this technology as part of their daily workflows. Robotics provides increased efficiency and laboratory throughput. When conducting SPE, the use of a 96-well SPE plate and a 96-well positive pressure manifold (off deck) is much more efficient than individual SPE columns processed by hand. The use of a positive pressure manifold is also more reliable and consistent in controlling sample loading, drip rate, and other variables that affect SPE. Lastly, the use of 96-well format has the advantage of being able to dry 96 samples at once with the appropriate dryer Figure 2.2c. In other laboratories, a liquid-handling robot may not process samples faster or increase the number of samples processed. There are benefits to implementing liquid-handling robots other than increased laboratory throughput. Manual extraction of lipids is labor intensive and time-consuming. By using a liquid-handling robot, the scientist can perform other tasks, while the robot performs the extractions. Also, a properly calibrated liquid-handling platform has greater pipetting accuracy and precision compared to a human. As a result, there is improved consistency when processing a large cohort of samples. Although the use of liquid-handling robots can be imperfect and has limitations, it has clear advantages when processing large numbers of samples, either from a single cohort or from multiple sample sets each day, making it a valuable tool for preanalytics in lipidomics.

2.9 Tips and Tricks

- Ultrasonic baths are often not used correctly. Ensure that the water level is correct and that samples are properly submerged, not resting directly on the bottom of the actual sonic bath. The samples should either be floated with a foam holder or placed in the tray that comes with the bath.

- When extracting lipids using any of the methods described here, a second extraction may be necessary to maximize the recovery. If being done using a test tube and Pasteur Pipette configuration for the LLE, prepare a rack of extra test tubes to hold the pipette between extractions so that it can be reused. This will ensure that extract and lipids retained in the pipette after the initial extraction is efficiently rinsed and transferred to the extract. This is only necessary when analyzing lipids with low abundance or poor ionization efficiency.
- The use of the highest quality solvents is always recommended. Background contaminants can vary between manufacturers, and changing sources without conducting a series of solvent blank experiments can lead to compromised data. Always ensure that enough solvent is available for a contiguous series of experiments to minimize this variable. If changing solvent sources is necessary, conduct the proper experiments to identify background contaminants that may interfere with lipidomics analysis.
- The use of glass, stainless steel, and Teflon/PTFE is always the best choice. However, working at the interface between biology and analytical chemistry will result in the use of plastics. Often biological samples are collected and stored in plastic tubes. In some cases, this is unavoidable, but in other cases where time allows for more advanced planning, tissues or fluids can be collected and stored into glass vials. This can have the added benefit of simplifying the extraction process by eliminating the transfer of samples between a plastic tube to a glass tube for solvent extraction.
- When using screw-cap test tubes, always use a Teflon or PTFE-lined cap. Many standard caps have liners and adhesives that are not compatible with many commonly used solvents in lipidomics analysis, leading to high background signals.
- Choice of caps for autosampler vials is important. Factors that influence this choice include configuration of an autosampler needle (possible coring and blockage), solvent evaporation, and solvent compatibility. Silicon septum with a Teflon/PTFE lining is common, but a recent report shows the background of siloxanes from these septa, especially multiple injections introduce increasing amounts of polysiloxanes along with the lipids [38]. This can have a negative impact on the analysis and should be carefully evaluated for the supplies used in each laboratory.
- When using multi-phase extraction methods that involve an aqueous component, it may be advisable to use water, a phosphate-buffered saline (PBS) solution, or a saturated brine solution. These options will influence phase separation, stability of a protein disc at the interface, and extraction efficiency of the more polar lipids. As an example, PBS yields a better protein disc and phase separation when extracting 100 μl of human plasma as described in Ref. [39].

- For unknown reasons, when centrifuging multi-phase samples, occasionally, one or more samples will not have a clean phase separation. Removing the sample from the centrifuge, gently inverting it two to three times, and recentrifuging the sample should resolve this issue. This phenomenon is generally observed when working with human plasma samples.

- It is common for scientists to utilize smaller "bench bottles" for commonly used solvents. The bottles are often accessed many times with a variety of pipettes, sometimes both glass and plastic. These bottles will over time become increasingly contaminated with plasticizers, slip-release agents, dust, skin oils, and anything else that was on the pipette or the hand (preferably gloved) that touched the pipettes. Even the most careful scientist will eventually contaminate their bench bottles. It is recommended that the researchers commit to changing out (or rinsing/cleaning) their bottles on a regular basis.
- It is preferable that any glassware used for lipidomic extractions be disposable. Washing glassware with any kind of soap or detergent should be avoided as the residue will remain in the glassware and may confound analytical results because of the commonalities of lipids, soaps, and detergents. To wash the glassware, consider using only solvents such as isopropyl alcohol, acetone, or other solvents. A final rinse with a minimum of three volumes or deionized or ultrapure water is also recommended. Also, consider baking clean glassware at 500 °C for 6–12 hours in order to remove any contaminants.
- Although there are many brands and styles of dryers for evaporating solvents in test tubes and other vials, it is important to clean the needles between samples. For those dryers that have removable needles, removing them and rinsing them in isopropanol (or sonicating them) is suggested. For dryers with fixed needles, wiping the needles with kimwipes dabbed in isopropanol is a good option.
- For some lipidomic extractions, it may be necessary to include a SPE step. This may be done to target a specific lipid class, separate polar from neutral lipids to reduce sample complexity, or remove contaminants such as traces of protein (perhaps more as a filtration step). The use of SPE is generally reserved for targeted analysis of specific lipid classes such as sterols, steroids, or other targeted lipid classes. The breadth of SPE and adequate description of the methods is beyond the scope of his chapter. An excellent resource for lipid SPE is Cyberlipid (http://cyberlipid.gerli.com) or manufacturers' websites that sell SPE products. There you will often find catalogs of SPE methods that will fit your needs.

- When cultured cells are prepared (and other biological samples), some techniques (fluorescence-activated cell sorting (FACS) sorting, organelle isolation, etc.) may use kits with reagents containing surfactants or polymers. Sometimes, these kits or procedures use solutions that are proprietary and do not list all components. If in doubt, it is always advisable to perform a preliminary lipidomics analysis on any suspect reagents before exposing valuable samples to them. Polymers and surfactants mimic lipids and can lead to challenges in sample preparation, MS, and data analysis. Identifying sources of these additives before the samples are collected and processed is important.

- The use of syringes made of glass-, metal-, and solvent-resistant polymers are ideal for transferring or dispensing small volumes of organic solvents but lack benefits of automation. Some vendors have incorporated automation with syringes (Figure 2.2b). These models are capable of multiple levels of automation, including repeat pipetting, which is ideal for addition of standards to large sets of samples when dispensing volumes of 10–20 μl. These tools are also useful for removing fixed volumes from LLEs, which is difficult to do manually with volumetric glass pipettes. Use of standard lab pipettes is not ideal because of the plastic tips and challenges with air-displaced pipetting and organic solvents. Although these syringe-based systems do not offer the convenience of disposable tips and must be thoroughly rinsed between steps, they can be a beneficial tool in preanalytics for lipidomics analysis.

- As a guide to the reader, Figure 2.5 offers a flowchart to help guide decisions and planning steps for all aspects of preanalytics.

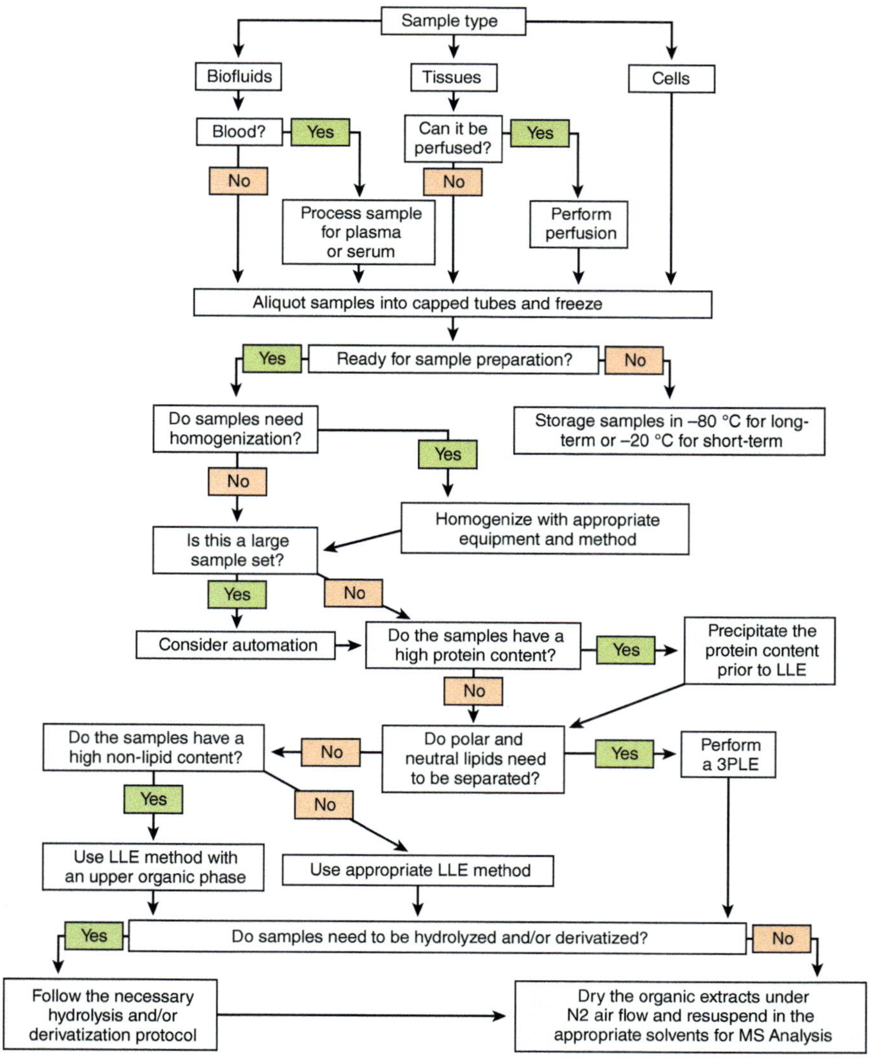

Figure 2.5 Flow chart summarizing preanalytics for lipidomics analysis.

Acknowledgments

We thank Nancy Heard for assistance preparing figures and Stacy McDonald for editorial review.

References

1 Lippi, G., Salvagno, G.L., Montagnana, M. et al. (2006). Influence of the needle bore size used for collecting venous blood samples on routine clinical chemistry testing. *Clin. Chem. Lab. Med.* 44 (8): 1009–1014.

2 WHO Organization (2010). *WHO Guidelines on Drawing Blood*. World Health Organization Press.

3 Burla, B. et al. (2018). MS-based lipidomics of human blood plasma: a community-initiated position paper to develop accepted guidelines. *J. Lipid Res.* 59 (10): 2001–2017.

4 Han, X. (2016). Lipidomics: comprehensive mass spectrometry of lipids. In: *Mass Spectrometry* (ed. D.M. Desiderio and J.A. Loo), 283–287. NJ: Wiley.

5 Ulmer, C.Z. et al. (2021). A review of efforts to improve lipid stability during sample preparation and standardization efforts to ensure accuracy in the reporting of lipid measurements. *Lipids* 56 (1): 3–16.

6 Wang, X. et al. (2015). Phenylmethanesulfonyl fluoride pretreatment stabilizes plasma lipidome in lipidomic and metabolomic analysis. *Anal. Chim. Acta* 893: 77–83.

7 Roche, I.A.D.L. and Andrews, C.J. (1973). Changes in phospholipid composition of a winter wheat cultivar during germination at 2C and 24C. *Plant Physiol.* 51: 468–473.

8 Xia, F. and Wan, J.B. (2021). Chemical derivatization strategy for mass spectrometry-based lipidomics. *Mass Spectrom. Rev.* e21729.

9 Liu, K., Liu, Y., and Chen, F. (2019). Effect of storage temperature on lipid oxidation and changes in nutrient contents in peanuts. *Food Sci. Nutr.* 7 (7): 2280–2290.

10 Wazir, H. et al. (2019). Effects of storage time and temperature on lipid oxidation and protein co-oxidation of low-moisture shredded meat products. *Antioxidants* 8 (10): 486, 1–417.

11 Bowden, J.A. et al. (2017). Harmonizing lipidomics: NIST interlaboratory comparison exercise for lipidomics using SRM 1950-metabolites in frozen human plasma. *J. Lipid Res.* 58 (12): 2275–2288.

12 Liu, X. et al. (2018). Serum or plasma, what is the difference? Investigations to facilitate the sample material selection decision making process for metabolomics studies and beyond. *Anal. Chim. Acta* 1037: 293–300.

13 Yu, Z. et al. (2011). Differences between human plasma and serum metabolite profiles. *PLoS One* 6 (7): e21230.

14 Ishikawa, M. et al. (2014). Plasma and serum lipidomics of healthy white adults shows characteristic profiles by subjects' gender and age. *PLoS One* 9 (3): e91806.

15 Gonzalez-Covarrubias, V. et al. (2013). The influence of citrate, EDTA, and heparin anticoagulants to human plasma LC-MS lipidomic profiling. *Metabolomics* 9: 337–348.

16 Khadka, M. et al. (2019). The effect of anticoagulants, temperature, and time on the human plasma metabolome and lipidome from healthy donors as determined by liquid chromatography-mass spectrometry. *Biomolecules* 9 (5): 200.

17 Jonasdottir, H.S. et al. (2018). Effects of anticoagulants and storage conditions on clinical oxylipid levels in human plasma. *Biochim. Biophys. Acta, Mol. Cell. Biol. Lipids* 1863 (12): 1511–1522.

18 Bowen, R.A. and Remaley, A.T. (2014). Interferences from blood collection tube components on clinical chemistry assays. *Biochem. Med.* 24 (1): 31–44.

19 Holcapek, M., Liebisch, G., and Ekroos, K. (2018). Lipidomic analysis. *Anal. Chem.* 90 (7): 4249–4257.

20 Liebisch, G. et al. (2017). Reporting of lipidomics data should be standardized. *Biochim. Biophys. Acta, Mol. Cell. Biol. Lipids* 1862: 747–751.

21 Matthan, N.R. et al. (2010). Long-term fatty acid stability in human serum cholesteryl ester, triglyceride, and phospholipid fractions. *J. Lipid Res.* 51 (9): 2826–2832.

22 Horing, M. et al. (2021). Accurate lipid quantification of tissue homogenates requires suitable sample concentration, solvent composition, and homogenization procedure – a case study in murine liver. *Metabolites* 11 (6): 365.

23 Folch, J., Lees, M., and Stanley, G.H.S. (1957). A simple method for the isolation and purification of total lipides from animal tissues. *J. Biol. Chem.* 226: 497–509.

24 Matyash, V. et al. (2008). Lipid extraction by methyl-*tert*-butyl ether for high-throughput lipidomics. *J. Lipid Res.* 49 (5): 1137–1146.

25 Blight, E.G. and Dyer, W.J. (1959). A rapid method of total lipid extraction and purification. *Can. J. Biochem. Physiol.* 37: 911–917.

26 Carlson, L. (1985). Extraction of lipids from human whole serum and lipoproteins and from rat liver tissue with methylene chloride – methanol: a comparison with extraction with chloroform-methanol. *Clin. Chim. Acta* 149: 89–93.

27 Vale, G. et al. (2019). Three-phase liquid extraction: a simple and fast method for lipidomic workflows. *J. Lipid Res.* 60 (3): 694–706.

28 Nagano, K. et al. (2006). Enhancement of renal carcinogenicity by combined inhalation and oral exposures to chloroform in male rats. *J. Toxicol. Environ. Health A* 69 (20): 1827–1842.

29 Adhikari, N. and Joshi, D.R. (2019). An overview on common organic solvents and their toxicity. *J. Pharmaceut. Res. Int.* 28 (3): 1–18.

30 Cequier-Sanchez, E. et al. (2008). Dichloromethane as a solvent for lipid extraction and assessment of lipid classes and fatty acids from samples of different natures. *J. Agric. Food Chem.* 56 (12): 4297–4303.

31 Lofgren, L. et al. (2012). The BUME method: a novel automated chloroform-free 96-well total lipid extraction method for blood plasma. *J. Lipid Res.* 53 (8): 1690–1700.

32 Alshehry, Z.H. et al. (2015). An efficient single phase method for the extraction of plasma lipids. *Metabolites* 5 (2): 389–403.

33 Wong, M.W.K. et al. (2019). Comparison of single phase and biphasic extraction protocols for lipidomic studies using human plasma. *Front. Neurol.* 10: 879.

34 Reis, A. et al. (2013). A comparison of five lipid extraction solvent systems for lipidomic studies of human LDL. *J. Lipid Res.* 54 (7): 1812–1824.

35 Rose, H.G. and Oaklander, M. (1965). Improved procedure for the extraction of lipids from human erythrocytes. *J. Lipid Res.* 6: 428–431.

36 Cruz, M. et al. (2016). Improved butanol-methanol (BUME) method by replacing acetic acid for lipid extraction of biological samples. *Lipids* 51 (7): 887–896.

37 McDonald, J.G. et al. (2008). Identification and quantitation of sorbitol-based nuclear clarifying agents extracted from common laboratory and consumer plasticware made of polypropylene. *Anal. Chem.* 80 (14): 5532–5541.

38 Benke, P.I. et al. (2020). Impact of ion suppression by sample cap liners in lipidomics. *Anal. Chim. Acta* 1137: 136–142.

39 McDonald, J.G. et al. (2012). A comprehensive method for extraction and quantitative analysis of sterols and secosteroids from human plasma. *J. Lipid Res.* 53 (7): 1399–1409.

3

Direct Infusion (Shotgun) Electrospray Mass Spectrometry

Marcus Höring and Gerhard Liebisch

University Hospital of Regensburg, Institute of Clinical Chemistry and Laboratory Medicine, Franz-Josef-Strauß-Allee 11, 93053 Regensburg, Germany

3.1 Introduction

The essential role of lipids for life is not merely limited to their function as a supplier of energy (storage of excess energy) or building blocks for cell membranes to form physical barriers [1, 2]. Lipids are also bioactive molecules either as signaling molecules [3–5] or as determinants of the biophysical properties of membranes regulating membrane budding/fission events and protein function [6–8]. Therefore, the lipid compositions of membranes of cell organelles are characteristic [2, 9] and tightly regulated [10] also in their asymmetric distribution [11]. In order to get more insights into the role of lipids, it is not sufficient to analyze only a subset of lipid molecules. Instead, it requires their quantitative and comprehensive analysis.

With the development of robust, easy-to-use mass spectrometers (MSs) in combination with electrospray ionization (ESI-MS), the analysis of lipid structure became possible [12]. In the 1990s, ESI-MS was applied for the analysis of lipid structures [13], and Han and Gross reported the use of ESI tandem mass spectrometry (ESI-MS/MS) for the quantification of human erythrocyte plasma membrane phospholipids [14] and structural analysis of phospholipids [15]. In 1997, Brügger et al. presented another seminal work that showed quantification of various phospholipid classes at the picomole level by nano-ESI-MS/MS [16]. The first application of flow injection analysis (FIA) coupled to ESI-MS/MS for lipid species quantification was reported in 1999 by Liebisch et al. for sphingosine-based ceramide species [17]. Ekroos et al. introduced a quadrupole time-of-flight MS (QTOF) for the quantitative profiling of phospholipids using multiple precursor ion scans (PISs) [18]. Further, the Shevchenko group pioneered the application of an automated nanospray chip ion source [19, 20]. It was also coupled to high resolution/accurate mass (HRAM) such as Orbitrap instruments [21] to quantify lipid species. In 2005, Han and Gross

Mass Spectrometry for Lipidomics: Methods and Applications, First Edition.
Edited by Michal Holčapek and Kim Ekroos.
© 2023 WILEY-VCH GmbH. Published 2023 by WILEY-VCH GmbH.

introduced the term "Shotgun lipidomics" [22], which is frequently used to describe the direct infusion analysis of crude lipid extracts.

Although direct infusion mass spectrometry constitutes the starting point of lipidomics, it still represents one of the three main lipidomic workflows used today [23]. This is mainly because of its simple instrumental setup, short analysis times, straightforward quantification, automated data processing, and broad applicability [24]. In the past years, the number of reports containing lipidomic data has been grown rapidly. However, the quality of data is sometimes substantially compromised by incorrect or false annotations [25–27]. Therefore, the Lipidomics Standards Initiative (LSI; https://lipidomics-standards-initiative.org), an interest group of the International Lipidomics Society (ILS; https://lipidomicssociety.org), started to develop guidelines for the major lipidomic workflows [28, 29].

In this chapter, we discuss the current concepts of direct infusion (shotgun) lipidomics with an emphasis on the current standards and potential pitfalls. For researchers new to the field, we introduce the complexity of lipidomes (see Section 3.2) and basic mass spectrometry principles to resolve the signals of lipid molecules (see Section 3.3).

3.2 Complexity of Crude Lipid Extracts

3.2.1 Main Lipid Classes in Mammalian Samples

Direct infusion MS typically analyzes the crude lipid extracts. Therefore, it is important to understand which lipid classes and species are expected within the respective sample material. In the following, we will focus on the lipid compositions of mammalian samples. Today, lipids are categorized according to the LIPID MAPS nomenclature introduced in 2005 by Fahy et al. [30]. This system defines eight lipid categories: fatty acyls (FAs), glycerolipids (GLs), glycerophospholipids (GPs), sphingolipids (SPs), sterol lipids (STs), prenol lipids (PRs), saccharolipids (SLs), and polyketides (PKs). Each of the categories is subdivided into lipid classes, e.g. phosphatidylcholine (PC) in the GP category.

The typical membranes of mammalian cells contain about two-thirds of glycerophospholipid, about 25% cholesterol, and 10% sphingolipid molecules (Figure 3.1) [31]. The main glycerophospholipid is commonly PC, followed by phosphatidylethanolamine (PE), phosphatidylserine (PS), and phosphatidylinositol (PI) [32]. The major sphingolipid class is sphingomyelin (SM), which could contribute at about 10% of the membrane lipids in human blood cells [32]. Cholesterol has a high impact on membrane fluidity [33] and therefore shows a substantial variation among cell types with up to 50% for red blood cells [32].

Besides membrane lipids, mammalian cells contain a variable content of storage lipids deposited in lipid droplets. The most prominent lipid classes in lipid droplets are triacylglycerols (TGs) and cholesteryl ester (CE) (Figure 3.2). In adipocytes, TGs represent the main lipid class [34], as well as in adipose tissue, with the TG content up to 99% [35]. In blood plasma from (fasted) healthy human subjects, the content

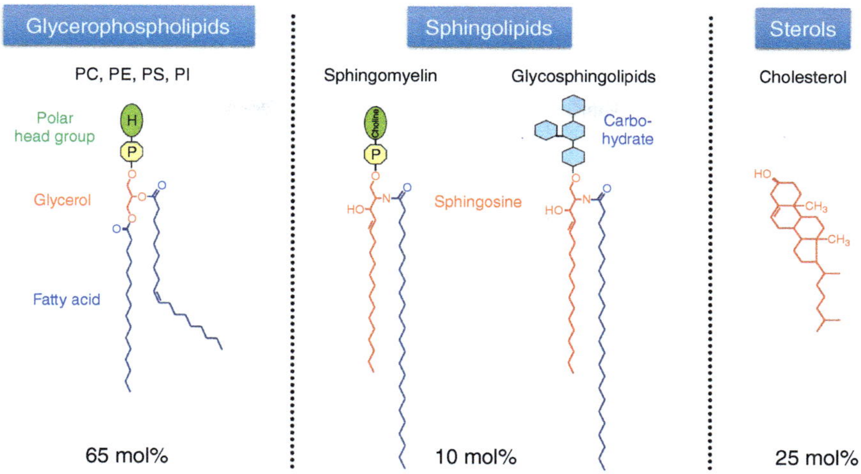

Figure 3.1 Lipid composition of mammalian cell membranes. The main lipid categories of mammalian cells are depicted. The major glycerophospholipid classes are phosphatidylcholine (PC), phosphatidylethanolamine (PE), phosphatidylserine (PS), and phosphatidylinositol (PI). Source: Adapted from van Meer and de Kroon [31].

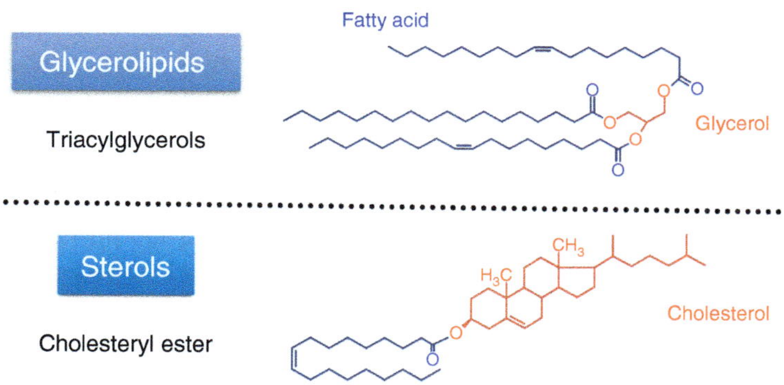

Figure 3.2 Main lipid classes stored in lipid droplets of mammalian cells.

of CE is higher than that of TG. The transporters of blood lipids, the lipoproteins, comprise TG-rich particles (chylomicrons and very low-density lipoprotein [VLDL]) as well as CE-rich lipoproteins (LDL and high-density lipoprotein [HDL]) [36]. In contrast to mammalian cells or tissues, blood plasma contains a high fraction of lysophosphatidylcholine (LPC) in HDL and bound to albumin. These examples demonstrate that the lipid composition may vary substantially between different sample materials and therefore may require adaptation of the analysis strategy.

3.2.2 Bond Types as Structural Features

Their polar head groups differentiate glycerophospholipid classes (Figure 3.3), which mainly consist of diacyl species. However, besides an ester bond at the

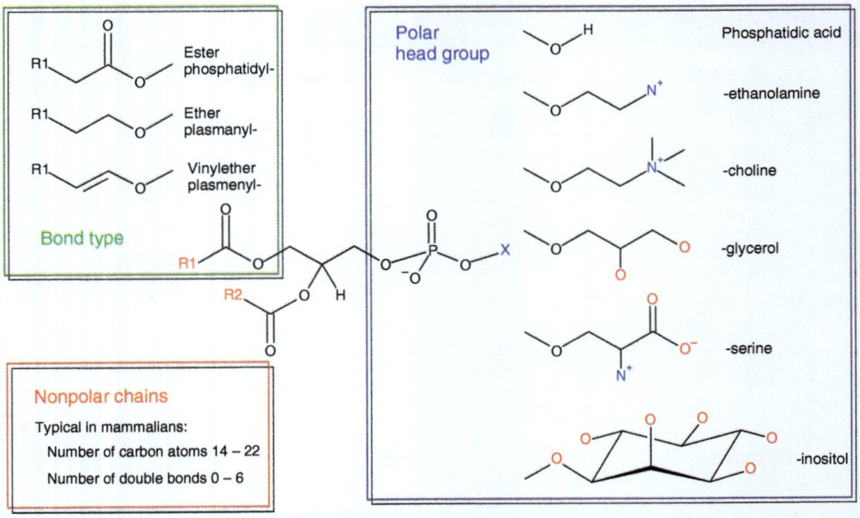

Figure 3.3 Glycerophospholipid structures in mammalian cells. The lipid class of glycerophospholipid is defined by its polar head group. Subclasses are defined by the type of bond at the *sn*1-position. The nonpolar chains vary in their number of carbon atoms and double bonds (DBs).

sn1-position, there also occur species with an ether bond and ethers with a double bond (DB) at position 1 termed as plasmanyl- or alkyl and plasmenyl- or plasmalogens, respectively. The occurrence of alkyl and plasmalogens is characteristic for cells or tissues. In particular, heart and brain [37, 38] contain high fractions of plasmalogens. Interestingly, heart contains a high fraction of PC plasmalogen, whereas brain almost exclusively contains PE plasmalogens. Typically, PE and PC are the only glycerophospolipid classes that contain relevant fractions of alkyl species, and the diacyl fraction is higher than the plasmalogen fraction. For example, granulocytes are the only human blood cells that contain a larger fraction of PE plasmalogens (PE P) than diacyl-PE [32], and in human plasma, the HDL fraction contains the highest amount of PE P compared to other lipoprotein fractions [39].

3.2.3 Fatty Acids as the Major Building Blocks

Lipidomic analysis provides information not only about lipid class but also about lipid species, i.e. their fatty acyls/alkyl linked to the core structure (see Section 3.3.1 for annotation of lipids). In order to set up the analysis and evaluate the data appropriately, it is necessary to have information about this elemental building block of the majority of lipid classes.

A convenient method to obtain fatty acid profiles is gas chromatography (GC) coupled to either flame ionization detection (FID) or GC-MS, which typically applies derivatization to fatty acid methyl ester (FAME) [40]. The most abundant fatty acids in mammalian samples are palmitic acid with 16 carbon atoms and no DB (FA 16:0) and FAs with 18 carbon atoms, i.e. saturated stearic acid,

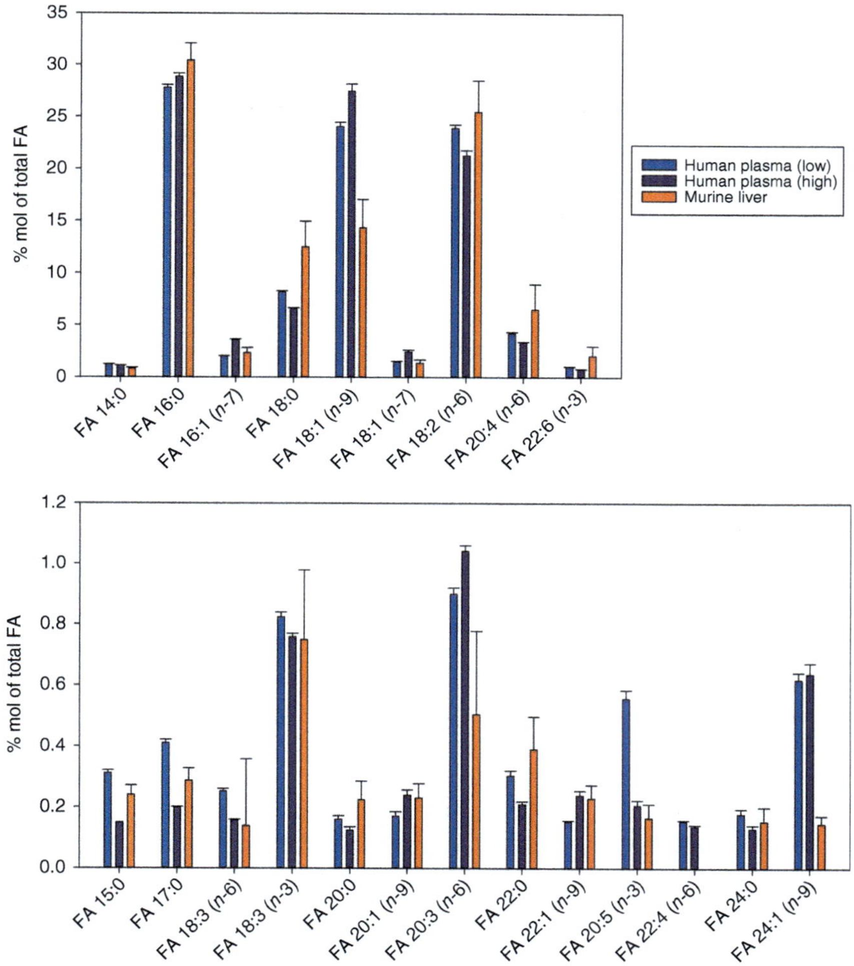

Figure 3.4 Fatty acid profiles. The total fatty acid compositions were analyzed by GC–MS of human plasma with low and high total lipid content (*n* = 6 replicates. Source: Adapted from Ecker et al. [40] and murine liver (*n* = 6; unpublished data).

monounsaturated oleic acid (cis DB at carbon 9; FA 18:1*n*-9), and linoleic acid (FA 18:2) (Figure 3.4). The main FAs with more than two DBs are arachidonic acid (FA 20:4*n*-6) and docosahexanoic acid (DHA, FA 22:6*n*-3).

3.2.4 Lipid Species and Double-Bond Series

The FAs available in a biological system, i.e. a cell, are used to synthesize complex lipids. However, FAs are not incorporated into distinct lipid classes randomly but instead highly regulated in order to create a specific composition of membranes required for their respective biological function [2, 9, 10]. As shown in Figure 3.4 in

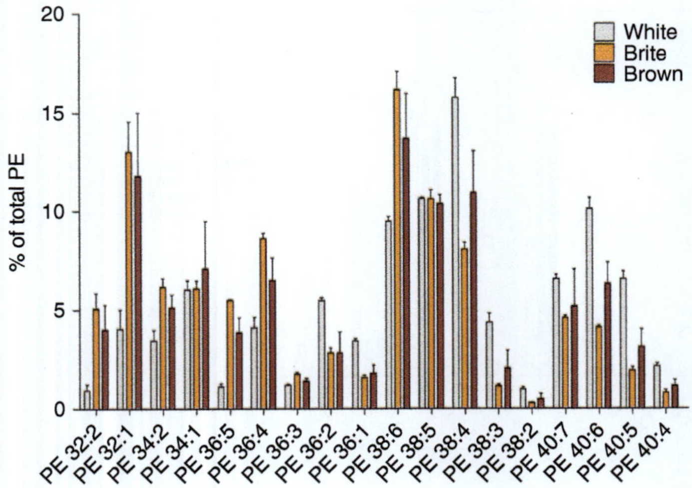

Figure 3.5 Lipid species of PE. PE species profiles of murine white, brite, and brown adipocytes analyzed by FIA–ESI–MS/MS. Preadipocytes, isolated from inguinal (white), epididymal white (brite), and intrascapular (brown) adipose tissue, were *ex vivo* differentiated to adipocytes ($n = 3$). Source: Schweizer et al. [34]/PLOS/CC BY-4.0.

mammals, FAs are dominated by even numbers of carbons, and the number of DBs increases with their length up to six DBs in DHA. The abundance of FAs represents the basis for species profiles observed for complex lipid classes. A basic lipidomic analysis provides data at the species level, i.e. sum of both acyl/alkyl chains (see details of annotation in 3.3.1). Thus, glycerophospholipids typically comprise a series of species with an increasing number of DBs for the same number of carbon atoms. For example, PE in adipocyte samples contains PE species with 38 carbons and two to six DBs (Figure 3.5). Advanced lipidomics analysis are eligible to differentiate acyl combinations, e.g. PE 18:0_20:4, PE 18:1_20:4, and PE 16:0_22:6.

3.3 Introduction to Mass Spectrometry of Lipids

3.3.1 Annotation of Lipid Structures Analyzed by MS

Annotation of lipid structures derived from MS follows two major principles:

(1) Annotate only what you see, i.e. only experimentally proven structural details are assigned.
(2) Use biological intelligence as the annotation principle, indicating that the current knowledge about lipid classes and its building blocks is applied for an appropriate annotation (eventually also for justified assumptions).

These principles are mirrored in a hierarchical annotation system [41, 42] that was updated in 2020 [43] (Figure 3.6).

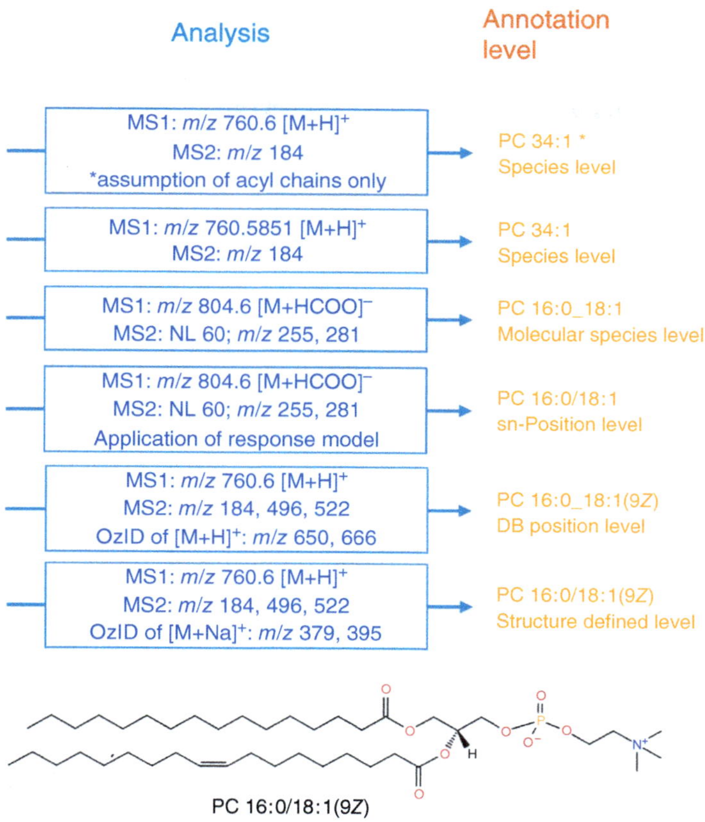

Figure 3.6 Hierarchical annotation of PC. Annotation of lipid species follows a hierarchical system for MS-derived lipid structures. Source: Adapted from Liebisch et al. [43]. Only structural details justified by experimental data are annotated. For mass spectrometric identification and OzID (ozone-induced dissociation) see Section 3.7. (*) Annotation is based on the assumption that only even carbon number fatty acyls are present.

The most frequently reported annotation levels are as follows:

- "Species level" as the lowest hierarchical level, representing the sum composition of the variable constituents, that is, the sum of carbon atoms and double-bond equivalents (DBEs); when additional oxygen atoms are present, their number is added separated by a semicolon. For example, PC 34:1, for oxygenated species, PC 38:4;O.
- "Molecular species level" describes the constituent fatty acyl/alkyl residues without the definition of their *sn*-position in glycerolipids indicated by an underscore. For example, PC 16:0_18:1 and PC 18:0_20:4;O.
- "*sn*-position level" defines the position of fatty acyl/alkyl constituents at the glycerol backbone indicated by a slash. For example PC 16:0/18:1 and PC 18:0/20:4;O.

The important rules/features for annotation are as follows:

- Report applied assumptions together with the data.
- DBEs are annotated instead of the number of DBs because cyclic structures, oxo, hydroxyl, and DBs are frequently isomeric and require additional MS data for structural verification.
- The number of O-atoms instead of hydroxy groups is applied for the annotation of sphingolipids, e.g. Cer d18:1/16:0 should be annotated as Cer 18:1;O2/18:0.
- The position of DB (if known) is indicated by a number according to the Δ-nomenclature (*Z* for cis and *E* for trans), for example, FA 20:4(5*Z*,8*Z*,11*Z*,14*Z*) for arachidonic acid.
- Only experimentally proven structural details are annotated (when known, including their position), for example, FA 20:4;12OH.
- Alkyl species are denoted with "O-" and plasmalogens (vinyl ether bond) with "P-," for example, PC O-34:1 and PE P-16:0/20:4.

3.3.2 Isomers

The additional complexity in the mass spectrometry analysis of lipids is the presence of multiple isomeric molecules (Figure 3.7). Isomers are defined as molecules or ions with identical sum formulae but with a distinct arrangement of atoms. Isomerism could occur between lipid classes such as PC and PE, where PE with three additional carbon atoms in the nonpolar chains is isomeric to PC, e.g. PC 33:1 is isomeric to PE 36:1. Moreover, different combinations of acyl/alkyl chains are isomeric, such as PE 18:0/18:1 and PE 16:0/20:1. Further, variations in the *sn*-position (PE 18:0/18:1 and PE 18:1/18:0) and DB positions result in multiple isomers, for example, 18:1(9*Z*) and 18:1(11*Z*), both of which are present in the samples of mammalian origin (Figure 3.4).

Because isomers (when they form the same ions) have identical mass-to-charge (*m/z*) ratios, their differentiation requires an additional analytical dimension, such as tandem mass spectrometry (MS/MS) or chromatographic separation.

A list of isomeric overlaps present in lipid extracts is shown in Table 3.1.

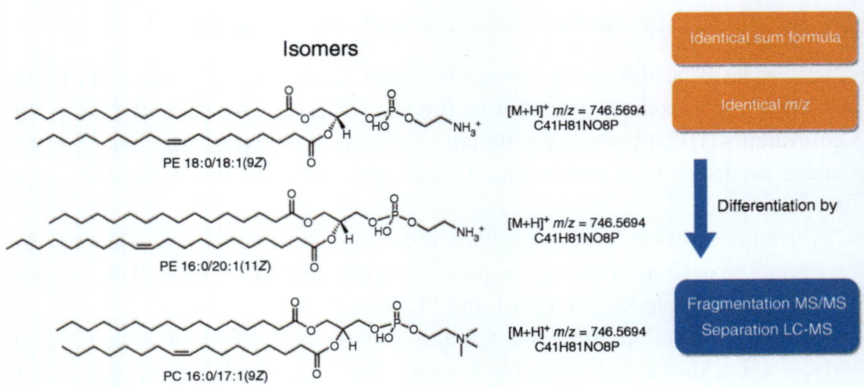

Figure 3.7 Isomeric lipid molecules.

Table 3.1 Isomerism of lipid species.

Lipid classes	Type of overlap	Example
(A) Positive- and negative-ion mode		
PE O-lysophosphatidylethanolamine (LPE)	PE O = LPE	$[PE\ O\text{-}26{:}1+H]^+ = [LPE\ 26{:}1+H]^+$
PC O-LPC	PC O = LPC	$[PC\ O\text{-}26{:}1+H]^+ = [LPC\ 26{:}1+H]^+$
(B) Positive-ion mode		
PC-PE	$PC = PE+3CH_2$	$[PC\ 32{:}0+H]^+ = [PE\ 35{:}0+H]^+$ $[PC\ 32{:}0+Na]^+ = [PE\ 35{:}0+Na]^+$
PC-PA	$[PC+H]^+ = [PA+5CH_2+DB+NH_4]^+$	$[PC\ 32{:}0+H]^+ = [PA\ 37{:}1+NH_4]^+$
PE-PA	$[PE+H]^+ = [PA+C_2H_4+DB+NH_4]^+$	$[PE\ 34{:}1+H]^+ = [PA\ 36{:}2+NH_4]^+$
PS-PG	$[PS+H]^+ = [PG+2DB+NH_4]^+$	$[PS\ 34{:}1+H]^+ = [PG\ 34{:}2+NH_4]^+$
SM-EPC	$SM = EPC+3CH_2$	$[SM\ 34{:}1;O2+H]^+ = [EPC\ 37{:}1;O2+H]^+$
(C) Negative-ion mode		
PC-PS[a]	$[PC+HCOO]^- = [PS+3CH_2\text{-}DB\text{-}H]^-$	$[PC\ 33{:}1+HCOO]^- = [PS\ 36{:}0\text{-}H]^-$
PC-PS	$[PC+CH_3COO]^- = [PS+4CH_2\text{-}DB\text{-}H]^-$	$[PC\ 32{:}1+CH_3COO]^- = [PS\ 36{:}0\text{-}H]^-$
All lipid classes that form acetate/formate adducts[a]	$[X+CH_2+HCOO]^- = [X+CH_3COO]$	$[PC\ 34{:}1+HCOO]^- = [PC\ 33{:}1+CH_3COO]^-$ $[Cer\ 35{:}1;O2+HCOO]^- = [Cer\ 34{:}1;O2+CH_3COO]^-$

Isomeric overlap present in (A) both, (B) positive-, and (C) negative-ion modes. DB = Double bond. For lipid class abbreviations, see Table 3.5.
[a]Acetate salts of LC–MS grade can be contaminated with trace amounts of formate, which can lead to false-positive identification. Methanol can be oxidized to formic acid during electrospray ionization.
Source: Reproduced from https://lipidomics-standards-initiative.org/resources/isomeric-overlap.

3.3.3 Isobars and the Type-II Isotopic Overlap

Another overlap in the mass spectra of lipid mixtures results from isobars. Isobars have the same nominal mass but differ in their exact m/z because of their different sum formulas (Figure 3.8). Thus, isobars can be differentiated by mass spectrometry but require sufficient mass resolution. For example, isobars resulting from different bond types such as diacyl PC 33:1 and alkyl PC O-34:1 have only a m/z difference of 36 mDa, which cannot be resolved by low mass resolving analyzers such as a quadrupole but can be resolved by high-resolution instruments such as a time-of-flight (TOF) analyzer (see Section 3.7 for instrument types).

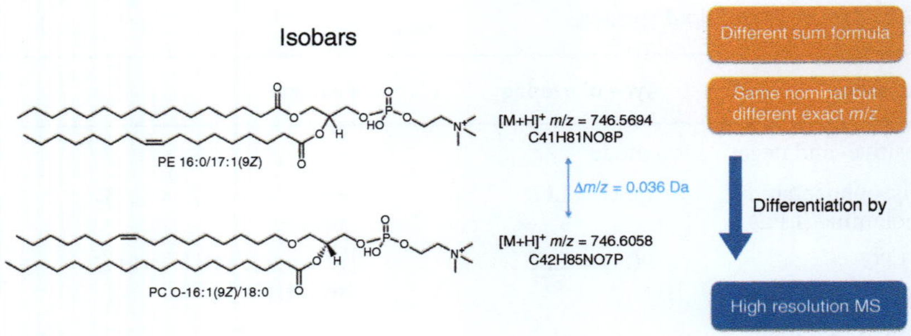

Figure 3.8 Isobaric lipid molecules.

A very important consideration in the analysis of lipidomes is the so-called Type-II isotopic overlap [44]. This isobaric interference occurs in DB series within the same lipid class (Figure 3.9). The second isotopic peak of a species with one additional DB overlaps with the monoisotopic peak of the adjacent species. For example, [PC 36:1+H+$^{13}C_2$]$^+$ overlaps with [PC 36:0+H]$^+$ and exhibits only a mass difference of 8.94 mDa. Table 3.2 shows a list of isobaric overlaps present in lipid extracts.

3.4 Overview of Direct Infusion MS Workflows

Besides separation-based lipidomics and imaging, direct infusion lipidomics represents one of the three main lipidomic workflows used today. It refers to the mass spectrometry analysis of lipid extracts without chromatographic separation (Figure 3.10). This workflow comprises in principle three analytical steps: sample preparation (preanalytics, lipid extraction, and preparation of lipid infusate), infusion of the lipid mixture, and mass spectrometry analysis. The analysis of mass spectra includes two subsequent steps: the identification and quantification of lipid molecules. All steps are discussed in the following sections with considerations, which are important to ensure a high data quality.

3.5 Sample Preparation

Details concerning sample stability and other preanalytical issues as well as extraction of lipids are discussed in detail in Chapter 2. In the following, we highlight only a few important points related to direct infusion lipidomics.

3.5.1 Preanalytics – Sample Stability

In general, the major lipid classes typically analyzed by direct infusion lipidomics are more stable compared to the minor products of oxygenation or lipolytic action. However, it is important to consider the stability of all lipids in any lipidomic

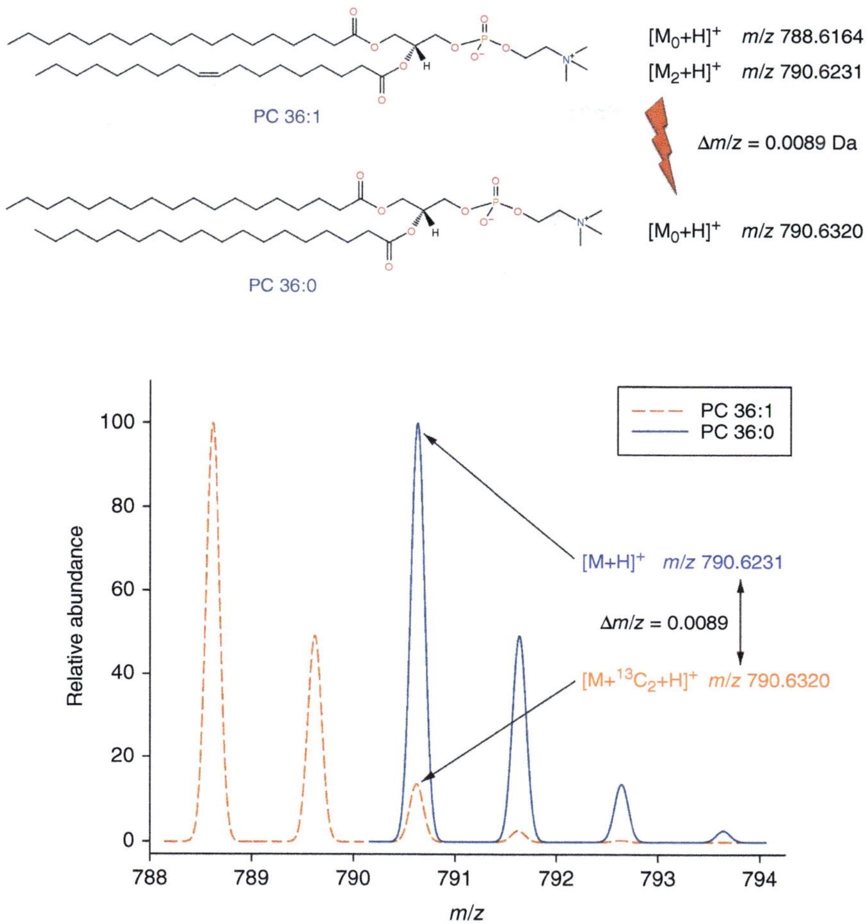

Figure 3.9 Type-II isotopic overlap. The figure displays the Type-II isotopic overlap of PC 36:1 and PC 36:0. The relative abundance of the isotopologues is normalized to the monoisotopic peak M+0. Source: Köfeler et al. [28]/Elsevier/CC BY-4.0.

workflow. Prevention of oxidative modification requires addition of radical scavengers such as butylated hydroxytoluene (BHT) or addition of inert gases [45]. Lipolytic degradation can be monitored by lipid class ratios, e.g. LPC/PC for phospholipase or Cer/SM for sphingomyelinase action [46]. In particular, the latter ratio exhibits a high sensitivity in mouse tissues.

When solid samples are subjected to lipid extraction, a homogenization step is required to ensure sufficient lipid recovery. Either samples are homogenized in the extraction solvent [47–49] or homogenized to generate a fluidic sample at a defined concentration [50]. The latter permits a straightforward handling of quasi-fluidic samples including their introduction into several workflows with exact defined amounts [51], which is important to control lipid concentration in the extracts (see below). Moreover, homogenization of larger sample portions avoids analysis of

Table 3.2 Isobaric overlap of lipid species.

Lipid classes	Type of overlap	Δ*m/z*	Examples
(A) Positive- and negative-ion modes			
DB-containing classes	$[M+DB+^{13}C_2]\approx[M]^a$	0.009	$[PC\ 32:1+H+^{13}C_2]^+\approx[PC\ 32:0+H]^+$
Glycerolipids	$[M]\approx[M+CH_2+O]$	0.036	$[PC\ 33:1+H]^+\approx[PC\ O\text{-}34:1+H]^+$
Sphingolipids	$[M]\approx[M+CH_2\text{-}DB\text{-}O\text{-}atom]$	0.036	[SM 42:2;O3] ≈ [SM 43:1;O2]
PI-PS	$[PI]\approx[PS+6CH_2+5DB+^{13}C]$	0.002	$[PI\ 34:1\text{-}H]^-\approx[PS\ 40:6\text{-}H+^{13}C]^-$
PC-SM	$[PC+^{13}C]\approx[SM$ with $2O\text{-}atoms+4CH_2\text{-}DB]$	0.065	$[PC\ 38:3+^{13}C]\approx[SM\ 42:2;O2]$
(B) Positive-ion mode			
DB-containing classes	$[M+Na]^+\approx[M+2CH_2+3DB+H]^+$	0.002	$[PC\ 34:1+Na]^+\approx[PC\ 36:4+H]^+$
DB-containing classes	$[M+^{13}C+Na]^+\approx[M+CH_2+4DB+NH_4]^+$	0.006	$[TG\ 52:2+^{13}C+Na]^+\approx[TG\ 53:6+NH_4]^+$
PC-PS	$[PC+H]^+\approx[PS+DB+H]^+$	0.073	$[PC\ 32:0+H]^+\approx[PS\ 32:1+H]^+$
DG-CE	$[CE\ X:Y+NH_4]^+\approx[DG\ X+30:Y+NH_4]^+$	0.015	$[CE\ 18:1+NH_4]^+\approx[DG\ 38:1+NH_4]^+$
(C) Negative-ion mode			
DB-containing classes	$[M+^{35}Cl]^-\approx[M+DB+^{37}Cl]^-$	0.019	$[PC\ 34:1+^{35}Cl]^-\approx[PC\ 34:2+^{37}Cl]^-$
$PA\text{-}CL^{2-}$	$[PA\ X:Y-H]^-\approx[CL\ 2X:2Y-2H]^{2-}$	0.018	$[PA\ 34:2\text{-}H]^-\approx[CL\ 64:4\text{-}2H]^{2-}$
(D) Isobaric fragment ions			
FA fragments	FA X:Y(+O) ≈ FA X+4:Y+6(−CO)	0.021	$[FA\ 18:0\text{-}H]^-\approx[FA\ 22:6\text{-}H\text{-}CO_2]^-$
FA fragments	FA X:Y(+O) ≈ FA X+3:Y-1(−CO)	0.073	$[FA\ 20:4\text{-}H]^-\approx[FA\ 23:3\text{-}H\text{-}CO_2]^-$

Isobaric overlap present in (A) both, (B) positive-, (C) negative-ion mode and (D) isobaric FA fragment ions. DB = double bond, O = ether linkage instead of ester linkage. Lipid class abbreviations see Table 3.5.

[a] Overlap resulting from natural ^{13}C abundance of 1.1% was selected as a prevailing overlap; other isotopes such as two deuterium or ^{18}O may lead to similar isobaric overlaps

Source: Reproduced from https://lipidomics-standards-initiative.org/resources/isobaric-overlap.

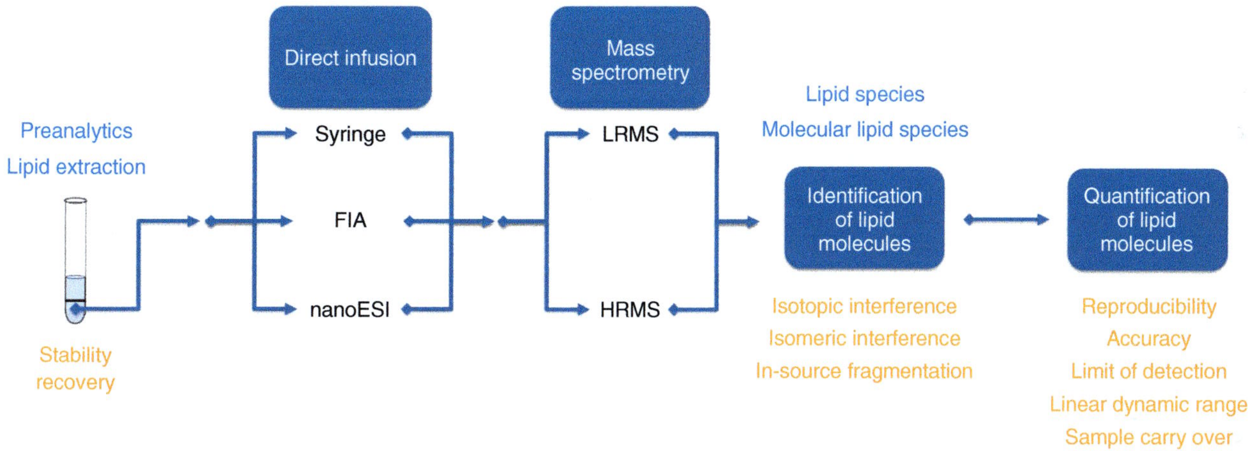

Figure 3.10 Workflows of direct infusion mass spectrometry. Crude lipid extracts are infused by a syringe, an LC system (flow injection analysis, FIA), or an automated nanospray chip-based ion source into mass spectrometers operated at nominal resolution, i.e. low mass resolution MS (LRMS) or high mass resolution (HRMS). Dedicated data analysis tools include identification and quantification of lipid molecules. Important considerations are indicated in orange to achieve high-quality results. Source: Adapted from Köfeler et al. [28].

nonrepresentative sample fractions as described for liver tissue [52]. Selection of homogenization method and solvent is important and should be evaluated for the respective samples. In particular, the degree of dispersion plays an important role, with bead-beating instruments providing a good performance [53].

3.5.2 Lipid Extraction

The most common methods for lipid extraction used for direct infusion lipidomics are chloroform based on Bligh and Dyer [54] and Folch et al. [55]. The chloroform-free alternatives are methyl tertiary-butyl ether (MTBE) [56] and butanol/methanol (BUME for plasma [57] and tissue [48]). To address lipid recovery, it is important to add the internal standards (ISs) used for quantification before extraction. For direct infusion lipidomics, only "clean" lipid extracts are recommended, indicating that contaminations with salts, proteins, or other polar molecules should be avoided.

Furthermore, specific lipid extractions can help to reduce the complexity of the lipid extract by selective recovery of lipid classes. For example, polar glycerophospholipids are practically insoluble in nonpolar solvents such as hexane. Thus, hexane could be applied to either extract or deplete nonpolar TG from samples or lipid mixtures [58]. Fractionation of the lipidome is also possible by sequential extraction as for instance by chloroform/methanol (10 : 1, v/v) for a nonpolar enriched fraction followed by chloroform/methanol (2 : 1, v/v) extracting lipid classes with a higher polarity [50].

3.5.3 Solvents, Additives, and Lipid Concentration

Crude lipid extracts are dissolved in organic solvents suitable to achieve efficient ionization of lipids. The main ionization method applied for direct infusion lipidomics is ESI. This step is of paramount importance as pH and respective additives substantially influence ionization of lipid classes [59]. These factors are applied in the concept of selective ionization described in the chapter "Multidimensional MS shotgun lipidomics" (see Section 3.7.3). Typically, quantitative direct infusion lipidomics uses solvents containing chloroform, methanol, and isopropanol with ammonium acetate [19, 60] or formate [61, 62] to promote formation of protonated or ammoniated ions in the positive-ion mode and deprotonated or acetate/formate adduct ions in the negative-ion mode [63]. A substantial increase in ionization efficiency for deprotonated ions (negative-ion mode) can be achieved by addition of amines such as methylamine [50] or trimethylamine [62]. For structural elucidation, lithiated ions formed by addition of LiOH are useful because of their information-rich product ion spectra [59, 63].

It is essential to adjust the total lipid concentration in the infusates because above 10 μM, aggregation of lipids is observed and higher than 100 μM multimers such as $[3M+2Na]^{2+}$ or $[2M+Na]^{+}$ are formed [14]. Formation of aggregates also depends on the solvent composition and lipid classes [64]. In solvents with higher polarity or for nonpolar lipid classes, aggregation could occur even at lower concentrations; thus, 10 μM is the recommended upper limit for a mixture of methanol/chloroform = 2/1 (v/v).

3.5.4 Sample Derivatization

Not all lipid classes are sufficiently ionized by ESI, in particular when polar groups are missing, e.g. for free cholesterol (FC). Moreover, less-abundant lipids are frequently not analyzable by direct infusion analysis in complex lipid mixtures because of insufficient intensities. Another drawback of direct analysis could be a lack of specificity, e.g. isomeric or isobaric overlap (see Sections 3.3.2 and 3.3.3). Therefore, various derivatization strategies are described to overcome these limitations (see for reviews, Refs. [65, 66]). Derivatizations aim to increase the ionization efficiency or permit mass spectrometric differentiation.

For example, ionization of FC can be enhanced by derivatization to an acetyl ester using acetylchloride and its analysis as an ammonium adduct ion together with endogenous CE [67]. The sensitivity of fatty acid analysis is boosted by AMPP (*N*-(4-aminomethylphenyl)pyridinium) derivatization, which introduces a fixed positive charge [68]. Differentiation of isomeric phosphatidylglycerol (PG) and bis-(monoacylglycero)phosphate (BMP) is facilitated by trimethylsilyl–diazomethane derivatization [69]. This type of derivatization for phosphate groups is also applicable for the analysis of polyphosphoinositides.

3.6 Direct Infusion

Lipid solutions are introduced into the MS by the following methods:

- Syringe pump: Samples are loaded into a glass syringe and are delivered at microliter/min flow rates [22].
- FIA: Samples are injected by a LC autosampler into a constant flow provided by LC pumps at flow rates of 10–20 μl/min [60, 70].
- Automated nanospray chip ion source: Each sample is introduced via separated nano-ESI needles at nanoliter/min flow rates [19, 20].

Although application of syringe pumps is the simplest way to introduce samples into MSs, it does not provide high sample throughput because it includes various manual steps such as loading the syringe with the sample, connecting to MS, and cleaning of the syringe. However, it provides extensive analysis time at relatively low sample consumption.

FIA methods using triple-quadrupole MS (QqQ) are developed for high-throughput analysis and applied for various lipid classes including ceramide [17], LPC [71], PC [60], and CE/FC [67]. Recently, FIA was also coupled to high-resolution MS [72]. These methods apply a constant flow rate during MS analysis window, run flow gradients for sample loading, and wash out. The latter is critical to avoid sample carryover that is a potential disadvantage of these methods. Carryover is excluded when a nano-ESI chip source is used, and each sample is introduced via a separate needle [19, 20]. This system combines high sample throughput with practically no restriction in sample analysis time because of low sample consumption. Typically, the nano-ESI chip source is coupled to HRAM such as Orbitrap instruments [21, 73]. Furthermore, nano-ESI facilitates analysis from a very low amount of sample [16].

3.7 Mass Spectrometry Analysis

A MS has three principal components that are an ion source, a mass analyzer, and a detector. Direct infusion lipidomics approaches almost exclusively apply ESI; hence, we will focus on this ionization method. In direct infusion lipidomics, a low mass resolution (LMR) analyzer operated only in the full scan MS mode commonly does not provide useful lipidomic data. Therefore, we limit our discussion to tandem mass spectrometry using a triple-quadrupole (QqQ) analyzer as well as high-resolution instruments as the main instrumentation applied for shotgun lipidomics. This chapter is focused on the analytical principles applied in these approaches, whereas details of lipid identification are in Section 3.8.

3.7.1 Electrospray Ionization of Lipids

ESI is considered a soft ionization method that typically generates intact molecular ions that are monomeric when appropriate lipid concentrations are used (see Section 3.5.3). Lipid classes with polar head groups such as glycerophospholipids, sphingolipids such as SM, and glycosphingolipids typically form protonated $[M+H]^+$ ions in the presence of ammonium formate/acetate in the positive-ion mode. Nonpolar lipid classes such as TG and CE ionize primarily as NH_4^+ adducts [74] (see also Table 3.5). Ammoniated ions are also formed for some anionic phospholipids such as phosphatidic acid (PA), PI, and PG. Despite that this modifier supports the generation of these ions, the formation of sodiated $[M+Na]^+$ or other adduct ions can be observed.

In the negative-ion mode, polar lipid classes occur as deprotonated ions $[M-H]^-$. Of note, phosphocholine-containing lipid classes such as PC and SM could not be ionized by deprotonation because of their quaternary ammonium. They can either form adducts with formate or acetate or ionize by demethylation [75]. Some lipid classes with higher molecular masses such as cardiolipin, polyphosphoinositides, or gangliosides may also be detected as doubly charged ions.

An important aspect of ESI is that ionization of the individual molecules does not only depend on the composition of the solvents and additives [59] but also on other molecules present in the charged droplet, the so-called "matrix effect" [76]. Because of the matrix effect, the quantification requires addition of ISs (see Section 3.9.1).

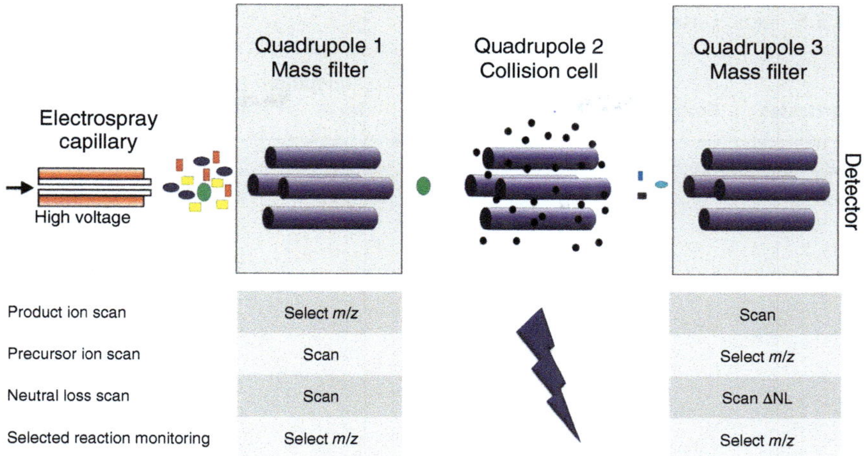

Figure 3.11 Electrospray ionization tandem mass spectrometry (ESI-MS/MS). ESI-MS/MS is typically performed using a triple-quadrupole mass spectrometer (QqQ). Displayed are the principal operation modes.

3.7.2 Tandem Mass Spectrometry

The origin of lipidomics was linked to the development of easy-to-use tandem MSs (MS/MS) based on a triple-quadrupole (QqQ) setup with ESI ion sources (Figure 3.11) [15, 16]. These instruments permit the generation of intact molecular ions by ESI and analysis of their product ions upon collision-induced dissociation (CID). Quadrupole analyzers are applicable as mass filters typically operated at unit mass resolution, i.e. differentiation of peaks separated by 1 Da (for singly charged ions) is possible. Such a mass resolution classifies them as LMR instruments.

While quadrupole 1 and 3 are operated as mass filters, the second quadrupole is filled with gas (commonly argon or nitrogen) to induce ion fragmentation by CID. For most lipid classes, the resulting fragment ions are characteristic for lipid classes. These lipid class-specific fragment ions (LCF, see Table 3.3) are used in PISs and neutral loss scans (NLSs) to analyze lipid extracts by direct infusion lipidomics. When lipid class information is combined with molecular lipid fragments (MLFs; Table 3.4), such as carboxylate anion (CA) fragments or neutral loss of acyl chains, it is possible to annotate molecular lipid species.

For example, in the positive-ion mode, protonated phosphocholine-containing lipid classes generate a prominent fragment ion of *m/z* 184.1 upon CID. A PIS of *m/z* 184 monitors these lipid classes including PC, SM [60] (Figure 3.12), and their lyso-products LPC [71] and lysosphingomyelin (LSM) [77].

Acquisition of numerous precursor ions is time-consuming by QqQ. In that case, a hybrid mass analyzer such as time QTOF could be advantageously applied in the so-called multiple precursor ion scans (MPISs) described in Section 3.7.3.

Table 3.3 Lipid class-specific fragments (LCF).

Lipid classes	Precursor ion	Neutral loss	Annotation level	Example (QqQ)	Remark
(A) Positive-ion mode					
PC	$[M+H]^+$	*m/z* 184.0733 NL 183.0661	Lipid species	Precursor *m/z* 746.6 PC O-34:1* PC 33:1**	1
PE	$[M+H]^+$	NL 141.0191	Lipid species	Precursor *m/z* 704.5 PE O-34:1* PE 33:1**	1
PS	$[M+H]^+$	NL 185.0089	Lipid species	Precursor *m/z* 748.5 PS O-34:1* PS 33:1**	1
PG	$[M+NH_4]^+$	NL 189.0402	Lipid species	Precursor *m/z* 752.5 PG O-34:1* PG 33:1**	1
PA	$[M+NH_4]^+$	NL 115.0035 NL 17.0266	Lipid species	Precursor *m/z* 678.5 PA O-34:1* PA 33:1**	1; NL of 17 has a low specificity
PI	$[M+NH_4]^+$	NL 277.0563	Lipid species	Precursor *m/z* 840.6 PI O-34:1* PI 33:1**	1
Lysophospholipid (LPX)	See respective nonlyso lipid class	Molecular lipid species		Precursor *m/z* 482.3 LPC O-16:0* LPC 15:0**	1
Diacylglycerol (DG)	$[M+NH_4]^+$	NL 35.0371 NL 17.0266	Lipid species	Precursor *m/z* 598.5 DG O-34:1* DG 33:1**	1; NL of 17 has a low specificity
SM	$[M+H]^+$	*m/z* 184.0733	Lipid species	Precursor *m/z* 703.6 SM 34:1;O2* SM 33:2;O3**	2
Cer HexCer Hex2Cer	$[M+H]^+$	Long-chain base specific product ions: e.g. *m/z* 264.2685 for sphingoid base (SPB) 18:1;O2 backbone	Molecular lipid species	Cer 18:1;O2/16:0	

Table 3.3 (Continued)

Lipid classes	Prec. ion	Neutral loss	Annotation level	Example	Remark
(B) Negative-ion mode					
PC	$[M+HCOO]^-$	NL 60.0211	Lipid species	Precursor *m/z* 790.6 PC O-34 : 1* PC 33 : 1**	1
PC	$[M+CH_3COO]^-$	NL 74.0368	Lipid species	Precursor *m/z* 804.6 PC O-34 : 1* PC 33 : 1**	1
PE	$[M-H]^-$	*m/z* 140.0118 *m/z* 196.0380	Lipid species	Precursor *m/z* 702.5 PE O-34 : 1* PE 33 : 1**	1
PG	$[M-H]^-$	*m/z* 152.9958 *m/z* 171.0063	Lipid species	Precursor *m/z* 733.5 PG O-34 : 1* PG 33 : 1**	1
PA	$[M-H]^-$	*m/z* 152.9958	Lipid species	Precursor *m/z* 659.5 PA O-34 : 1* PA 33 : 1**	1
PI	$[M-H]^-$	*m/z* 241.0119 *m/z* 223.0013 *m/z* 152.9958 *m/z* 259.0224	Lipid species	Precursor *m/z* 821.5 PI O-34 : 1* PI 33 : 1**	1
PS	$[M-H]^-$	*m/z* 152.9958 NL 87.0320	Lipid species	Precursor *m/z* 746.5 PS O-34 : 1* PS 33 : 1**	1
SM	$[M+HCOO]^-$	*m/z* 168.0431 NL 60.0211	Lipid species	Precursor *m/z* 747.6 SM 34:1;O2* SM 33:2;O3**	2
SM	$[M+CH_3COO]^-$	*m/z* 168.0431 NL 74.0368	Lipid species	Precursor *m/z* 761.6 SM 34:1;O2* SM 33:2;O3**	2
LPXs	See respective nonlyso lipid class		Molecular lipid species	Precursor *m/z* 438.3 LPE O-16:0* LPE 15:0**	1

Fragment/neutral loss characteristic for lipid classes in (A) positive- and (B) negative-ion modes. For lipid class abbreviations, see Table 3.5.
Remarks:
1) Isobaric overlap of species may require the following assumptions:
*Only acyl chains with even number of C-atoms.
**Only ester bonds are present.
2) The isobaric overlap of species may require the following assumptions:
*Sphingoid base with two hydroxyl groups.
**Sphingoid base with three hydroxyl groups.
Source: Reproduced from https://lipidomics-standards-initiative.org/resources/lipid-class-specific-fragments.

Table 3.4 Molecular lipid fragments (MLF).

Lipid classes	Prec. ion	Neutral loss	Annotation level	Example	Remark
(A) Positive-ion mode					
Glycero-phospholipids	$[M+H]^+$	NL – FA X1:Y1(+HO) NL – FA X2:Y2(+HO) NL – FA X1:Y1(−H) NL – FA X2:Y2(−H)	Molecular lipid species	PC 16:0_18:1	NL of fatty acid and ketene
LPX	See the respective diradyl lipid class		Molecular lipid species	Precursor *m/z* 482.3 LPC O-16:0* LPC 15:0**	1
Cer HexCer Hex2Cer	$[M+H]^+$	Long-chain base-specific product ions: e.g. *m/z* 264.2685 for SPB 18:1;O2 backbone	Molecular lipid species	Cer 18:1;O2/16:0	

Lipid classes	Prec. ion	Neutral loss	Annotation level	Example	Remark
(B) Negative-ion mode					
Glycero-phospholipids (except PC)	$[M-H]^-$	FA X1:Y1(+O) FA X2:Y2(+O) Additional: NL – FA X1:Y1(+HO) NL – FA X2:Y2(+HO) NL – FA X1:Y1(−H) NL – FA X2:Y2(−H)	Molecular lipid species	PX 16:0_18:1	Both acyl chain fragments should be observed; additional evidence from NL of fatty acid and ketene
PC	$[M-CH_3COO]^-$ $[M-HCOO]^-$	FA X1:Y1(+O) FA X2:Y2(+O) additional: NL – FA X1:Y1(+HO) NL – FA X2:Y2(+HO) NL – FA X1:Y1(−H) NL – FA X2:Y2(−H)	Molecular lipid species	PC 16:0_18:1	Both acyl chain fragments should be observed; additional evidence from NL of fatty acid and ketene

(Continued)

Table 3.4 (Continued)

Lipid classes	Prec. ion	Neutral loss	Annotation level	Example	Remark
LPX	See the respective nonlyso lipid class		Molecular lipid species	Precursor *m/z* 438.3 LPE O-16:0* LPE 15:0**	1

Fragment/neutral loss characteristic for molecular lipid species in (A) positive- and (B) negative-ion modes. For lipid class abbreviations, see Table 3.5.
Remarks:
1) Isobaric overlap of species may require the following assumptions:
*Only acyl chains with even number of C-atoms.
**Only ester bonds are present.
Source: Reproduced from https://lipidomics-standards-initiative.org/resources/lipid-molecular-species-fragments.

3.7.3 Multidimensional MS Shotgun Lipidomics

The concept "multidimensional mass spectrometry-based shotgun lipidomics" (MDMS-SL) was developed in the 2000s by Han and Gross [78, 79]. They applied different pHs and additives to favor the ionization of different lipid classes. Such selective ionization conditions provided "intra-source" separation because some lipid classes reveal high intensities in contrast to others [59]. These conditions were combined with two-dimensional mass spectrometry analysis, i.e. various neutral loss (NL) and PIS to evaluate lipid molecule structures (Figure 3.13). For a detailed description of this concept, we refer to Ref. [78].

3.7.4 High-Resolution Mass Spectrometry

The development of high-resolution mass spectrometers (HRMSs) such as TOF and Orbitrap facilitates the separation of isobaric ions. As described in Section 3.3.3, the mass spectra of crude lipid extracts comprise numerous signals of isobaric ions such as diacyl PC 33:1 and ether PC O-34:1 (Figure 3.14). Sufficient mass-resolving power separates these peaks. Hybrid instruments use a quadrupole to filter precursor ions for MS/MS experiments, as described above. Such instruments provide not only enhanced mass resolution but also accurate mass measurements (typically better than 3 ppm) that enable the determination of elemental composition of precursor and fragment masses. A combination of HRAM analysis with MS/MS data is required to differentiate isomeric lipid molecules (Table 3.1). When such an overlap is not present, accurate mass measurement could provide in principle specific detection of lipid species [21].

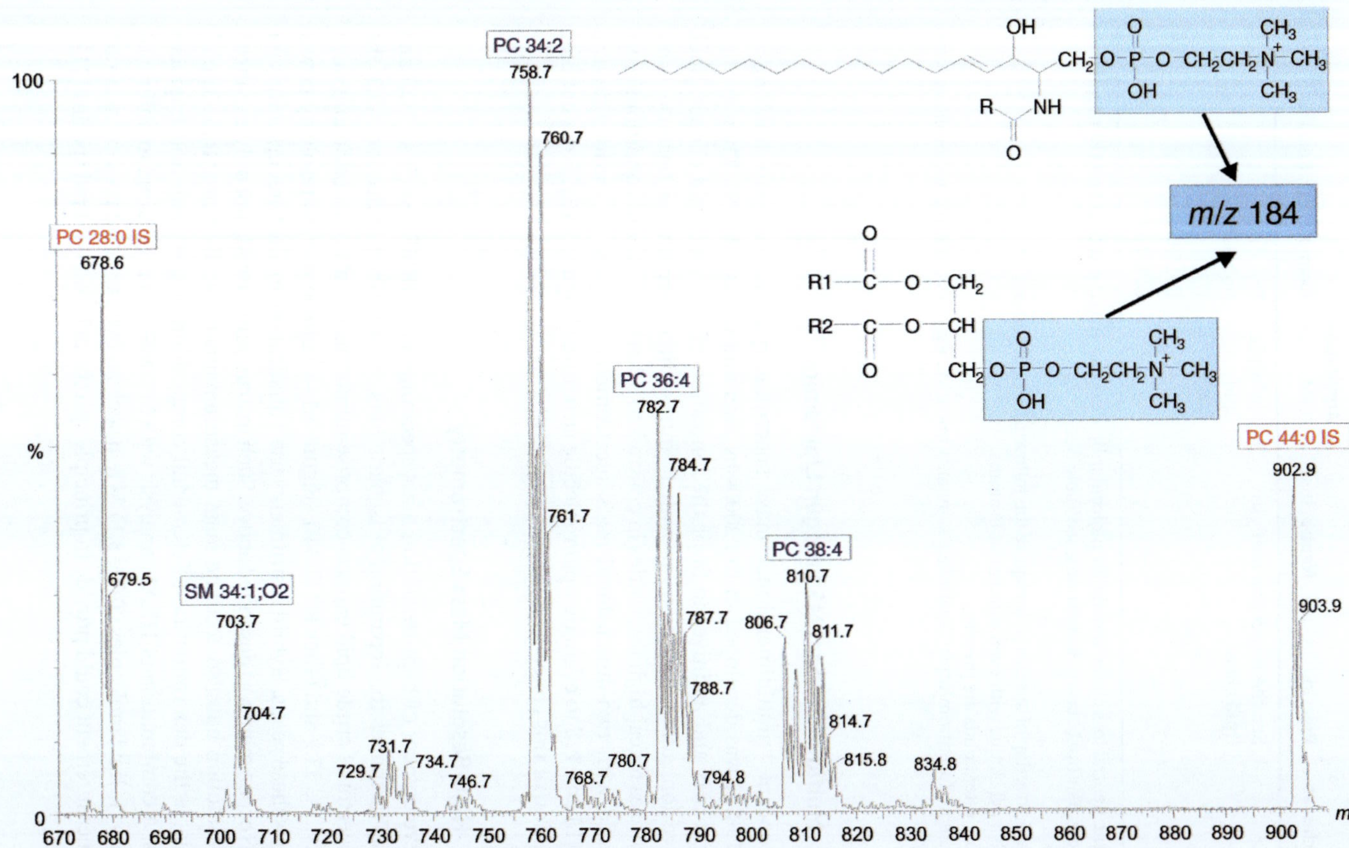

Figure 3.12 Precursor ion scan *m/z* 184 of human plasma. Human plasma was extracted according to Bligh and Dyer [54] after the addition of PC 28:0 and PC 44:0 as internal standards. Crude lipid extract was analyzed by FIA-ESI-MS/MS using a QqQ instrument operated in the positive-ion mode precursor ion scan *m/z* 184. Source: Adapted from Liebisch et al. [60].

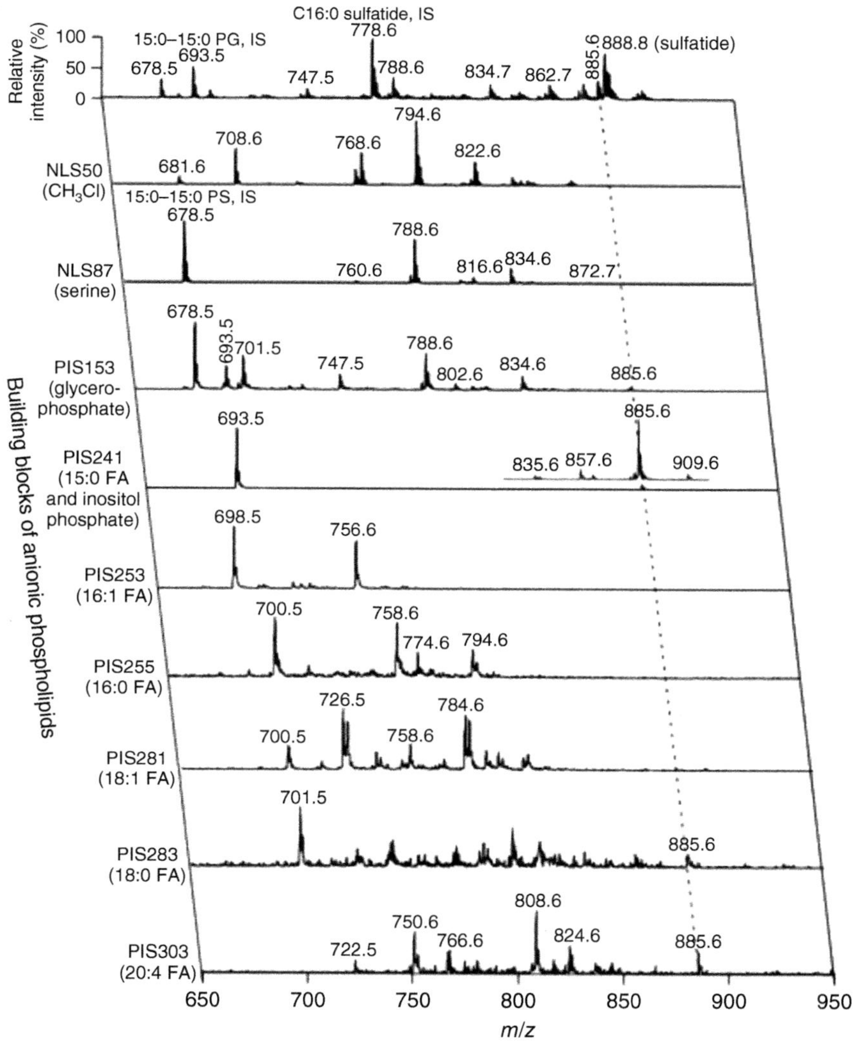

Figure 3.13 Two-dimensional mass spectrometry analyses of anionic phospholipids in the mouse cortex. The lipid extract was infused into an ESI QqQ mass spectrometer operated in the negative-ion mode. PIS – precursor-ion scan, NLS – neutral-loss scan. Source: Reprinted with permission from Han et al. [78]/John Wiley & Sons.

Hybrid instruments such as QTOF or Q-Orbitrap instruments capture full product ion spectra and do not require scan experiments as QqQ. Therefore, analysis of multiple product ions, e.g. carboxylic ions from acyl chain isomers in the negative-ion mode formed from glycerophospholipids, is straightforward with such instruments [19, 20]. Data generated by MPISs permit analysis of molecular lipid species.

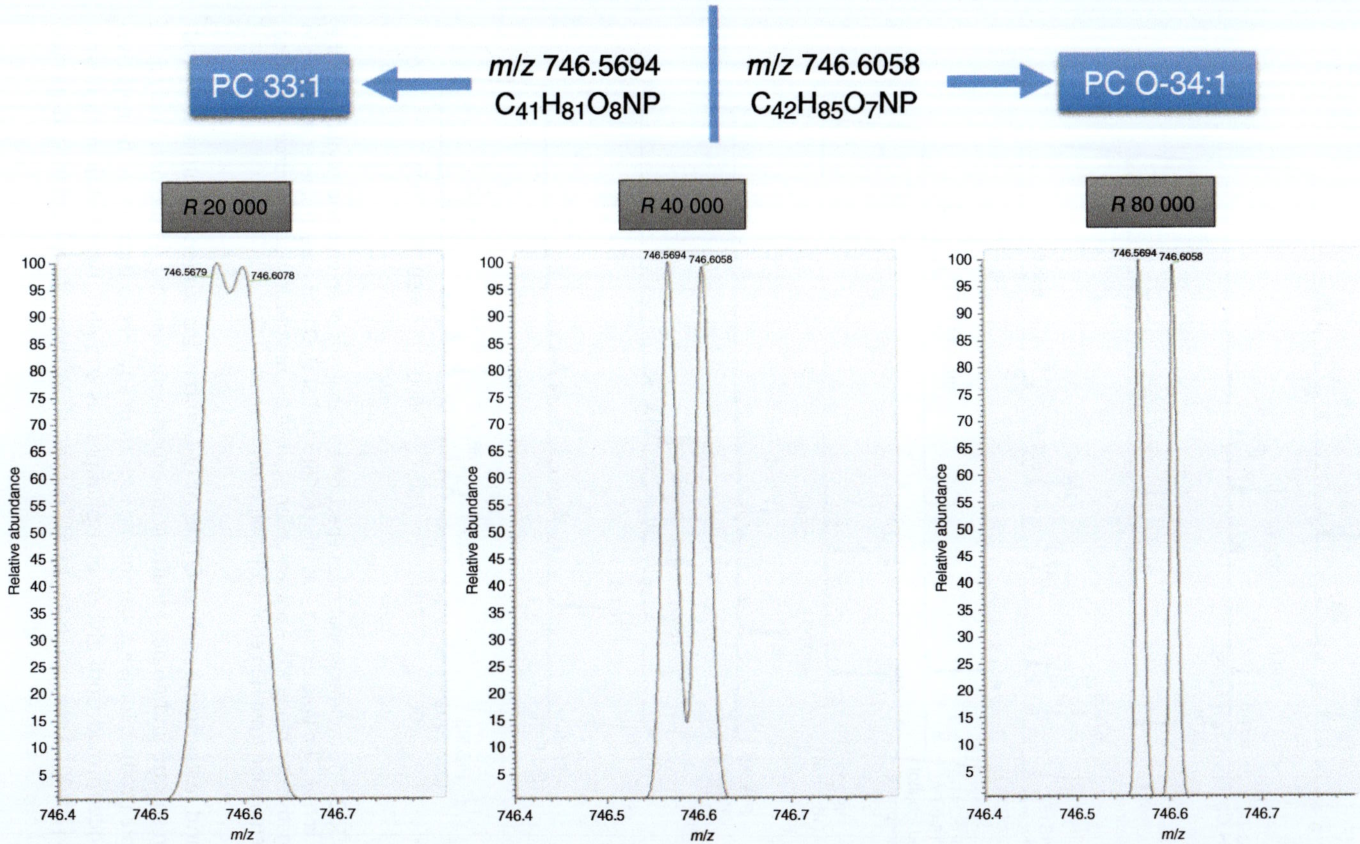

Figure 3.14 Application of mass resolution to differentiate isobaric ions. Depicted are simulations of $[M+H]^+$ of diacyl PC 33:1 and ether PC O-34:1. Isobaric ions are separated by sufficient resolving power (*R* in figure) $R = \frac{M}{\Delta M}$ with mass of the peak M and peak width ΔM frequently as full width at half-maximum (FWHM).

3.8 Lipid Identification

Identification of lipid molecules needs to consider the complexity described in Section 3.2, i.e. the presence of numerous lipid classes and their huge structural variety because of a range of carbon chain lengths, number of double bonds in acyl/alkyl chains, and different linkages. Because the crude lipid extracts contain numerous isomeric and isobaric peaks (Tables 3.1 and 3.2), successful identification requires mass spectrometric differentiation of these peaks. This chapter describes two main strategies applied in direct infusion lipidomics, i.e. tandem mass spectrometry and high mass resolution.

3.8.1 Identification by MS/MS

Application of tandem mass spectrometry (MS/MS) is the initial and still main strategy to resolve the described complexity in direct infusion lipidomics. The success of this strategy is based on the PIS and NLS characteristic for lipid classes (LCF), as well as acyl chains/sphingoid bases (MLF). Such mass spectrometric transitions are available for most polar lipid classes (Table 3.3 for LCF and Table 3.4 for MLF). Following this strategy, it is, for example, possible to differentiate isomeric PC and PE in the positive-ion mode because PC generates a fragment of m/z 184 while PE undergoes a NL of 141 Da. Similarly, LCF m/z 184 and NL 185 can differentiate protonated isobaric PC and PS ions, respectively. Of note, the application of LCF does not differentiate acyl chains and consequently only permits the annotation of their sum, i.e. lipid species. A combination of lipid class information with MLF, in particular of acyl and lyso-fragments, is required for annotation of molecular lipid species (see Section 3.8.4 for annotation hierarchy).

3.8.2 Identification by HRMS

Identification of lipid molecules by HRMS is based on the determination of accurate m/z values representing the chemical sum formula. Because of their different heteroatom contents, m/z values are characteristic for most lipid classes [74] (Table 3.5). It is important to keep in mind that mass spectrometry analysis cannot resolve isomeric ions (Table 3.1). For example, protonated PC species overlap with PE species with three additional C-atoms. In the negative-ion mode, the PC species typically form acetate/formate adduct ions and the PE species ionize primarily deprotonated, leading to a different heteroatom content of those ions enabling their differentiation by HRMS. Considering isobaric interferences (Table 3.2), HRMS is only capable of separating peaks when the resolving power of the instrument is sufficient for the respective peak pair (Figure 3.14). Therefore, successful identification by HRMS should consider the abundance of lipid classes and species in the respective sample material (described in Section 3.2) to delineate potential isomeric and isobaric overlaps in complex lipid extracts.

Table 3.5 Heteroatoms of the main lipid classes.

Lipid class	Abbreviations	Positive mode	Negative mode	N	O	P
Diacylglycerols	DG	—	$[DG+CH_3COO]^-$ $[DG+HCOO]^-$	0	7	0
Triacylglycerols	TG	—	$[TG+CH_3COO]^-$ $[DG+HCOO]^-$	0	8	0
Phosphatidic acids	PA	—	$[PA-H]^-$	0	8	1
Cholesteryl esters	CE	$[CE+NH_4]^+$	-	1	2	0
Ceramides (dihydroxy)	Cer X:Y;O2	$[Cer\ X:Y;O2+H]^+$	$[Cer\ X:Y;O2-H]^-$	1	3	0
Ceramides (trihydroxy)	Cer X:Y;O3	$[Cer\ X:Y;O3+H]^+$	$[Cer\ X:Y;O3-H]^-$	1	4	0
Diacylglycerols	DG	$[DG+NH_4]^+$	—	1	5	0
Triacylglycerols	TG	$[TG+NH_4]^+$	—	1	6	0
Phosphatidy-lethanolamine ethers	PE O	$[PE\ O+H]^+$	$[PE\ O-H]^-$	1	7	1
Lysophosphatidy-lethanolamines	LPE	$[LPE+H]^+$	$[LPE-H]^-$	1	7	1
Phosphatidylcholine ethers	PC-O	$[PC\ O+H]^+$	—	1	7	1
Lysophosphati-dylcholines	LPC	$[LPC+H]^+$	—	1	7	1
Hexosylceramides (dihydroxy)	HexCer	$[HexCer+H]^+$	$[HexCer-H]^-$	1	8	0
Phosphatidy-lethanolamines	PE	$[PE+H]^+$	$[PE-H]^-$	1	8	1
Phosphatidylcholines	PC	$[PC+H]^+$	—	1	8	1
Phosphatidic acids	PA	$[PA+NH_4]^+$	—	1	8	1
Phosphatidylcholine ethers	PC O	—	$[PC\ O+CH_3COO]^-$ $[PC\ O+HCOO]^-$	1	9	1
Lysophosphati-dylcholines	LPC	—	$[LPC+CH_3COO]^-$ $[LPC+HCOO]^-$	1	9	1
Phosphatidylglycerols	PG	—	$[PG-H]^-$	0	10	1
Phosphatidylserines	PS	$[PS+H]^+$	$[PS-H]^-$	1	10	1
Phosphatidylglycerols	PG	$[PG+NH_4]^+$	—	1	10	1
Phosphatidylcholines	PC	—	$[PC+CH_3COO]^-$ $[PC+HCOO]^-$	1	10	1
Phosphatidylinositols	PI	—	$[PI-H]^-$	0	13	1
Phosphatidylinositols	PI	$[PI+NH_4]^+$	—	1	13	1
Sphingomyelins (dihydroxy)	SM X:Y;O2	$[SM\ X:Y;O2+H]^+$	—	2	6	1

Table 3.5 (Continued)

Lipid class	Abbreviations	Positive mode	Negative mode	N	O	P
Ethanolamine-phosphorylceramides (dihydroxy)	EPC X:Y;O2	[EPC X:Y;O2+H]$^+$	—	2	6	1
Sphingomyelins (dihydroxy)	SM X:Y;O2	—	[SM X:Y;O2+CH_3COO]$^-$ [SM X:Y;O2+HCOO]$^-$	2	8	1

Ions typically formed in methanol, chloroform, and isopropanol mixtures containing ammonium acetate/formate as a modifier. X as the number of carbons and Y as the number of double-bond equivalents.
Source: Adapted from Schwudke et al. [74].

3.8.3 Consideration of Type-II Overlap

It is essential in all lipidomics approaches to consider Type-II overlap in DB series (see Section 3.3.3). In direct infusion lipidomics MS/MS with a QqQ instrument, this isobaric overlap is typically corrected based on the calculated isotope profiles [60]. Of note, the isotopic pattern used in such stepwise correction algorithms does not reflect the profile of the precursor ion but needs to take into account which fragment is used for analysis [19, 80]. Analysis of isotopic pattern and spike experiments could be applied to demonstrate the validity of such mathematical corrections.

Because Type-II overlap represents an isobaric overlap with ~9 mDa mass difference, HRMS is in principle capable of resolving M+2 and M+0 isotopologues. For example, high-end Orbitrap instruments could provide sufficient mass resolving power to separate M+2 from M+0 (Figure 3.15) and correction of Type-II overlap is not required [73] (see also Section 3.9.3).

3.8.4 Identification Hierarchy

As described in Section 3.3.1, annotation of lipid molecules should only include structural details justified by analytical data. Therefore, annotation requires a hierarchical scheme representing the levels of structural elucidation [43]. Because additional analytical dimensions such as characteristic retention times following chromatographic separation are not available in direct infusion lipidomics, annotation is just based on mass spectrometry analysis. This way, lipid class identification either by MS/MS or by accurate mass in HRMS results in lipid species annotation. The unambiguity of the annotation depends not only on the respective MS data but also on the presence of isomeric and isobaric overlap in the lipidome of the respective sample material. For example, determination of PE by detection of an LCF in MS/MS using a QqQ is not sufficient to resolve a typical isobaric overlap present in mammalian samples from the occurrence of diacyl and acyl/alkyl species such as PE 34:1 ([M−H]$^-$ *m/z* 716.5236) and PE O-35:1 ([M−H]$^-$ *m/z* 716.5600) (Figure 3.16). Thus, without further data such as accurate mass of the precursor ion, an assumption is required for annotation, e.g. that only even carbon number acyl chains are present to annotate PE 34:1. Additional

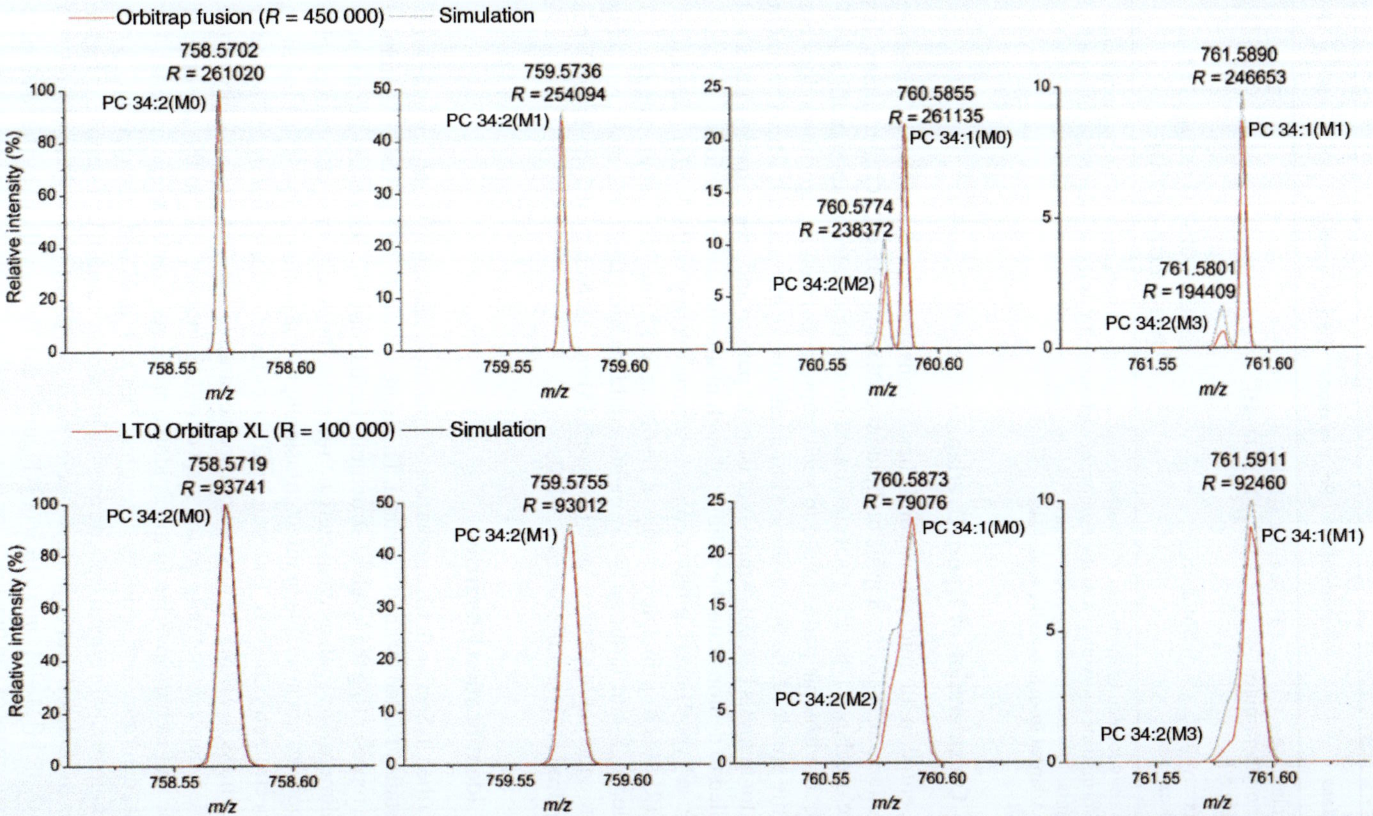

Figure 3.15 Resolution of Type-II by HRMS. PC 34:2 and PC 34:1 were analyzed in a molar ratio of 5:1 with Orbitrap Fusion (upper panel) operated with a resolution setting of 450 000 and LTQ Orbitrap XL (lower panel) operated with a resolution setting of 100 000 (shown in red). Simulated isotope profiles are colored black. Source: Reproduced with permission from Almeida et al. [73]/American Chemical Society.

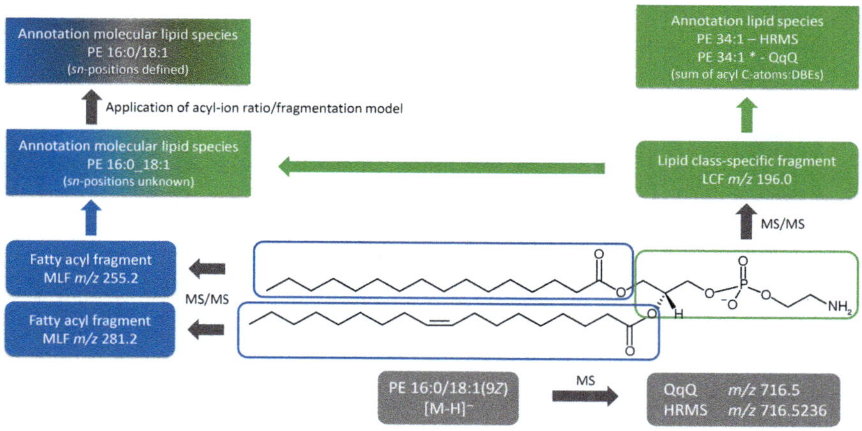

Figure 3.16 Hierarchical annotation of PE 16:0/18:1(9*Z*). Precursor mass and lipid class specific fragment ion (LCF) are required for annotation at the lipid species level: High-resolution MS (HRMS) allows the separation of isobaric PE O-35:1 ($[M-H]^-$ *m/z* 716.5600); annotation of PE 34:1 using QqQ (*) applies the assumption that only even carbon number fatty acyls are present. Annotation of molecular lipid species PE 16:0_18:1 needs LCF and both molecular lipid fragments (MLF, carboxylate anion fragments). *sn*-position level PE 16:0/18:1 demands application of fatty acyl ion ratios [81], fragmentation models [82], or LC-based methods [83]. Source: Köfeler et al. [28]/Elsevier/CC BY-4.0.

MS-derived information, like the detection of carboxylate ions *m/z* 255 and 281 as MLF matching the number of C-atoms permits the annotation of PE 16:0_18:1 a molecular lipid species without definition of *sn*-positions. To determine the *sn*-positions, the ratio of these carboxylate ions could be applied because the response of these fragments depends on their position at the glycerol backbone [81] (see also response model Section 3.9.3). Annotation of DB positions or other structural details requires sophisticated methods such as ozone-induced cleavage [84] or derivatization [85] to generate structure-specific ions (discussed in Chapters 4, 6–8).

3.8.5 Caveats/Pitfalls

An important consideration in direct infusion lipidomics is that precursor ion isolation using a quadrupole typically applies a 1 Da mass window selecting not only the target precursor but also other ions because of the complexity of lipid extracts. Therefore, fragments observed in product ion spectra are frequently not generated from the target precursor ion but originate from isotopic peaks (Type-II overlap) or other isobaric ions. An analysis of full-scan spectra could provide essential information about the presence of such interference and may avoid misinterpretation.

Furthermore, it is important to consider the potential in-source fragmentation of lipid molecules. Analysis of synthetic lipid standards provides sufficient information, whether respective lipid molecules undergo in-source fragmentation at the selected ionization conditions. High source temperatures or declustering potential may induce degradation of lipid ions [86, 87]. Such product ions frequently match the precursor ions of other lipid classes (Table 3.6) and thus may lead to misidentification.

Table 3.6 In-source fragmentation.

Lipid classes	In-source fragmentation
(A) Positive-ion mode	
Cer	NL of one or two molecules of water – generation of isomeric species, e.g. [Cer 34:1;O2+H]$^+$ = [Cer 34:0;O3+H-H_2O]$^+$, or isobaric species, e.g. [Cer 34:1;O2+H]$^+$ = [Cer 34:0;O3+H-H_2O]$^+$
CE-FC	NL of FA – generation of cholestadien ion
SM-LSM	NL of FA – generation of LSM
HexCer-Cer	NL of hexose – generation of Cer
SHexCer-HexCer	NL of SO_3 – generation of HexCer
Sterols	NL of water – generation of [M+H-H_2O]$^+$
DG and monoacylglycerols (MG)	NL of water from [M+Na]$^+$ or [M+NH_4]$^+$
TG-DG	NL of FA – generation of DG
PS and PC–PA	NL of serine/choline head group – generation of PA
Lysophosphatidylserine (LPS) and LPC–lysophosphatidic acid (LPA)	NL of serine/choline head group – generation of LPA
Phospholipid (PL)–lysophospholipid (LPL)	NL of FA – generation of LPL
(B) Negative-ion mode	
PL and SL	Generation of [RCOO]$^-$
PS–PA	NL of serine head group – generation of PA
LPS–LPA	NL of serine head group – generation of LPA

Potential in-source fragmentation in (A) positive- and (B) negative-ion modes.
Source: Reproduced https://lipidomics-standards-initiative.org/resources/in-source-fragmentation. In-source fragmentation depends on the type of ion source and ionization conditions such as declustering potential and temperature settings.

3.9 Lipid Quantification

As discussed in the Introduction section, quantification of lipid classes is important in many aspects, including in-depth interpretation, e.g. of biological function of membranes based on their lipid composition. In this chapter, we discuss the necessity and selection of appropriate ISs, the consideration of isotopic effect Type-I (and other isotopic overlaps), and analytical response as important steps before calculation of concentrations of accurate identified lipid molecules.

3.9.1 Internal Standards

A prerequisite for quantification in ESI-MS methods is the application of ISs because of the substantial influence of the matrix on the ionization process (see Section 3.7.1).

In direct infusion, samples are infused at constant concentrations and flow rates. Thus, the ionization conditions remain constant during the entire MS analysis. This fact represents a major advantage compared to LC-based methods where solvents and matrix change with time because of the chromatographic separation. The ionization efficiency of lipid classes during ESI is associated with the (polar) head groups; hence, it is important that each lipid class requires an IS matching the respective lipid class. Ideally, ISs match not only the head groups but also the chain length and DB content of the analyte. However, in particular, for polar lipid classes, the number of C-atoms and DBs show only a minor influence on ionization efficiency (own unpublished data). In contrast, for nonpolar lipid classes such as CE, the C-atom and DB number substantially affect their ionization (see Section 3.9.3). Thus, application of matching stable isotope-labeled IS or fully labeled lipid mixtures [88], e.g. ^{13}C-labeled yeast extracts [89], as recommended in reversed-phase separation, is not required for accurate quantification in direct infusion lipidomics. Typically, it is sufficient to add one or two ISs per lipid class for quantification. The applied ISs should not be present in the individual sample, and their addition needs to be in advance to lipid extraction to address a potential loss of lipids during sample preparation (i.e. they compensate for potential reduced lipid recovery). Furthermore, the addition of two (or more) ISs per lipid class permits a quality control for individual samples by monitoring their ratio, which should remain constant within a batch [60, 67]. The amount of IS should be in the range of the target analytes. For minor lipid classes, the amount could exceed the concentration of the most abundant lipid species of this class to minimize analytical variation in the IS analysis and consequently increase the reproducibly of quantification (Table 3.7).

3.9.2 Type-I Isotopic Effect

A factor affecting all lipid classes is the so-called Type-I isotopic effect [44]. The effect describes the proportional decrease of the monoisotopic peaks with increasing number of carbon atoms (Figure 3.17). Because the concentrations are typically calculated from the M+0 isotopologue, an increase in C-atom numbers leads to lower intensities and thus concentrations. A simple strategy to correct for this effect is the application of a factor adjusting the intensities of the monoisotopic peaks based on the theoretical isotopic pattern [44]. It is noteworthy that ISs need to be included into such corrections unless the fraction of M+0 is very similar to their respective analyte. Importantly, correction of all other isobaric overlaps, such as Type-II, needs to precede the compensation of the Type-I effect.

3.9.3 Evaluation and Correction of Isotopic Overlap

As discussed in Section 3.8.3, correct identification requires consideration of Type-II overlap in lipid classes with DB series, which of course also applies to accurate quantification. A special case is the deconvolution of spectra acquired by PIS *m/z* 184 in the positive-ion mode. In these spectra apart from M+2 and M+0 within each lipid class (Type-II), M+1 and M+0 isotopologues of SM and PC species overlap

Table 3.7 Internal standard mixtures typically used in direct infusion lipidomics.

Lipid category	Lipid class	nESI-FTMS [90]	FIA-MS/MS; FIA-FTMS ([53], [34])	nESI-FTMS MS^{ALL} [50]
GL	DG	[D5] 34:0	14:0/14:0 20:0/20:0	[D5] 17:0/17:0
	TG	[D5] 50:0	17:0/17:0/17:0 19:0/19:0/19:0	[D5] 17:0/17:1/17:0
GP	PC	25:0	14:0/14:0 22:0/22:0	16:0[D3]/16:0[D3]
	PE	25:0	14:0/14:0 20:0/20:0	O-20:0/O-20:0
	PG	25:0	14:0/14:0 20:0/20:0	17:0/14:1
	PS	25:0	14:0/14:0 20:0/20:0	17:0/20:4
	PI	25:0	17:0/17:0	17:0/20:4
	LPC	13:0	13:0 19:0	O-17:0
	LPE	13:0	13:0	O-16:0
SL	SM	18:1;O2/12:0	18:1;O2/12:0	18:1;O2/17:0
	Cer	18:1;O2/12:0	18:1;O2/14:0 18:1;O2/17:0	18:1;O2/17:0
	HexCer	18:1;O2/12:0	18:1;O2/12:0 18:1;O2/17:0	18:1;O2/12:0
ST	CE	[D7] 16:0	17:0 22:0	19:0
	FC	[D7]	[D7]	[D7]

(Figure 3.12). Because of the insufficient mass resolving power, a QqQ instrument cannot resolve this isobaric overlap; consequently, it needs to be corrected by stepwise correction of intensities using a calculated isotopic pattern [60]. Spike experiments can prove the validity of applied correction algorithms (Table 3.8).

Similarly, Type-II overlap could be tested in Fourier transform MS (FTMS) spectra (Figure 3.18) [70]. A species with an additional DB is spiked in increasing amounts, and the isobaric overlap of its M+2 with the M+0 isotopologue of the adjacent species is evaluated. Because the mass resolving power of Orbitrap instruments decreases with increasing *m/z*, the Type-II overlap remains unresolved for TG 54:0. In such a case, the measured peak intensities could be underestimated because the overlapping isobaric peaks are not additive. To quantify accurately in such situation, it is also possible to use the M+1 peak, which is less affected by Type-II overlap [70, 91].

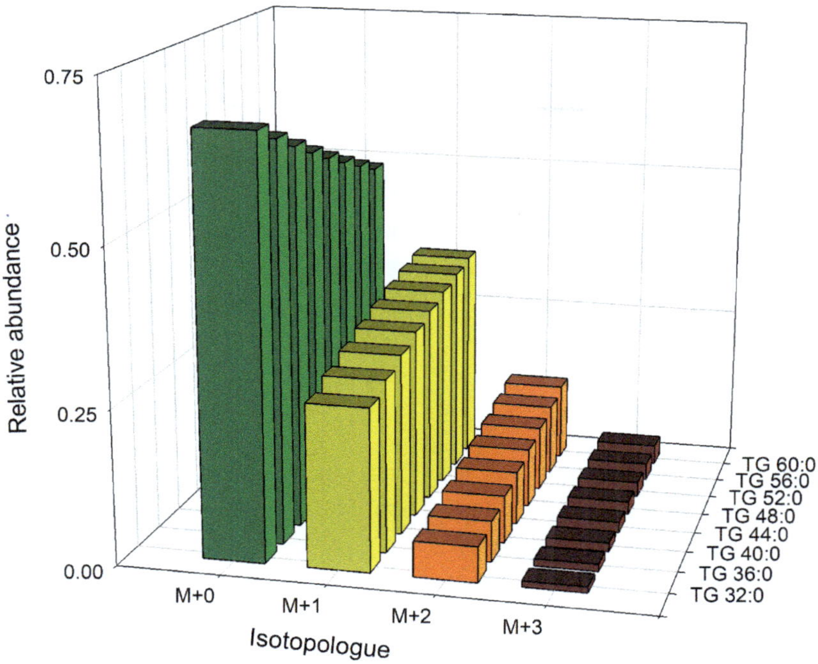

Figure 3.17 Type-I isotopic effect. Illustrated is the abundance of isotopologues for triacylglycerols with increasing number of carbon atoms. The abundance is normalized to the sum of all isotopologues. The monoisotopic peak (M+0) decreases and higher isotopologues increase with the number of carbon atoms. Source: Köfeler et al. [28]/Elsevier/CC BY-4.0.

In addition to Type-II overlap, isobaric overlaps can originate from different adduct ions (Table 3.2). For example, sodiated ions interfere with the protonated ions of species of the same lipid class with two additional CH_2 and three DBs ($\Delta m/z = 0.0025$). Similarly, the first isotopic peak of a sodiated ion overlaps with the ammoniated ions of a species with one additional CH_2 and four DBs ($\Delta m/z = 0.0057$). In such cases, the overlap could be corrected by experimentally determined factors, reflecting the ratio of sodiated to protonated ions calculated from ISs [92]. The procedure works similar to the correction of Type-II overlap. Sample-specific factors could be applied for a stepwise correction of intensities affected by this particular overlap as demonstrated for the quantification of PC species in human serum samples by positive-ion mode FIA-FTMS (Figure 3.19).

3.9.4 Species Response

The analytical response of lipid molecules is defined by its ionization efficiency and its gas-phase chemistry when the respective ion is subjected to fragmentation. Quantification is always based on the ratio to IS, which should belong to the same lipid class as the analyte (see Section 3.9.1). Therefore, in most cases, the ionization

Table 3.8 Isotope correction of overlapping PC and SM isotopologues.

m/z	731	732	782	783	784	810	811	812	813	814
(A) Uncorrected analyte/IS ratios										
C (mM)	SM 36:1;O2	PC 32:1	PC 36:4	SM 40:3;O2	PC 36:3	PC 38:4	SM 42:3;O2	PC 38:3	SM 42:2;O2	PC 38:2
0	0.149	0.306	0.999	0.470	0.865	0.569	0.428	0.390	0.542	0.260
0.045	0.310	0.366	1.205	0.568	0.882	0.793	0.533	0.419	0.546	0.269
0.113	0.549	0.452	1.539	0.721	0.923	1.126	0.693	0.461	0.565	0.275
0.188	0.821	0.577	1.931	0.900	0.964	1.513	0.879	0.527	0.574	0.284
0.300	1.229	0.731	2.460	1.128	0.998	2.037	1.123	0.584	0.588	0.279
(B) Corrected analyte/IS ratios										
C (mM)	SM 36:1;O2	PC 32:1	PC 36:4	SM 40:3;O2	PC 36:3	PC 38:4	SM 42:3;O2	PC 38:3	SM 42:2;O2	PC 38:2
0	0.136	0.247	0.982	0.030	0.748	0.528	0.173	0.245	0.397	0.036
0.045	0.279	0.245	1.186	0.037	0.741	0.752	0.173	0.247	0.395	0.044
0.113	0.493	0.238	1.517	0.042	0.744	1.086	0.177	0.249	0.406	0.044
0.188	0.735	0.258	1.907	0.046	0.743	1.472	0.182	0.269	0.397	0.053
0.300	1.098	0.255	2.434	0.040	0.724	2.000	0.180	0.266	0.403	0.046

SM 36:1;O2, PC 36:4, and PC 38:4 (marked blue) were added to a plasma sample at the indicated concentrations. Displayed are ratios counts (analyte) to counts (PC 28:0 as IS) of (A) uncorrected and (B) after correction with calculated isotopologue profiles. Crude lipid extracts were analyzed by FIA-ESI-MS/MS using a QqQ instrument operated in the positive-ion mode precursor ion scan *m/z* 184. Correction applied a self-programmed Excel Macro; for details, see [60].
Source: Adapted from Liebisch et al. [60].

response of IS and the respective lipid species is similar (see above). However, for nonpolar lipid classes, the acyl chain length and the number of DBs could affect the formation of ions in ESI. For example, CE species exhibit a substantially higher ionization efficiency as ammoniated ions when the DB number increases (more than twofold higher for CE 18:3 compared to CE 18:0) (Figure 3.20) [72]. Moreover, the longer the acyl chain, the higher the response. A major determinant for these response differences is the susceptibility of CE to in-source fragmentation, leading to cholestadiene fragment. In particular, introduction of DBs reduces the degree of in-source fragmentation. Application of experimentally determined response factors permits correction and accurate CE quantification.

Consideration of gas-phase chemistry, i.e. fragmentation characteristics, is important when CAs are used for quantification of glycerophospholipid molecular lipids. Analytical response of these species depends on the *sn*-position, chain length, and number of DBs of the acyl chain. Therefore, quantification based on CAs needs application of response models (Figure 3.21) [82].

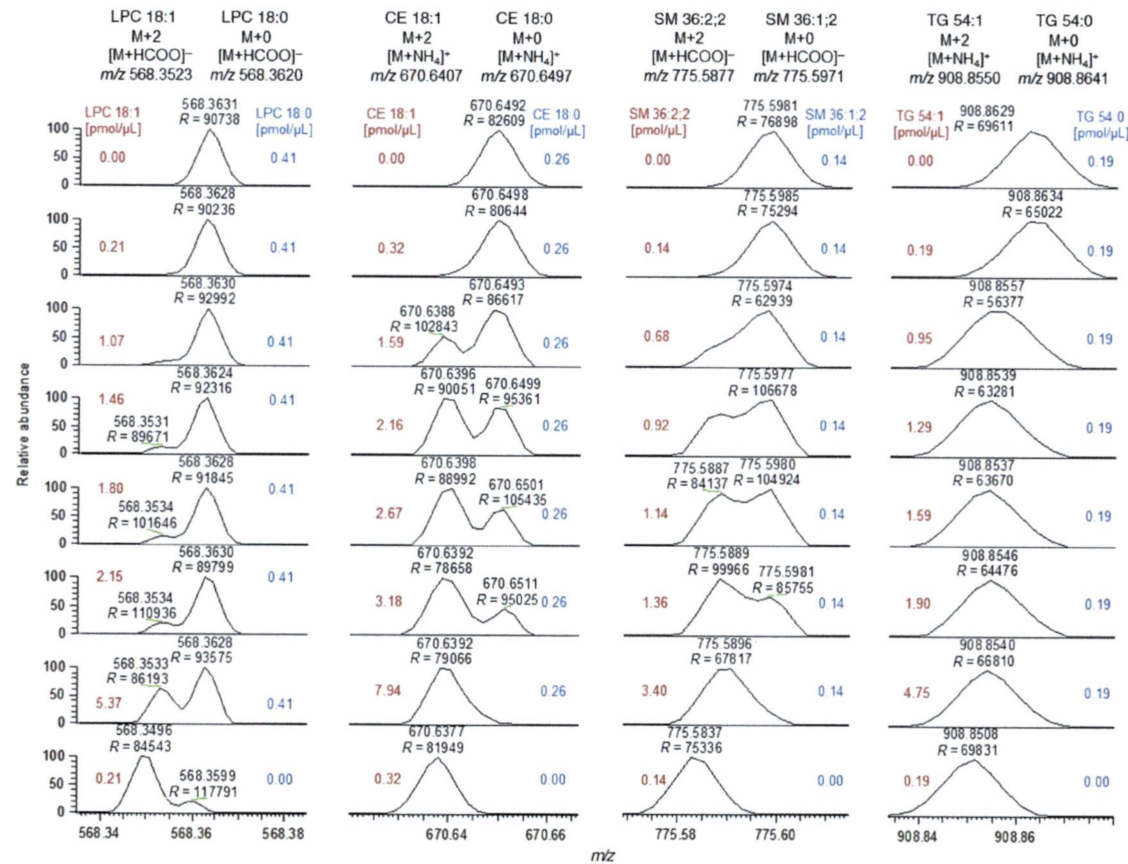

Figure 3.18 Type-II overlap in FTMS spectra. Displayed are the mass spectra of selected lipid species pairs. The species with one additional DB was spiked in increasing concentrations (indicated in red), while the saturated species was kept at a constant concentration (in blue). Data were recorded on a QExactive Orbitrap at a resolution setting of 140 000 (at m/z 200). Source: Reproduced from Höring et al. [70]/Elsevier/CC BY-4.0.

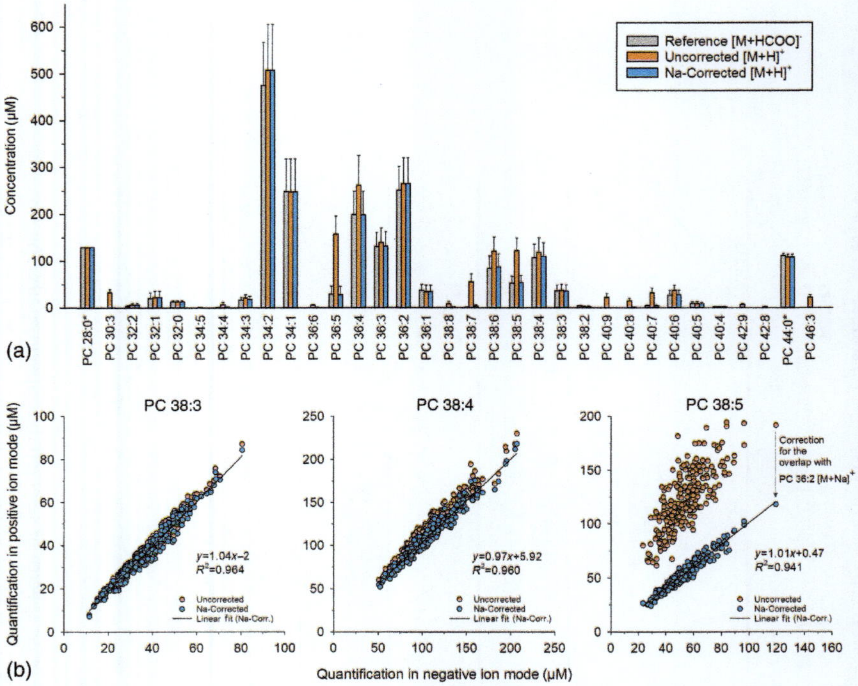

Figure 3.19 Isobaric overlap of sodiated with protonated ions. Sodiated ions overlap with protonated ions of the species of the same lipid class with two additional CH_2 and three double bonds ($\Delta m/z$ = 0.0025). (a) PC species quantified in human serum samples (mean ± SD) as $[M+HCOO]^-$ in the negative-ion mode and in the positive-ion mode as $[M+H]^+$ with and without sodium correction. ISs PC 28:0 and PC 44:0 were used to calculate the correction factor. (b) Correlation of individual concentrations after correction of sodium overlap (Na-Corr) and those determined in positive ion mode for PC 38:3, PC 38:4, and PC 38:5. Data were generated with a QExactive using a mass resolution setting of 140 000 (at m/z 200) (n = 260 serum samples). Source: Reproduced with permission from Horing et al. [92]/American Chemical Society.

3.9.5 Calculation of Concentration

Before the calculation of concentrations, the peak intensities are subjected to the respective correction steps, which include correction of Type-II overlap (and if present, other isotopic overlaps) as well as adjustment of the Type-I effect. Then, the intensities are set in relation to their IS. The simplest way to calculate concentrations from these corrected ratios is multiplication with the spiked amount of the IS.

When the analytical response is different for individual lipid species (as described above), response factor models could be applied to both corrected intensities or ratios of analyte/IS (equivalent to concentrations). Alternatively, variations in analytical response could be addressed by calibration lines generated for lipid species ideally covering the range of C-atoms and DBs in the acyl chains of the respective lipid class [60, 67]. To consider the effect of the sample matrix, such calibration lines are typically generated by the addition of standards to the respective pooled sample material.

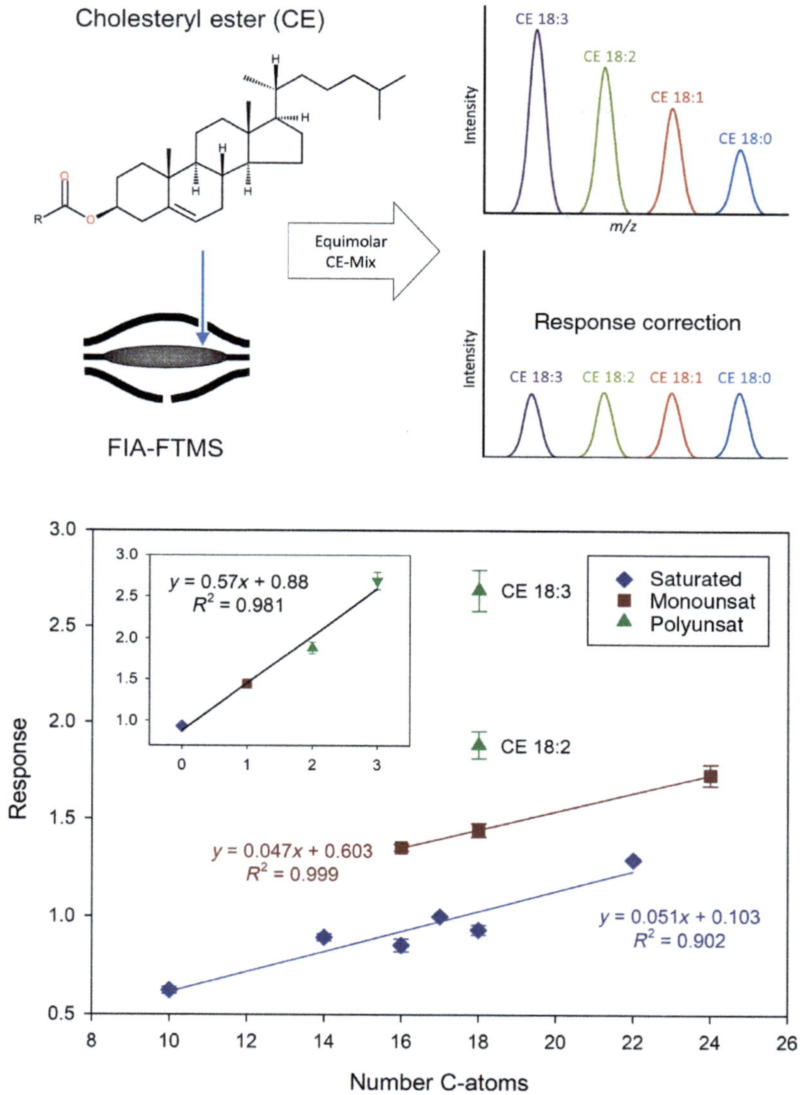

Figure 3.20 Analytical response of cholesteryl ester (CE) species. Nonpolar CE species response is related to their number of C-atoms and double bonds. Plotted are responses of saturated (blue), monounsaturated (dark red), and polyunsaturated species (green) against the acyl chain length. The inset displays the response of CE species with 18 carbons plotted against the number of double bonds. CE 17:0 was used as IS for quantification. Data were analyzed by FIA-FTMS. Source: Reproduced from Horing et al. [72]/American Chemical Society.

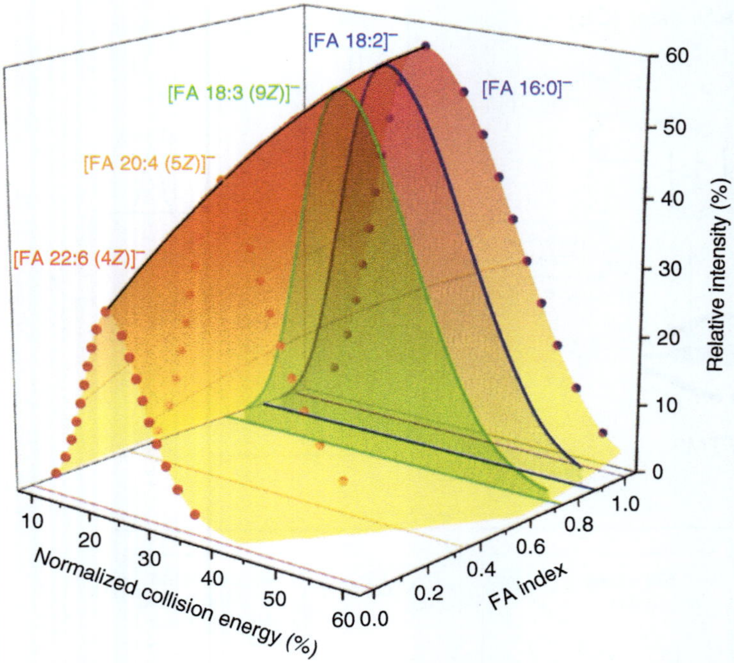

Figure 3.21 Response model for PC carboxylate (CA) fragments. Computational model for symmetrical PC species. Fatty acid index, which is the numeric measure for CA fragmentation propensity, is 0 for the fatty acid with the lowest (22:6) and 1.0 for saturated FAs (16:0 or 18:0) with highest relative intensity at the maxima. Source: Schuhmann et al. [82]/American Chemical Society/CC BY-4.0.

3.10 Data Analysis/Software

Data analysis tools are essential for all omics disciplines to process the raw data and to perform all steps described above, including lipid molecule identification, required corrections, and quantification. Until now, commercial software packages for direct infusion lipidomics are not available. Therefore, lipidomics groups frequently develop their own in-house software as for the example based on Excel Macros [60, 70, 72]. An open-source software package supporting direct infusion lipidomics is LipidXplorer (https://lifs-tools.org/lipidxplorer.html) [93, 94]. It applies a script language, the so-called molecular fragmentation query language (MFQL), which is used to describe fragmentation pathways to interpret mass spectra. This software also processes data subjected to a noise filtering tool (PeakStrainer) for FTMS data [95] or lipid derivatives derived from click chemistry [96]. Another python-based open-access software for the analysis of shotgun lipidomics data is ALEX (Analysis of Lipid Experiments; http://mslipidomics.info/contents/?page_id=2) [97]. This framework features automated identification (modifiable target lists) and export of lipid species intensity from mass spectral data files. These data could be linked to further data processing and visualization.

ALEX[123] (http://alex123.info) is a search tool for typical adduct ions of lipid molecules as well as lipid fragmentation information for more than 430 000 potential lipid molecules from 47 lipid classes [98].

3.11 Limitations

The main drawback of direct infusion lipidomics is the limited ionization capacity of ESI, which may lead to insufficient ion formation of less-abundant lipid classes because of predominance of major lipid classes. Therefore, minor lipid classes are frequently analyzed by chromatographic methods such as hydrophilic interaction liquid chromatography (HILIC) [77, 80, 99–101] permitting quantification also with a limited number of ISs because of its lipid class-based separation principle (see Chapter 4). Another workaround is derivatization of minor lipid classes to enhance their ionization efficiency, e.g. by introduction of a fixed charged (see Section 3.5.4).

Other caveats and pitfalls of direct infusion lipidomics (see Section 3.8.5) are the presence of in-source fragmentation that is not easily detected without sample separation, hence require evaluation with synthetic standards in advance. Another limitation is the presence of a chemical background for some lipid classes; however, this is not only a problem known for direct infusion approaches. Information about potential background ions could be discovered by an extraction blank. Consideration of contamination or noise is in particular important, when less-abundant lipid molecules close to the limit of detection (LoD) or low amounts of sample are analyzed. A lipid class with a typical high background is free fatty acids, particularly saturated acids such as palmitic acid and stearic acid [102].

3.12 Selected Applications

In this chapter, we discuss selected applications of direct infusion lipidomics to highlight its versatility and analytical power. Other chapters in this book will discuss the respective topics in more detail.

3.12.1 Analysis of Plasma

Analysis of plasma samples is one of the main lipidomics applications [103]. Direct infusion lipidomics was applied to profile plasma [104] and lipoprotein fractions [36] of healthy subjects. Moreover, numerous studies used this strategy to discover a novel lipid biomarker. In one of the first clinical studies, increased Cer/SM and decreased LPC/PC ratios were found in the plasma of sepsis patients [105]. These ratios also showed a correlation with mortality. FIA-MS/MS also identified specific Cer species as risk factors for cardiovascular mortality [106] that was proven by targeted LC-MS/MS analysis [107] [108]. Recently, a higher risk of cognitive decline was associated with several plasma lipid species, i.e. lower levels of TG 50:5,

SM 40:2;O2, PE 38:5, PE O-34:3, PC O-34:1, and higher levels of PC O-32:0 [109]. Moreover, a multicenter study including both direct infusion and chromatography-based lipidomics demonstrated a potential application of lipid signatures as a biomarker for pancreatic cancer [110].

To find genome-wide associations of lipid species, large-scale studies with several thousands of samples applied direct infusion methods [111, 112]. Associations with lipid metabolism gene loci showed a proof of concept, and unexpected loci led to further functional analysis [113].

In summary, direct infusion lipidomics proved as a useful and robust tool for large-scale plasma studies capable of discovering genomic associations and disease biomarkers.

3.12.2 Analysis of Tissues and Cells

Direct infusion lipidomics has also been applied in multiple studies for the analysis of tissue samples, either biopsies or from model organisms. Recently, biopsies from colorectal patients revealed a tumor-specific lipid species signature for colorectal cancer. Notably, this signature could be reproduced in several cohorts measured by direct infusion platforms [114]. Lipidomic profiling of liver biopsies by nESI-FTMS revealed lipid signatures that enabled patient's stratification at different stages of nonalcoholic fatty liver disease [115]. Furthermore, nESI-FTMS was used to investigate the lipidome of murine adipose tissue, brain, full blood, plasma, intestine, kidney, liver, lung, muscle, and spleen [116]. This study demonstrated that each organ has a unique lipid fingerprint. Additionally, the study evaluated the effect of diet, sex, and genotype on the individual lipidomes. Analysis of cells by direct infusion methods is straightforward for both cultured [117] and isolated cells such as blood cells [32].

3.12.3 Analysis of Lipid Metabolism

Applications of direct lipidomic methods to study lipid metabolism were based either on time series, e.g. in the analysis of circadian rhythm [50], or on the introduction of a stable isotope-labeled precursor [118]. Labeling strategies could also be applied to investigate lipid transport processes such as cellular lipid efflux [119].

A seminal study by DeLong et al. [120] used [D4]-ethanolamine and [D9]-choline as a tracer to investigate major pathways of the glycerophospholipid biosynthesis (Figure 3.22). In hepatic cells, they could demonstrate that PC species derived from choline incorporation were more saturated and shorter than those derived via PE *N*-methyltransferase (PEMT) from PE. In mammalians, this pathway is only active in hepatocytes, and intermediates of PE methylation (monomethyl-PE [MMPE] and DMPE) could also be analyzed by direct infusion analysis [50]. Addition of labeled serine provides a parallel monitoring of PS synthesis [122]. Combination of data from fatty acid and phospholipid synthesis could provide valuable insights into cellular [117] and tissue/organ [123] specific lipid metabolism. Labeling with ^{15}N

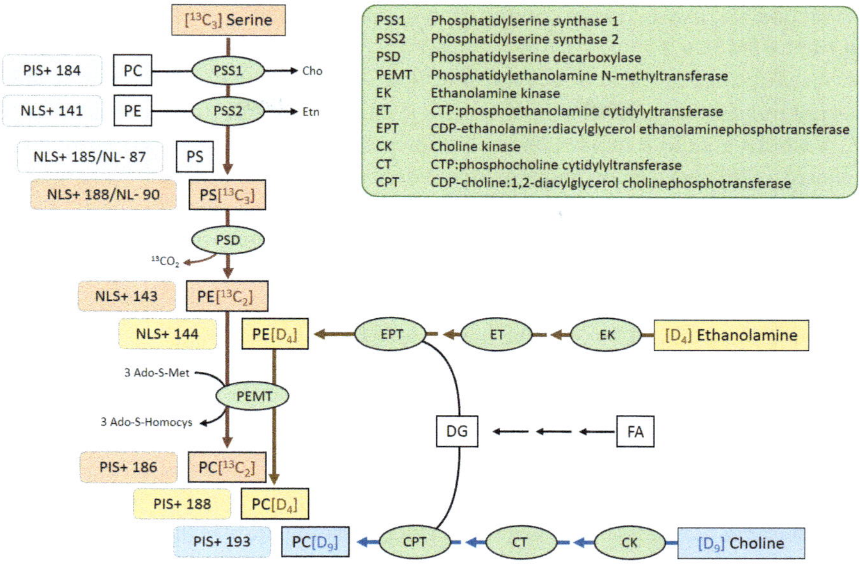

Figure 3.22 Analysis of glycerophospholipid metabolism. Incorporation of labeled choline, ethanolamine, and serine into PC, PE, PS, and their MS/MS analysis by PIS and NLS. Source: Adapted from Refs. [118, 121].

permits a metabolic profiling of PC, PE, PS, and sphingolipids by shotgun-FTMS, but analysis of the labeled products requires ultrahigh mass resolution [62].

An alternative strategy to stable isotope labeling is tracing with alkyne-labeled lipids [124]. These fatty acids provide upon incorporation into complex lipid classes and modification by click chemistry with charge-tagged reporters a specific, highly sensitive detection with direct infusion MS [96].

3.13 Outlook

Direct infusion lipidomics is one of the main approaches in lipidomics because it could provide robust, accurate quantification and permits a high sample throughput because of automated data analysis. These features led to its broad application in biomarker search, basic research, and metabolic tracing. Despite that HRMS is invaluable for the resolution of isobaric lipid molecules, triple quadrupole (QqQ)-based shotgun lipidomics is still a workhorse of this lipidomic workflow as it could provide accurate, reproducible, and quantitative lipidome analysis.

However, an ongoing issue of lipidomics analysis represents misidentifications, mainly observed for LC-based studies [26, 27]. Therefore, the Lipidomics Standards Initiative (LSI; https://lipidomics-standards-initiative.org) started the development of guidelines for the main lipidomic MS-based workflows [29]. Besides these guidelines, data quality could be improved by considering the basic knowledge of lipid classes/species and their metabolism occurring in the respective sample material (see Section 3.2) as well as the combination of data from various workflows, such as QqQ and FTMS data.

A disadvantage of basic direct infusion lipidomics is that identification usually does not exceed the molecular lipid species level. For example, the identification of DB positions requires more advanced strategies such as ozone- [84] or radical-mediated [125] cleavage or photochemical derivatization of DBs [126] (see related Chapters 7, 8). Another way to improve the structural resolution of shotgun lipidomics is the application of ion mobility as an additional separation dimension (see Chapter 6). Such enhanced structural resolution capabilities implemented into user-friendly software packages could expand the usability and acceptance of direct infusion methods further and make them applicable to researchers new to the field of lipid research.

References

1 Harayama, T. and Riezman, H. (2018). Understanding the diversity of membrane lipid composition. *Nat. Rev. Mol. Cell Biol.* 19: 281–296.

2 Van Meer, G., Voelker, D.R., and Feigenson, G.W. (2008). Membrane lipids: where they are and how they behave. *Nat. Rev. Mol. Cell Biol.* 9: 112–124.

3 Cartier, A. and Hla, T. (2019). Sphingosine 1-phosphate: lipid signaling in pathology and therapy. *Science* 366: eaar5551.

4 Dennis, E.A. and Norris, P.C. (2015). Eicosanoid storm in infection and inflammation. *Nat. Rev. Immunol.* 15: 511–523.

5 Hammond, G.R.V. and Burke, J.E. (2020). Novel roles of phosphoinositides in signaling, lipid transport, and disease. *Curr. Opin. Cell Biol.* 63: 57–67.

6 Covino, R., Hummer, G., and Ernst, R. (2018). Integrated functions of membrane property sensors and a hidden side of the unfolded protein response. *Mol. Cell* 71: 458–467.

7 Ernst, R., Ejsing, C.S., and Antonny, B. (2016). Homeoviscous adaptation and the regulation of membrane lipids. *J. Mol. Biol.* 428: 4776–4791.

8 Wang, H.Y., Bharti, D., and Levental, I. (2020). Membrane heterogeneity beyond the plasma membrane. *Front. Cell Dev. Biol.* 8: 580814.

9 Wenk, M.R. (2010). Lipidomics: new tools and applications. *Cell* 143: 888–895.

10 Levental, K.R., Malmberg, E., Symons, J.L. et al. (2020). Lipidomic and biophysical homeostasis of mammalian membranes counteracts dietary lipid perturbations to maintain cellular fitness. *Nat. Commun.* 11: 1339.

11 Doktorova, M., Symons, J.L., and Levental, I. (2020). Structural and functional consequences of reversible lipid asymmetry in living membranes. *Nat. Chem. Biol.* 16: 1321–1330.

12 Han, X. and Gross, R.W. (2021). The foundations and development of lipidomics. *J. Lipid Res.* 63: 100164.

13 Weintraub, S.T., Pinckard, R.N., and Hail, M. (1991). Electrospray ionization for analysis of platelet-activating factor. *Rapid Commun. Mass Spectrom.* 5: 309–311.

14 Han, X. and Gross, R.W. (1994). Electrospray ionization mass spectroscopic analysis of human erythrocyte plasma membrane phospholipids. *Proc. Natl. Acad. Sci. U.S.A.* 91: 10635–10639.

15 Han, X. and Gross, R.W. (1995). Structural determination of picomole amounts of phospholipids via electrospray ionization tandem mass spectrometry. *J. Am. Soc. Mass Spectrom.* 6: 1202–1210.

16 Brügger, B., Erben, G., Sandhoff, R. et al. (1997). Quantitative analysis of biological membrane lipids at the low picomole level by nano-electrospray ionization tandem mass spectrometry. *Proc. Natl. Acad. Sci. U.S.A.* 94: 2339–2344.

17 Liebisch, G., Drobnik, W., Reil, M. et al. (1999). Quantitative measurement of different ceramide species from crude cellular extracts by electrospray ionization tandem mass spectrometry (ESI-MS/MS). *J. Lipid Res.* 40: 1539–1546.

18 Ekroos, K., Chernushevich, I.V., Simons, K., and Shevchenko, A. (2002). Quantitative profiling of phospholipids by multiple precursor ion scanning on a hybrid quadrupole time-of-flight mass spectrometer. *Anal. Chem.* 74: 941–949.

19 Ejsing, C.S., Duchoslav, E., Sampaio, J. et al. (2006). Automated identification and quantification of glycerophospholipid molecular species by multiple precursor ion scanning. *Anal. Chem.* 78: 6202–6214.

20 Schwudke, D., Oegema, J., Burton, L. et al. (2006). Lipid profiling by multiple precursor and neutral loss scanning driven by the data-dependent acquisition. *Anal. Chem.* 78: 585–595.

21 Schwudke, D., Hannich, J.T., Surendranath, V. et al. (2007). Top-down lipidomic screens by multivariate analysis of high-resolution survey mass spectra. *Anal. Chem.* 79: 4083–4093.

22 Han, X. and Gross, R.W. (2005). Shotgun lipidomics: electrospray ionization mass spectrometric analysis and quantitation of cellular lipidomes directly from crude extracts of biological samples. *Mass Spectrom. Rev.* 24: 367–412.

23 Holcapek, M., Liebisch, G., and Ekroos, K. (2020). Lipidomic analysis. *Anal. Bioanal. Chem.* 412: 2187–2189.

24 Wang, J., Wang, C., and Han, X. (2019). Tutorial on lipidomics. *Anal. Chim. Acta* 1061: 28–41.

25 Koelmel, J.P., Ulmer, C.Z., Jones, C.M. et al. (2017). Common cases of improper lipid annotation using high-resolution tandem mass spectrometry data and corresponding limitations in biological interpretation. *Biochim. Biophys. Acta, Mol. Cell. Biol. Lipids* 1862: 766–770.

26 Köfeler, H.C., Eichmann, T.O., Ahrends, R. et al. (2021). Quality control requirements for the correct annotation of lipidomics data. *Nat. Commun.* 12: 4771.

27 Liebisch, G., Ejsing, C.S., and Ekroos, K. (2015). Identification and annotation of lipid species in metabolomics studies need improvement. *Clin. Chem.* 61: 1542–1544.

28 Köfeler, H.C., Ahrends, R., Baker, E.S. et al. (2021). Recommendations for good practice in MS-based lipidomics. *J. Lipid Res.* 62: 100138.

29 Liebisch, G., Ahrends, R., Arita, M. et al. (2019). Lipidomics needs more standardization. *Nat. Metab.* 1: 745–747.

30 Fahy, E., Subramaniam, S., Brown, H.A. et al. (2005). A comprehensive classification system for lipids. *J. Lipid Res.* 46: 839–861.

31 Van Meer, G. and De Kroon, A.I. (2011). Lipid map of the mammalian cell. *J. Cell Sci.* 124: 5–8.

32 Leidl, K., Liebisch, G., Richter, D., and Schmitz, G. (2008). Mass spectrometric analysis of lipid species of human circulating blood cells. *Biochim. Biophys. Acta* 1781: 655–664.

33 Holthuis, J.C. and Menon, A.K. (2014). Lipid landscapes and pipelines in membrane homeostasis. *Nature* 510: 48–57.

34 Schweizer, S., Liebisch, G., Oeckl, J. et al. (2019). The lipidome of primary murine white, brite, and brown adipocytes-impact of beta-adrenergic stimulation. *PLoS Biol.* 17: e3000412.

35 Lange, M., Angelidou, G., Ni, Z. et al. (2021). AdipoAtlas: a reference lipidome for human white adipose tissue. *Cell Rep. Med.* 2: 100407.

36 Wiesner, P., Leidl, K., Boettcher, A. et al. (2009). Lipid profiling of FPLC-separated lipoprotein fractions by electrospray ionization tandem mass spectrometry. *J. Lipid Res.* 50: 574–585.

37 Panganamala, R.V., Horrocks, L.A., Geer, J.C., and Cornwell, D.G. (1971). Positions of double bonds in the monounsaturated alk-1-enyl groups from the plasmalogens of human heart and brain. *Chem. Phys. Lipids* 6: 97–102.

38 Schmid, H.H.O. and Takahashi, T. (1968). The ALK-i-enyl ether and alkyl ether lipids of bovine heart muscle. *Biochim. Biophys. Acta, Lipids Lipid Metab.* 164: 141–147.

39 Scherer, M., Bottcher, A., and Liebisch, G. (2011). Lipid profiling of lipoproteins by electrospray ionization tandem mass spectrometry. *Biochim. Biophys. Acta* 1811: 918–924.

40 Ecker, J., Scherer, M., Schmitz, G., and Liebisch, G. (2012). A rapid GC-MS method for quantification of positional and geometric isomers of fatty acid methyl esters. *J. Chromatogr. B Analyt. Technol. Biomed. Life Sci.* 897: 98–104.

41 Ekroos, K. (2012). *Lipidomics: Technologies and Applications*. Weinheim/ Chichester: Wiley-VCH/Wiley.

42 Liebisch, G., Vizcaino, J.A., Köfeler, H. et al. (2013). Shorthand notation for lipid structures derived from mass spectrometry. *J. Lipid Res.* 54: 1523–1530.

43 Liebisch, G., Fahy, E., Aoki, J. et al. (2020). Update on LIPID MAPS classification, nomenclature, and shorthand notation for MS-derived lipid structures. *J. Lipid Res.* 61: 1539–1555.

44 Han, X. and Gross, R.W. (2001). Quantitative analysis and molecular species fingerprinting of triacylglyceride molecular species directly from lipid extracts of biological samples by electrospray ionization tandem mass spectrometry. *Anal. Biochem.* 295: 88–100.

45 Tsikas, D. (2017). Assessment of lipid peroxidation by measuring malondialdehyde (MDA) and relatives in biological samples: analytical and biological challenges. *Anal. Biochem.* 524: 13–30.

46 Krautbauer, S., Blazquez, R., Liebisch, G. et al. (2021). Application of lipid class ratios for sample stability monitoring-evaluation of murine tissue homogenates and SDS as a stabilizer. *Metabolites* 11: 277.

47 Kirkwood, J.S., Maier, C., and Stevens, J.F. (2013). Simultaneous, untargeted metabolic profiling of polar and nonpolar metabolites by LC-Q-TOF mass spectrometry. *Curr. Protoc. Toxicol.*, Chapter 4, Unit4 39.

48 Lofgren, L., Forsberg, G.B., and Stahlman, M. (2016). The BUME method: a new rapid and simple chloroform-free method for total lipid extraction of animal tissue. *Sci. Rep.* 6: 27688.

49 Ulmer, C.Z., Patterson, R.E., Koelmel, J.P. et al. (2017). A robust lipidomics workflow for mammalian cells, plasma, and tissue using liquid-chromatography high-resolution tandem mass spectrometry. *Methods Mol. Biol.* 1609: 91–106.

50 Sprenger, R.R., Hermansson, M., Neess, D. et al. (2021). Lipid molecular timeline profiling reveals diurnal crosstalk between the liver and circulation. *Cell Rep.* 34: 108710.

51 Liebisch, G., Plagge, J., Horing, M. et al. (2021). The effect of gut microbiota on the intestinal lipidome of mice. *Int. J. Med. Microbiol.* 311: 151488.

52 Hall, Z., Bond, N.J., Ashmore, T. et al. (2017). Lipid zonation and phospholipid remodeling in nonalcoholic fatty liver disease. *Hepatology* 65: 1165–1180.

53 Höring, M., Krautbauer, S., Hiltl, L. et al. (2021). Accurate lipid quantification of tissue homogenates requires suitable sample concentration, solvent composition, and homogenization procedure – a case study in murine liver. *Metabolites* 11: 365.

54 Bligh, E.G. and Dyer, W.J. (1959). A rapid method of total lipid extraction and purification. *Can. J. Biochem. Physiol.* 37: 911–917.

55 Folch, J., Lees, M., and Sloane Stanley, G.H. (1957). A simple method for the isolation and purification of total lipides from animal tissues. *J. Biol. Chem.* 226: 497–509.

56 Matyash, V., Liebisch, G., Kurzchalia, T.V. et al. (2008). Lipid extraction by methyl-*tert*-butyl ether for high-throughput lipidomics. *J. Lipid Res.* 49: 1137–1146.

57 Lofgren, L., Stahlman, M., Forsberg, G.B. et al. (2012). The BUME method: a novel automated chloroform-free 96-well total lipid extraction method for blood plasma. *J. Lipid Res.* 53: 1690–1700.

58 Sun, G., Yang, K., Zhao, Z. et al. (2008). Matrix-assisted laser desorption/ ionization time-of-flight mass spectrometric analysis of cellular glycerophospholipids enabled by multiplexed solvent dependent analyte-matrix interactions. *Anal. Chem.* 80: 7576–7585.

59 Han, X., Yang, K., Yang, J. et al. (2006). Factors influencing the electrospray intrasource separation and selective ionization of glycerophospholipids. *J. Am. Soc. Mass Spectrom.* 17: 264–274.

60 Liebisch, G., Lieser, B., Rathenberg, J. et al. (2004). High-throughput quantification of phosphatidylcholine and sphingomyelin by electrospray ionization tandem mass spectrometry coupled with isotope correction algorithm. *Biochim. Biophys. Acta* 1686: 108–117.

61 Gallego, S.F., Hojlund, K., and Ejsing, C.S. (2018). Easy, fast, and reproducible quantification of cholesterol and other lipids in human plasma by combined high resolution MSX and FTMS analysis. *J. Am. Soc. Mass Spectrom.* 29: 34–41.

62 Schuhmann, K., Srzentic, K., Nagornov, K.O. et al. (2017). Monitoring membrane lipidome turnover by metabolic ^{15}N labeling and shotgun ultra-high-resolution orbitrap Fourier transform mass spectrometry. *Anal. Chem.* 89: 12857–12865.

63 Hsu, F.F. (2018). Mass spectrometry-based shotgun lipidomics – a critical review from the technical point of view. *Anal. Bioanal. Chem.* 410: 6387–6409.

64 Wang, M., Wang, C., and Han, X. (2017). Selection of internal standards for accurate quantification of complex lipid species in biological extracts by electrospray ionization mass spectrometry-what, how and why? *Mass Spectrom. Rev.* 36: 693–714.

65 Hu, C., Wang, C., He, L., and Han, X. (2019). Novel strategies for enhancing shotgun lipidomics for comprehensive analysis of cellular lipidomes. *TrAC, Trends Anal. Chem.* 120: 115330.

66 Ryan, E. and Reid, G.E. (2016). Chemical derivatization and ultrahigh resolution and accurate mass spectrometry strategies for "shotgun" lipidome analysis. *Acc. Chem. Res.* 49: 1596–1604.

67 Liebisch, G., Binder, M., Schifferer, R. et al. (2006). High throughput quantification of cholesterol and cholesteryl ester by electrospray ionization tandem mass spectrometry (ESI-MS/MS). *Biochim. Biophys. Acta* 1761: 121–128.

68 Wang, M., Han, R.H., and Han, X. (2013). Fatty acidomics: global analysis of lipid species containing a carboxyl group with a charge-remote fragmentation-assisted approach. *Anal. Chem.* 85: 9312–9320.

69 Pan, M., Qin, C., and Han, X. (2021). Quantitative analysis of polyphosphoinositide, bis(monoacylglycero)phosphate, and phosphatidylglycerol species by shotgun lipidomics after methylation. *Methods Mol. Biol.* 2306: 77–91.

70 Höring, M., Ejsing, C.S., Krautbauer, S. et al. (2021). Accurate quantification of lipid species affected by isobaric overlap in Fourier-transform mass spectrometry. *J. Lipid Res.* 62: 100050.

71 Liebisch, G., Drobnik, W., Lieser, B., and Schmitz, G. (2002). High-throughput quantification of lysophosphatidylcholine by electrospray ionization tandem mass spectrometry. *Clin. Chem.* 48: 2217–2224.

72 Höring, M., Ejsing, C.S., Hermansson, M., and Liebisch, G. (2019). Quantification of cholesterol and cholesteryl ester by direct flow injection high-resolution Fourier transform mass spectrometry utilizing species-specific response factors. *Anal. Chem.* 91: 3459–3466.

73 Almeida, R., Pauling, J.K., Sokol, E. et al. (2015). Comprehensive lipidome analysis by shotgun lipidomics on a hybrid quadrupole-orbitrap-linear ion trap mass spectrometer. *J. Am. Soc. Mass Spectrom.* 26: 133–148.

74 Schwudke, D., Schuhmann, K., Herzog, R. et al. (2011). Shotgun lipidomics on high resolution mass spectrometers. *Cold Spring Harbor Perspect. Biol.* 3: a004614.

75 Hsu, F.F. and Turk, J. (2009). Electrospray ionization with low-energy collisionally activated dissociation tandem mass spectrometry of glycerophospholipids:

mechanisms of fragmentation and structural characterization. *J. Chromatogr. B Analyt. Technol. Biomed. Life Sci.* 877: 2673–2695.

76 Matuszewski, B.K., Constanzer, M.L., and Chavez-Eng, C.M. (2003). Strategies for the assessment of matrix effect in quantitative bioanalytical methods based on HPLC-MS/MS. *Anal. Chem.* 75: 3019–3030.

77 Scherer, M., Leuthauser-Jaschinski, K., Ecker, J. et al. (2010). A rapid and quantitative LC-MS/MS method to profile sphingolipids. *J. Lipid Res.* 51: 2001–2011.

78 Han, X., Yang, K., and Gross, R.W. (2012). Multi-dimensional mass spectrometry-based shotgun lipidomics and novel strategies for lipidomic analyses. *Mass Spectrom. Rev.* 31: 134–178.

79 Yang, K., Cheng, H., Gross, R.W., and Han, X. (2009). Automated lipid identification and quantification by multidimensional mass spectrometry-based shotgun lipidomics. *Anal. Chem.* 81: 4356–4368.

80 Scherer, M., Schmitz, G., and Liebisch, G. (2010). Simultaneous quantification of cardiolipin, bis(monoacylglycero)phosphate and their precursors by hydrophilic interaction LC-MS/MS including correction of isotopic overlap. *Anal. Chem.* 82: 8794–8799.

81 Ekroos, K., Ejsing, C.S., Bahr, U. et al. (2003). Charting molecular composition of phosphatidylcholines by fatty acid scanning and ion trap MS3 fragmentation. *J. Lipid Res.* 44: 2181–2192.

82 Schuhmann, K., Moon, H., Thomas, H. et al. (2019). Quantitative fragmentation model for bottom-up shotgun lipidomics. *Anal. Chem.* 91: 12085–12093.

83 Wozny, K., Lehmann, W.D., Wozny, M. et al. (2019). A method for the quantitative determination of glycerophospholipid regioisomers by UPLC-ESI-MS/MS. *Anal. Bioanal. Chem.* 411: 915–924.

84 Marshall, D.L., Criscuolo, A., Young, R.S.E. et al. (2019). Mapping unsaturation in human plasma lipids by data-independent ozone-induced dissociation. *J. Am. Soc. Mass Spectrom.* 30: 1621–1630.

85 Ma, X., Chong, L., Tian, R. et al. (2016). Identification and quantitation of lipid C=C location isomers: a shotgun lipidomics approach enabled by photochemical reaction. *Proc. Natl. Acad. Sci. U.S.A.* 113: 2573–2578.

86 Criscuolo, A., Zeller, M., and Fedorova, M. (2020). Evaluation of lipid in-source fragmentation on different orbitrap-based mass spectrometers. *J. Am. Soc. Mass Spectrom.* 31: 463–466.

87 Hu, C., Luo, W., Xu, J., and Han, X. (2022). Recognition and avoidance of ion source-generated artifacts in lipidomics analysis. *Mass Spectrom. Rev.* 41: 15–31.

88 Krautbauer, S., Buchler, C., and Liebisch, G. (2016). Relevance in the use of appropriate internal standards for accurate quantification using LC-MS/MS: Tauro-conjugated bile acids as an example. *Anal. Chem.* 88: 10957–10961.

89 Schoeny, H., Rampler, E., El Abiead, Y. et al. (2021). A combined flow injection/reversed-phase chromatography-high-resolution mass spectrometry workflow for accurate absolute lipid quantification with ^{13}C internal standards. *Analyst* 146: 2591–2599.

90 Wang, Y., Hinz, S., Uckermann, O. et al. (2019). Shotgun lipidomics-based characterization of the landscape of lipid metabolism in colorectal cancer. *Biochim. Biophys. Acta, Mol. Cell. Biol. Lipids* 1865 (3): 158579.

91 Wang, M., Huang, Y., and Han, X. (2014). Accurate mass searching of individual lipid species candidates from high-resolution mass spectra for shotgun lipidomics. *Rapid Commun. Mass Spectrom.* 28: 2201–2210.

92 Höring, M., Ekroos, K., Baker, P.R.S. et al. (2020). Correction of isobaric overlap resulting from sodiated ions in lipidomics. *Anal. Chem.* 92: 10966–10970.

93 Herzog, R., Schuhmann, K., Schwudke, D. et al. (2012). LipidXplorer: a software for consensual cross-platform lipidomics. *PLoS One* 7: e29851.

94 Herzog, R., Schwudke, D., Schuhmann, K. et al. (2011). A novel informatics concept for high-throughput shotgun lipidomics based on the molecular fragmentation query language. *Genome Biol.* 12: R8.

95 Schuhmann, K., Thomas, H., Ackerman, J.M. et al. (2017). Intensity-independent noise filtering in FT MS and FT MS/MS spectra for shotgun lipidomics. *Anal. Chem.* 89: 7046–7052.

96 Yaghmour, M.H., Thiele, C., and Kuerschner, L. (2021). An advanced method for propargylcholine phospholipid detection by direct-infusion MS. *J. Lipid Res.* 62: 100022.

97 Husen, P., Tarasov, K., Katafiasz, M. et al. (2013). Analysis of lipid experiments (ALEX): a software framework for analysis of high-resolution shotgun lipidomics data. *PLoS One* 8: e79736.

98 Pauling, J.K., Hermansson, M., Hartler, J. et al. (2017). Proposal for a common nomenclature for fragment ions in mass spectra of lipids. *PLoS One* 12: e0188394.

99 Cifkova, E., Hajek, R., Lisa, M., and Holcapek, M. (2016). Hydrophilic interaction liquid chromatography-mass spectrometry of (lyso)phosphatidic acids, (lyso) phosphatidylserines and other lipid classes. *J. Chromatogr. A* 1439: 65–73.

100 Lisa, M. and Holcapek, M. (2015). High-throughput and comprehensive lipidomic analysis using ultrahigh-performance supercritical fluid chromatography-mass spectrometry. *Anal. Chem.* 87: 7187–7195.

101 Scherer, M., Schmitz, G., and Liebisch, G. (2009). High-throughput analysis of sphingosine 1-phosphate, sphinganine 1-phosphate, and lysophosphatidic acid in plasma samples by liquid chromatography-tandem mass spectrometry. *Clin. Chem.* 55: 1218–1222.

102 Gallego, S.F., Hermansson, M., Liebisch, G. et al. (2018). Total fatty acid analysis of human blood samples in one minute by high-resolution mass spectrometry. *Biomolecules* 9: 7.

103 Burla, B., Arita, M., Arita, M. et al. (2018). MS-based lipidomics of human blood plasma: a community-initiated position paper to develop accepted guidelines. *J. Lipid Res.* 59: 2001–2017.

104 Sales, S., Graessler, J., Ciucci, S. et al. (2016). Gender, contraceptives and individual metabolic predisposition shape a healthy plasma lipidome. *Sci. Rep.* 6: 27710.

105 Drobnik, W., Liebisch, G., Audebert, F.X. et al. (2003). Plasma ceramide and lysophosphatidylcholine inversely correlate with mortality in sepsis patients. *J. Lipid Res.* 44: 754–761.

106 Sigruener, A., Kleber, M.E., Heimerl, S. et al. (2014). Glycerophospholipid and sphingolipid species and mortality: the Ludwigshafen Risk and Cardiovascular Health (LURIC) study. *PLoS One* 9: e85724.

107 Havulinna, A.S., Sysi-Aho, M., Hilvo, M. et al. (2016). Circulating ceramides predict cardiovascular outcomes in the population-based FINRISK 2002 cohort. *Arterioscler. Thromb. Vasc. Biol.* 36: 2424–2430.

108 Laaksonen, R., Ekroos, K., Sysi-Aho, M. et al. (2016). Plasma ceramides predict cardiovascular death in patients with stable coronary artery disease and acute coronary syndromes beyond LDL-cholesterol. *Eur. Heart J.* 37: 1967–1976.

109 Lefevre-Arbogast, S., Hejblum, B.P., Helmer, C. et al. (2021). Early signature in the blood lipidome associated with subsequent cognitive decline in the elderly: a case-control analysis nested within the Three-City cohort study. *EBioMedicine* 64: 103216.

110 Wolrab, D., Jirasko, R., Cifkova, E. et al. (2022). Lipidomic profiling of human serum enables detection of pancreatic cancer. *Nat. Commun.* 13: 124.

111 Demirkan, A., Van Duijn, C.M., Ugocsai, P. et al. (2012). Genome-wide association study identifies novel loci associated with circulating phospho- and sphingolipid concentrations. *PLoS Genet.* 8: e1002490.

112 Hicks, A.A., Pramstaller, P.P., Johansson, A. et al. (2009). Genetic determinants of circulating sphingolipid concentrations in European populations. *PLoS Genet.* 5: e1000672.

113 Sigruener, A., Wolfrum, C., Boettcher, A. et al. (2017). Lipidomic and metabolic changes in the P4-type ATPase ATP10D deficient C57BL/6J wild type mice upon rescue of ATP10D function. *PLoS One* 12: e0178368.

114 Ecker, J., Benedetti, E., Kindt, A.S.D. et al. (2021). The colorectal cancer lipidome: identification of a robust tumor-specific lipid species signature. *Gastroenterology* 161: 910–923.e19.

115 Vvedenskaya, O., Rose, T.D., Knittelfelder, O. et al. (2021). Nonalcoholic fatty liver disease stratification by liver lipidomics. *J. Lipid Res.* 62: 100104.

116 Surma, M.A., Gerl, M.J., Herzog, R. et al. (2021). Mouse lipidomics reveals inherent flexibility of a mammalian lipidome. *Sci. Rep.* 11: 19364.

117 Ecker, J., Liebisch, G., Englmaier, M. et al. (2010). Induction of fatty acid synthesis is a key requirement for phagocytic differentiation of human monocytes. *Proc. Natl. Acad. Sci. U.S.A.* 107: 7817–7822.

118 Ecker, J. and Liebisch, G. (2014). Application of stable isotopes to investigate the metabolism of fatty acids, glycerophospholipid and sphingolipid species. *Prog. Lipid Res.* 54: 14–31.

119 Schifferer, R., Liebisch, G., Bandulik, S. et al. (2007). ApoA-I induces a preferential efflux of monounsaturated phosphatidylcholine and medium chain sphingomyelin species from a cellular pool distinct from HDL(3) mediated phospholipid efflux. *Biochim. Biophys. Acta* 1771: 853–863.

120 Delong, C.J., Shen, Y.J., Thomas, M.J., and Cui, Z. (1999). Molecular distinction of phosphatidylcholine synthesis between the CDP-choline pathway and phosphatidylethanolamine methylation pathway. *J. Biol. Chem.* 274: 29683–29688.

121 Hermansson, M., Hokynar, K., and Somerharju, P. (2011). Mechanisms of glycerophospholipid homeostasis in mammalian cells. *Prog. Lipid Res.* 50: 240–257.

122 Binder, M., Liebisch, G., Langmann, T., and Schmitz, G. (2006). Metabolic profiling of glycerophospholipid synthesis in fibroblasts loaded with free cholesterol and modified low density lipoproteins. *J. Biol. Chem.* 281: 21869–21877.

123 Kindt, A., Liebisch, G., Clavel, T. et al. (2018). The gut microbiota promotes hepatic fatty acid desaturation and elongation in mice. *Nat. Commun.* 9: 3760.

124 Thiele, C., Wunderling, K., and Leyendecker, P. (2019). Multiplexed and single cell tracing of lipid metabolism. *Nat. Methods* 16: 1123–1130.

125 Pham, H.T., Ly, T., Trevitt, A.J. et al. (2012). Differentiation of complex lipid isomers by radical-directed dissociation mass spectrometry. *Anal. Chem.* 84: 7525–7532.

126 Ma, X., Zhang, W., Li, Z. et al. (2021). Enabling high structural specificity to lipidomics by coupling photochemical derivatization with tandem mass spectrometry. *Acc. Chem. Res.* 54: 3873–3882.

4

Liquid Chromatography – and Supercritical Fluid Chromatography – Mass Spectrometry

Michal Holčapek, Ondřej Peterka, Michaela Chocholoušková, and Denise Wolrab

University of Pardubice, Faculty of Chemical Technology, Department of Analytical Chemistry, Studentská 573, 532 10, Pardubice, Czech Republic

4.1 Introduction

Mass spectrometry (MS) is a key technology and an indispensable tool in lipidomic analysis, as described in more detail in multiple chapters of this book. MS can be used in standalone modes, such as direct infusion (Chapter 3), flow injection analysis, and various types of desorption ionization techniques, which can be easily applied for MS imaging (Chapter 5). Here, we describe the added potential of MS coupling with chromatographic techniques for tailored separations of selected types of lipid isomers. There are many different separation modes based on various types of interactions of analytes with the mobile and stationary phases, leading to different retention mechanisms and, therefore, providing different separation selectivities. This chapter includes only the most important chromatographic methods for lipidomic analysis using high-performance liquid chromatography (HPLC) or supercritical fluid chromatography (SFC) but excludes gas chromatography with common applications in the analysis of fatty acid methyl esters (FAMEs) to determine the relative abundances of individual fatty acyls after the transesterification of intact lipid molecules [1, 2] and the analysis of triacylglycerols (TGs) using dedicated columns stable at high temperatures [3].

The most common division of separation techniques in the analysis of lipids is lipid class separation, lipid species separation, and special separation approaches [4, 5]. The retention mechanisms for individual approaches and typical applications are described in the following chapters. Figure 4.1 shows the schematic visualization of the retention principles and the expected type of separation in a simplified example of phosphatidylcholines (PCs) and lysophosphatidylcholines (LPCs) containing shorter and longer fatty acyl chains. The lipid class separation (Figure 4.1a) presents an example of the silica gel stationary phase typically used in hydrophilic

Mass Spectrometry for Lipidomics: Methods and Applications, First Edition.
Edited by Michal Holčapek and Kim Ekroos.
© 2023 WILEY-VCH GmbH. Published 2023 by WILEY-VCH GmbH.

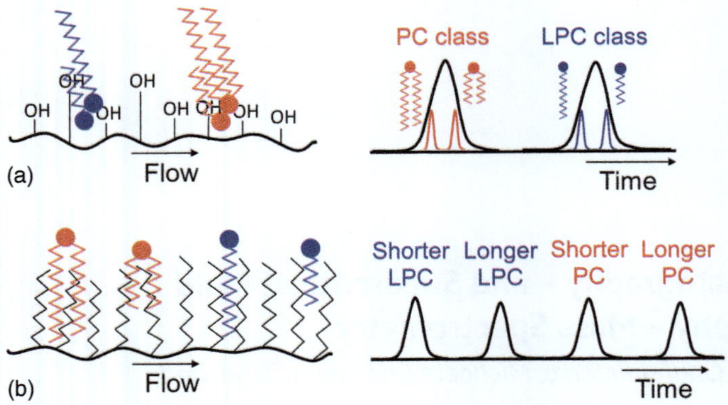

Figure 4.1 The main retention mechanisms involved in (a) lipid class separation and (b) lipid species separation illustrated on the example of phosphatidylcholines (PC) and lysophosphatidylcholines (LPC) with longer and shorter fatty acyl chains. The schematic representation of PC and LPC includes the polar head group (colored circles) and connected fatty acyl chain(s).

interaction liquid chromatography (HILIC) or ultrahigh-performance supercritical fluid chromatography (UHPSFC) systems. Primary interactions are between the polar head groups (e.g. phosphate moiety) and the hydroxyl groups in the silica-based stationary phase. This retention mechanism results in the separation of lipid classes, which differ in their polar functionality. The length of fatty acyls and the structure of the hydrophobic part play a secondary role and cause only partial in-group separation hidden within the envelope of the whole lipid class, as schematically shown in Figure 4.1a. In the case of lipid species separation (Figure 4.1b), the primary interaction is between the fatty acyl chains in the lipid molecule and the hydrophobic aliphatic chains of the stationary phase used in reversed-phase (RP) chromatography, e.g. C18, C8, or C30. Moreover, the secondary interactions of the polar head groups with the stationary phase are not negligible, providing the chromatographic resolution according to the fatty chain lengths and the polar head group in parallel.

Figure 4.2 highlights the differences in data processing for the lipid class and lipid species approaches. In the case of lipid class separation, the whole peak corresponding to all species from this particular class is integrated, which results in the lipid class mass spectrum (Figure 4.2b), as illustrated by the example of PC class showing 10 PC species and an internal standard (IS). The deisotoping procedure is essential in this case, but the overall data processing may be easily automated and provides advantages for quantitation because of the (partial) coelution of lipid species and IS. On the other hand, the lipid species separation (Figure 4.2b) provides much better selectivity for individual lipid species, including some isomeric lipids, but the data processing and quantitation are more demanding.

More detailed descriptions on the method development using advanced chromatographic methods coupled with MS could be found in a recently published book on this topic with several chapters focused on the analysis of lipids [6] or in scientific journals focused on chromatographic techniques or bioanalytical chemistry. Here, we

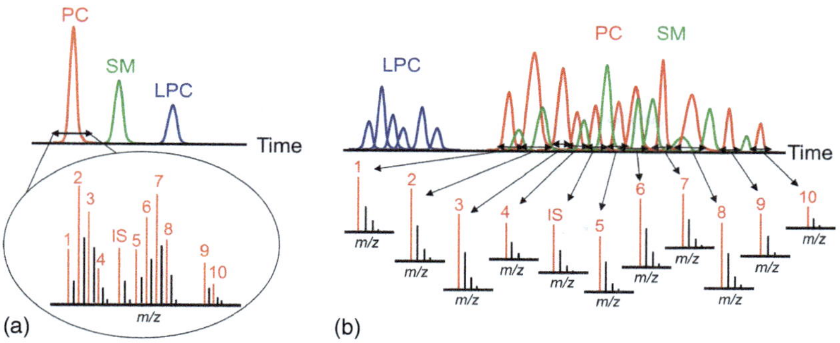

Figure 4.2 Illustrative chromatograms and corresponding mass spectra for (a) lipid class separation and (b) lipid species separation. The illustrative example shows 10 PC species and internal standard (IS).

provide only a brief introduction to the main separation modes that are convenient for the separation of particular subgroups of the lipidome or are focused on a certain type of isomerism. The primary decision is to select the suitable type of separation mode for a given problem. The second most critical issue is the selection of the chromatographic column, where preference should be given to the newest columns with a small particle size (below 2 μm particle diameter) coupled with chromatographic systems with the high maximum operating backpressure of the system. Such configurations are called ultrahigh-performance liquid chromatography (UHPLC) or UHPSFC in the case of the supercritical fluid used as the mobile phase. If the laboratory is not equipped with UHPLC or UHPSFC systems, then the alternative solution for conventional HPLC systems is the use of core–shell particles with the diameter below 3 μm, which could provide almost comparable performance to UHPLC systems but with the conventional device without additional costs. Chromatographic columns with particle size greater than 3 μm cannot compete in their performance with smaller particle size columns; therefore, they should be used only for less-demanding applications or in case a better alternative simply does not exist commercially [7], which could be the case of some dedicated column packing such as chiral columns. When the method is transferred from the previous use with non-MS detection, special care should be paid to the use of nonvolatile mobile phase additives (inorganic buffers, e.g. phosphate buffer or ion-pairing agents), which should be replaced by more volatile alternatives (organic buffers, e.g. ammonium acetate) at the lowest possible concentration to avoid ion suppression effects in the mass spectrometer. More detailed considerations could be found in individual references of this chapter.

4.2 Lipid Class Separation

The retention mechanism in the lipid class separation approach is based on primarily interactions between the polar head group of lipids and the polar stationary phase, whereas the effect of hydrophobic fatty acyl chains is mostly relatively low.

This results in the separation of individual lipid classes, while the separation of individual lipid species within a particular class is suppressed and shows only minor partial selectivity, as shown in the example in Figure 4.1a. The almost complete coelution of all lipid species within a lipid class with exogenous IS is a significant advantage for lipidomic quantitation because coionization guarantees the same matrix effect and therefore a more robust quantitation, as confirmed in our previous validation study [8]. On the other hand, the drawback of lipid class separation approaches is that only the summary formula with the carbon number and double-bond (DB) number (lipid species level [9]) is typically determined but without the isomeric separation, which results in c. two to three times less-detected species compared to the lipid species approach. There are three chromatographic modes that provide the lipid class separation: normal phase (NP), HILIC, and SFC using polar stationary phases, such as silica gel.

4.2.1 Normal-Phase Liquid Chromatography

At present, NP liquid chromatography is rarely used because it requires chromatographic experience and the right practice, and even for the experienced user, the reproducibility is mostly worse than for other well-established approaches. The stationary phase is polar, and the mobile phase is nonpolar with a small amount of added polar modifier to elute polar analytes. The typical stationary phase is silica gel, which prevails in the application in the analysis of lipids [10–12]. Other options are medium polar stationary phases based on modified silica, such as amino or diol columns [13]. The application range of normal chromatography is limited only to nonpolar and medium polar lipids, considering the reasonable analysis time, but it is not suitable for polar phospholipid or sphingolipid classes, which could be too strongly retained on the stationary phase or may not be eluted at all. Mobile phases typically contain hexane or heptane as the major component with relatively small addition of a polar modifier, such as 2-propanol, ethanol, acetonitrile, or their mixtures with other solvents. It is important to ensure that the polar modifier is fully miscible with hexane/heptane, e.g. methanol is not miscible, but the addition of 2-propanol could make it miscible at defined ratios. The most critical feature of NP-HPLC is to carefully control the amount of residual water in solvents, which requires the use of molecular sieves for the removal of any residual water from all solvents [10]; otherwise, serious reproducibility problems could occur. These mobile phases have limited compatibility with electrospray ionization (ESI), and therefore, atmospheric pressure chemical ionization (APCI) is typically preferred. The typical analytes for NP-HPLC are tri-, di-, and monoacylglycerols (TG, DG, and MG); cholesterol esters (CEs); sterols; or other low-to-medium polar lipid classes, as illustrated in the example of NP-UHPLC/APCI-MS analysis in Figure 4.3, where the silica gel column and the following gradient have been used: 0 minutes – 99% A + 1% B, 20 minutes – 32% A + 68% B, where A is hexane and B is a mixture of hexane-2-propanol–acetonitrile (96 : 2 : 2, v/v/v) [10]. The applicability of NP is rather limited and could be successfully replaced by robust and faster alternatives described in the following chapters, such as HILIC or UHPSFC. In the past, the term NP was

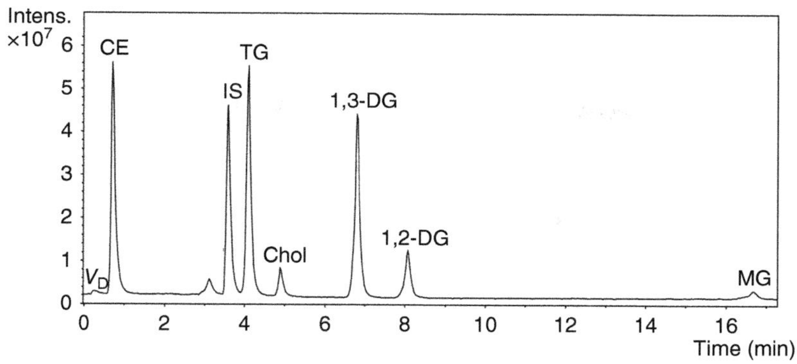

Figure 4.3 Normal-phase (NP) UHPLC/APCI-MS chromatogram of nonpolar lipid class standards and the internal standard using Acquity UPLC HILIC column (50 mm × 2.1 mm, 1.7 μm). Source: Reprinted with permission from Holčapek et al. [10].

incorrectly used in the literature for mobile phases containing water, resulting in the HILIC mechanism described in the follow-up chapter.

4.2.2 Hydrophilic Interaction Liquid Chromatography

HILIC chromatography uses basically the same type of stationary phases as NP, but the mobile phase is different, resulting in a different retention mechanism. In general, the mobile phase contains at least 3% of water, some ionic additives, and the main component acetonitrile with a typical content of 60–95%. The presence of water results in the formation of an aqueous multilayer on the surface of silica gel or other polar stationary phases. This aqueous layer acts as an embedded stationary phase, where the chromatographic partition of the analytes occurs between the adsorbed aqueous layer and the acetonitrile-rich mobile phase, which is responsible for the retention mechanism. It is important to realize that the different mobile-phase compositions compared to NP provide completely different retention mechanism and selectivity. Here, nonpolar lipid classes, such as TG, DG, MG, CE, etc., coelute in the void volume of the system, and only medium to strongly polar lipid classes are retained and well separated (Figure 4.4). In general, HILIC chromatography requires longer time for full equilibration of the chromatographic column, which could reduce the sample throughput. Fortunately, the solution is the so-called partial equilibration [14], when the relatively short time is used for equilibration, but this time must be always constant, and then the reproducibility is very good except for starting two to three injections used for the column equilibration. This approach has been used for large-scale clinical studies in cancer biomarker research, and the method has been fully validated according to the requirements of the Food and Drug Administration (FDA) [15] and the European Medicines Agency (EMA) [16]. The strongest application of HILIC/MS is the analysis of highly polar phospholipids [17, 18], sphingolipids, and mainly glycosphingolipids, as illustrated by the example of detailed characterization of anionic ganglioside subclasses (Figure 4.5). Glycosphingolipids with larger saccharide parts provide structurally

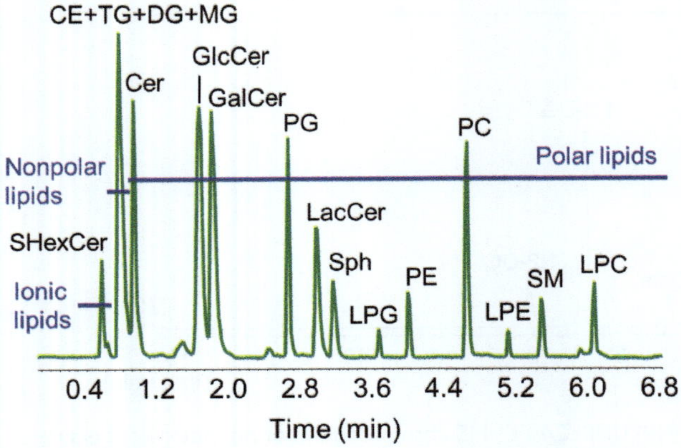

Figure 4.4 Base peak intensity chromatogram of lipid class standards measured by hydrophilic liquid chromatography (HILIC) UHPLC/MS using the Viridis BEH column (100mm × 3 mm, 1.7 μm). Source: Reprinted and adapted with permission from Wolrab et al. [8].

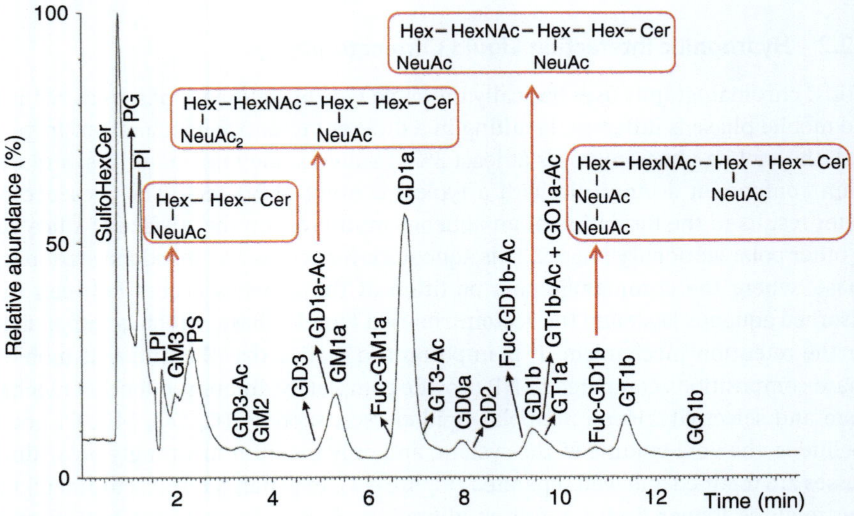

Figure 4.5 Total ion current chromatogram of porcine brain extract measured by HILIC/ESI-MS using the Ascentis Si column (150 mm × 2.1 mm, 3 μm) in the negative-ion mode. Structures of selected ganglioside subclasses are shown. The explanation of all abbreviations and structures is described in the original publication. Source: Reprinted and adapted with permission from Hájek et al. [19].

rich MS/MS spectra useful for the unambiguous determination of the glycan sequence including branching [19–21]. The retention behavior of glycosphingolipids follows regular patterns (Figure 4.6), which can be used as an additional tool for unambiguous identification in addition to MS data. Many useful applications can be found in the literature, for example, the lipid analysis of plants [22], bacteria [23, 24], tissues [25–27], cells [28, 29], body fluids [30, 31], and food [32].

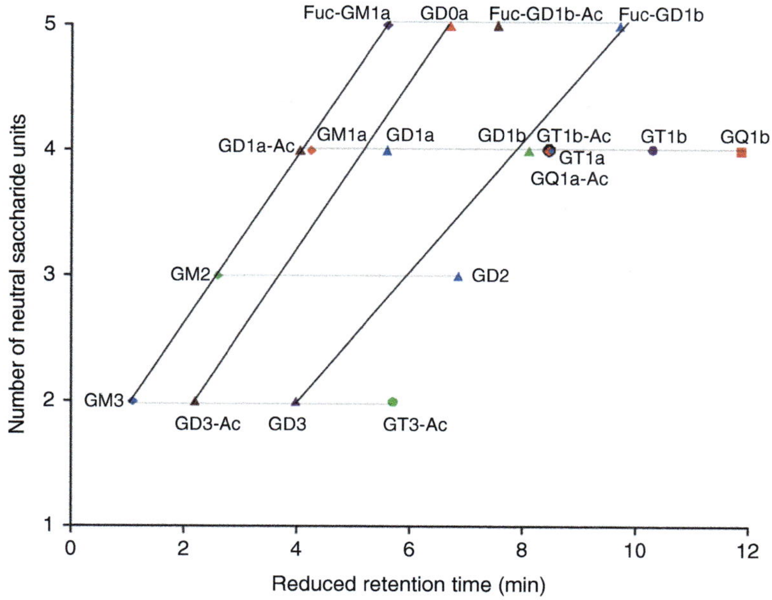

Figure 4.6 Dependences of reduced retention times in HILIC/ESI-MS on the number of neutral saccharide units. The explanation of all abbreviations and structures is described in the original publication. Source: Reprinted with permission from Hájek et al. [19].

4.2.3 Supercritical Fluid Chromatography

SFC has been known for decades, but the main limitation of the past was low reproducibility. At present, modern instruments equipped with a backpressure regulator have overcome this problem, and the reproducibility is comparable to that of liquid chromatography [33, 34]. Similar to UHPLC, SFC also strongly benefits from the use of sub-2 μm particles and higher pressure. This approach is called UHPSFC in analogy to UHPLC. The key reason for the successful application of UHPSFC/MS in lipidomic analysis is the fact that the supercritical fluid maintains the advantages of both gas and liquid phases because the viscosity is comparable to gas, the density is close to the liquid, and the diffusivity has a value between but still sufficiently high [35]. As a consequence, UHPSFC provides a very fast analysis of lipids with uncompromised resolution [36]. Another important aspect is the relatively low backpressure (Figure 4.7a), which allows the use of higher flow rates, but again without the loss of chromatographic resolution, because the dependence of the height equivalent of the chromatographic plate in van Deemter curves has a plateau over a rather wide range of flow rates, unlike in liquid chromatography (Figure 4.7b). The most common mobile phase in UHPSFC is supercritical carbon dioxide (scCO_2) because of the moderate values of critical pressure and critical temperature, miscibility with common organic solvents, nontoxicity, and relatively low price for the highest purity of CO_2. All UHPSFC/MS applications in lipidomic analysis in the literature are based on supercritical CO_2 with the addition of suitable modifiers to elute more polar lipid classes because the

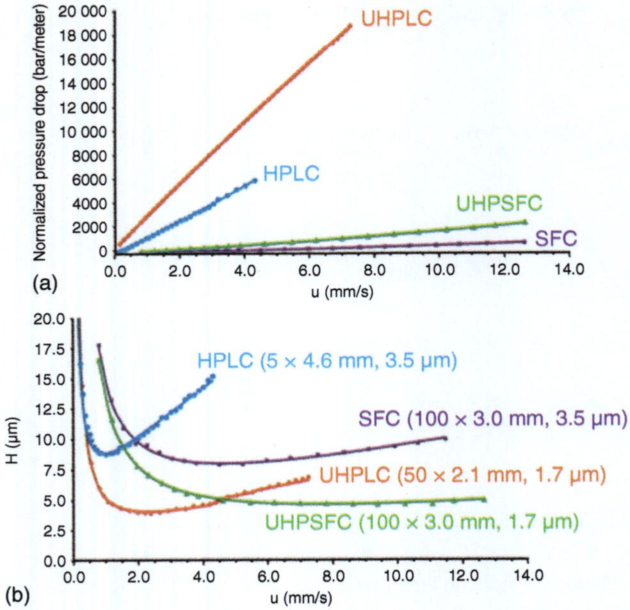

Figure 4.7 Comparison of characteristic parameters for HPLC, UHPLC, SFC, and UHPSFC chromatographic systems: (a) dependence of system backpressure on the linear velocity of mobile phase and (b) van Deemter curves showing the dependences of the theoretical plate equivalent versus the linear velocity. Source: Reprinted and adapted with permission from Perrenoud et al. [35].

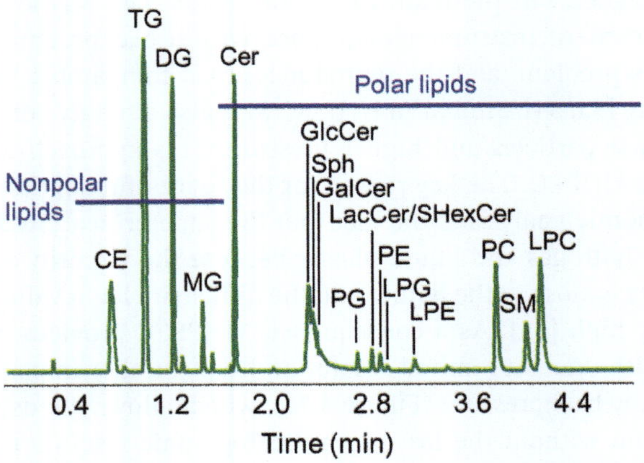

Figure 4.8 Base peak intensity chromatogram of lipid class standards measured by UHPSFC/MS using the Viridis BEH column (100mm × 3 mm, 1.7 µm). Source: Reprinted and adapted with permission from Wolrab et al. [8].

polarity of $scCO_2$ is similar to hexane; therefore, the addition of polar modifier and polar organic buffer in the gradient mode is essential for the elution of phospholipids and sphingolipids. The nonpolar characteristic of $scCO_2$ is perfectly compatible with the separation of nonpolar lipid classes, such as TG, DG, and CE, resulting in the ultimate sensitivity for these classes. An example of very fast UHPSFC separation of multiple nonpolar polar and polar lipid classes is shown in Figure 4.8. This method has been fully validated [8] and is then used for several thousands of clinical samples, especially in cancer biomarker research [37–40]. It is also the technology selected for the clinical translation of the method for the early detection of pancreatic cancer into real clinical screening, which is currently in progress [41, 42]. Similar to HILIC, partial in-class separation can be observed for lipid species differing in the number of DB and carbon atoms (CN) in fatty acyl chains, and these retention time changes have a very regular characteristic (Figure 4.9) [43]. UHPSFC can be used either in the HILIC-like mode for lipid class separation using silica, amino, or diol stationary phases or in the RP-like mode using conventional RP stationary phases, such as C18, adjusting the modifier composition depending on the applied mode. The real retention mechanism in SFC is more complex because of the absence or a very small amount of water and the specific characteristic of $scCO_2$ [44]; therefore, it is preferred to term it as HILIC-like and RP-like modes rather than HILIC and RP, which would not be accurate. The number of lipidomics groups with the implementation of UHPSFC/MS is still relatively low, but several worthy methods have already been published, both for the lipid class [45] and the lipid species [46]. The large potential of UHPSFC/MS in the lipidomic analysis is based on very fast and high-throughput lipidomic quantitation of biological samples convenient for clinical analysis [36, 47].

4.3 Lipid Species Separation

4.3.1 Reversed-Phase Liquid Chromatography

The lipid species separation is typically represented by RP-UHPLC, typically using C18 columns or less frequently with shorter (e.g. C8) or longer (C30) alkyl chains bonded to the silica. The clear and strong advantage is the universal applicability for many lipid classes with the highest number of separated lipid species; therefore, most of lipid analysis is done by RP-UHPLC using the C18 column. The retention mechanism is governed by nonpolar interactions between the hydrophobic parts of lipids (i.e. fatty acyl chains) and the hydrophobic part of the stationary phase, as already explained in the example in Figure 4.1b. The selectivity to resolve various types of isomers is quite attractive because RP-UHPLC methods can provide resolution of isomers differing in the positions and geometry of DB, the arrangement of carbon atoms in fatty acyl chains, regioisomers, or even branching of fatty acyl chains [48–51]. Many research groups [52–54] use RP-UHPLC for various lipidomic applications, either targeted to certain lipid classes or, more frequently, for the comprehensive analysis of lipidomic extracts containing the most abundant lipid classes (Figure 4.10). Typical mobile phases are based on acetonitrile – water or methanol – water with suitable ionic volatile additives, but sometimes, the mobile phase contains a less-polar component to foster the elution of nonpolar lipid classes, such as TG and CE. The typical mobile phases in published papers are the gradients of aqueous mixtures of

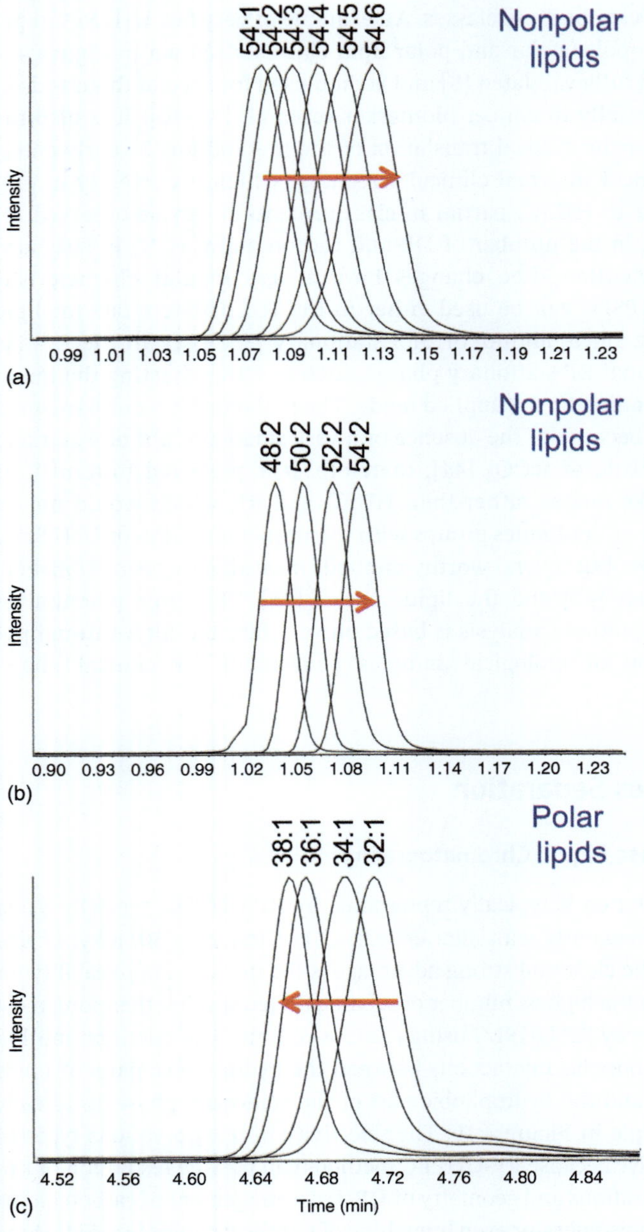

Figure 4.9 Effects of double-bond number and fatty acyl chain length on the retention behavior of lipids using UHPSFC/MS. Reconstructed ion chromatograms from the analysis of porcine brain extract (a) TG with 54 carbon atoms and different numbers of DB, (b) TG with 2 DB and different numbers of carbon atoms, and (c) PC with 1 DB and different numbers of carbon atoms. Source: Reprinted and adapted with permission from Lísa and Holčapek [43].

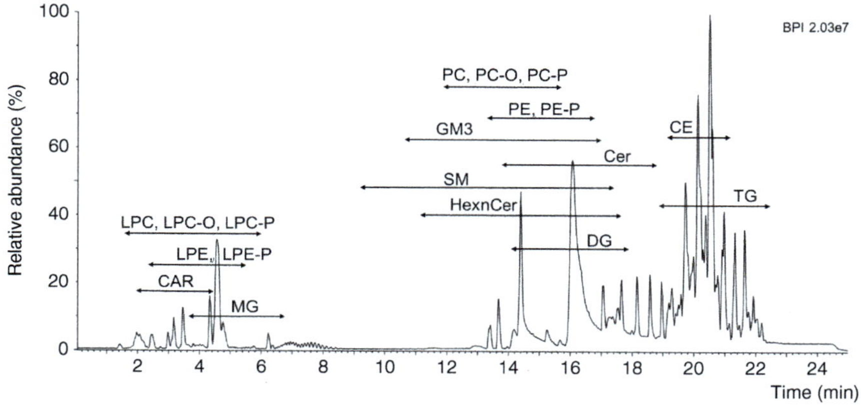

Figure 4.10 Base peak intensity chromatogram of NIST SRM 1950 human plasma measured by reversed-phase (RP) UHPLC/MS using the Acquity UPLC BEH C18 column (150 mm × 2.1 mm, 1.7 μm) in the positive ion mode. Source: Reprinted and adapted with permission from Vaňková et al. [48].

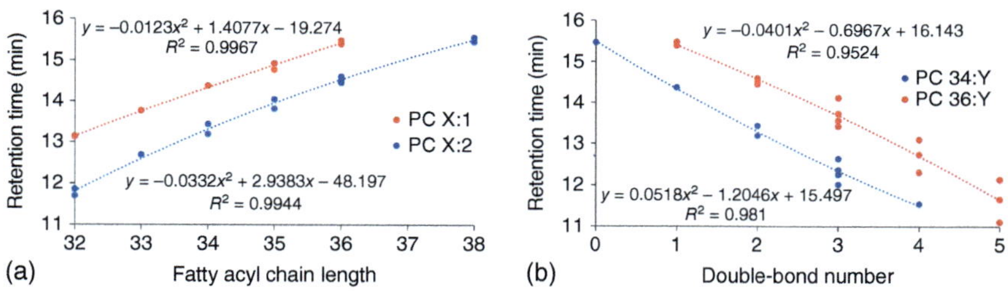

Figure 4.11 Retention dependencies of retention times on (a) the length of fatty acyl chains (X = carbon number) and (b) the number of double bonds (Y). Source: Reprinted with permission from Vaňková et al. [48].

acetonitrile or methanol, often with the addition of 2-propanol to increase the elution strength and to improve the dissolution of nonpolar lipid classes, such as TG and CE. The addition of volatile ionic additives (ammonium formate or acetate) at the concentration of 5–20 mM is common, sometimes in combination with adjusting the pH with the addition of a small amount of formic or acetic acid. Isomeric lipid molecules may have different biological properties; therefore, their differentiation could be important. The typical example is the analysis of oxylipins with numerous isomers differing in the positions of DB, hydroxyl groups, etc., which can be efficiently separated by RP-UHPLC [55, 56]. The retention behavior in RP-UHPLC follows logical patterns and increases with increasing length of fatty acyls and decreasing number of DB. The characteristic retention dependences for the constant DB number (Figure 4.11a) or the constant carbon number (CN) in all fatty acyl chains (Figure 4.11b) provide an additional tool to support unambiguous identification [48, 49, 51, 57–59]. The retention follows the equivalent carbon number (ECN) defined as ECN = CN − 2*DB.

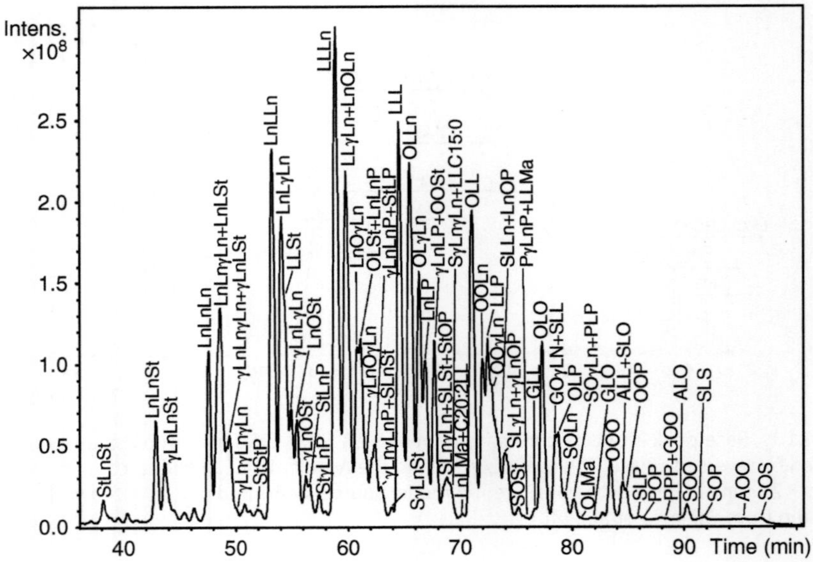

Figure 4.12 NARP-HPLC/APCI-MS analysis of redcurrant (*Ribes rubrum*) seed oil using Nova-Pak C18 columns connected in series (300 + 150 mm × 3.9 mm, 4 μm). The annotation of all triacylglycerols is described in the original publication. Source: Reprinted with permission from Lísa and Holčapek [63].

4.3.2 Nonaqueous Reversed-Phase Liquid Chromatography

Nonaqueous reversed-phase liquid chromatography (NARP-HPLC) is a variant of RP-HPLC but without the content of water in the mobile phase. Such conditions are convenient for very nonpolar molecules, such as TG and CE, because they have limited solubility in polar solvents, including water [60]. NARP conditions have been used in numerous papers for the characterization of TG in plant oils and animal fats. The typical mobile-phase conditions include solvents, such as 2-propanol, hexane, or chloroform, in addition to the common methanol and acetonitrile typical for RP separation. The retention of NARP follows the same rules as in the case of RP according to the ECN number. Some groups use the term partition number instead of ECN [61]. For the analysis of nonpolar lipid classes, such as TG, APCI [2, 62–64] or eventually atmospheric pressure photoionization (APPI) [65, 66] could provide better results than ESI; therefore, most NAPR papers are based on APCI-MS [67]. The characteristic ratios of fragment ions $[M+H-R_iCOOH]^+$ allow us to determine the predominant fatty acyl in the middle position *sn*-2 because the cleavage from this position is less energetically favored, resulting in a lower relative abundance of this fragment ion compared to the statistically expected abundance [64, 68–72]. Moreover, the number and positions of DB also influence the relative abundances of individual ions, where fragment ions containing more unsaturations have higher abundances. Figure 4.12 illustrates an example of optimized NAPR separation of redcurrant plant oil as an example of complex plant oil. The series of works on the analysis of plant oils and animal fats based on the use of HPLC/APCI-MS methodology resulted in the

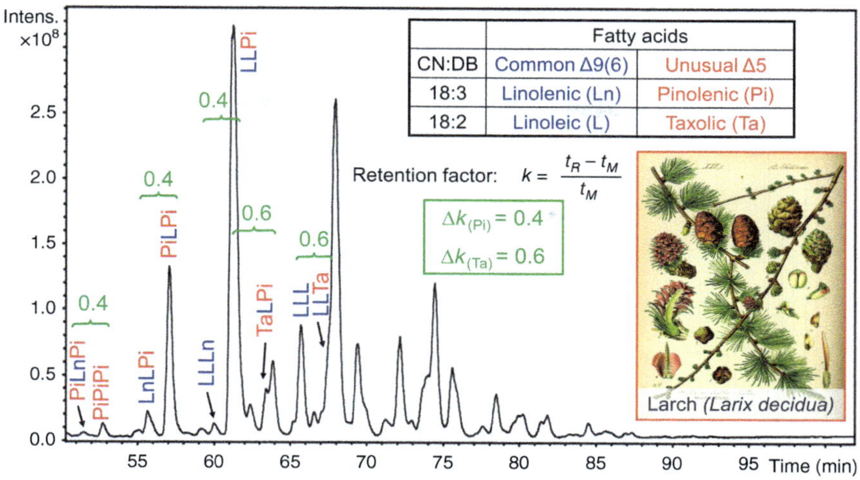

Figure 4.13 HPLC/APCI-MS analysis of European Larch oil (*Larix decidua*) oil using Nova-Pak C18 columns (300 + 150 mm × 3.9 mm, 4 μm) connected in series. The annotation of all triacylglycerols is described in the original publication. Chromatogram reprinted and adapted with permission from Lísa et al. [62], Larix decidua from [73].

identification of 264 TG containing 28 fatty acyls from 6 to 26 carbon atoms and up to 4 DB. The selectivity in NAPR enables the chromatographic resolution of the positional isomers of DB, as illustrated by the example of conifer seed oils known because of the presence of an unusual position of DB at Δ5 (Figure 4.13). These isomers can be easily recognized based on the characteristic shifts of the capacity factors and the characteristic changes in the ratio of fragment ions compared to the usual positions of DB [62].

4.4 Other Separation Approaches

Here, we report examples of silver ion chromatography, chiral chromatography, and multidimensional approaches in offline and online configuration, but less frequently other special modes could be found in the literature for tailored applications.

4.4.1 Silver Ion Chromatography

Silver ion chromatography (also termed as argentation chromatography) represents a relatively unusual separation mode in chromatography, which is known mainly in the analysis of TG, but it may be applied to any analytes that differ in the arrangement of DB in their molecules. The key retention mechanism is the interaction between a silver ion embedded in the strong cation exchanger as the stationary phase and DB in the analyte molecule [74]. The simple rule is that more DB means stronger interaction and higher retention, but the positions and geometry (*cis* versus *trans*) also play a role (Figure 4.14). The spatial configuration of *trans-DB* is closer to the saturated

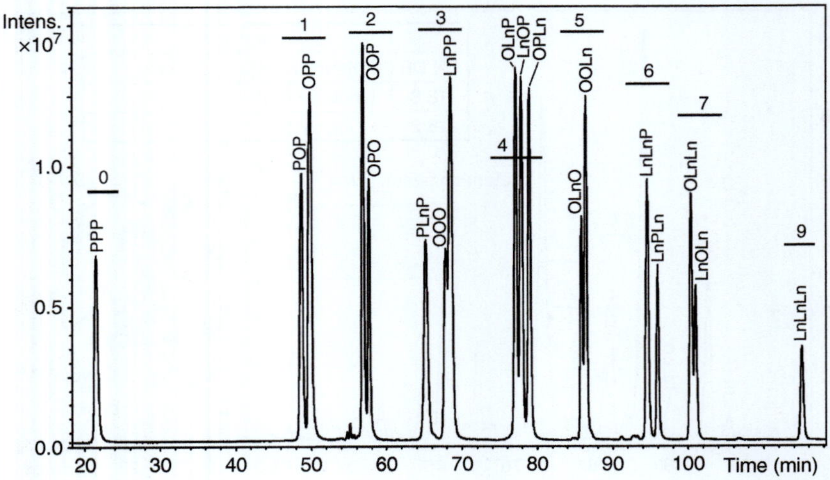

Figure 4.14 Silver ion HPLC/APCI-MS analysis of the randomization mixture of PPP, OOO, and LnLnLn using three ChromSpher Lipids columns (250 mm × 4.6 mm, 5 μm) connected in series. Source: Reprinted with permission from Lísa et al. [75].

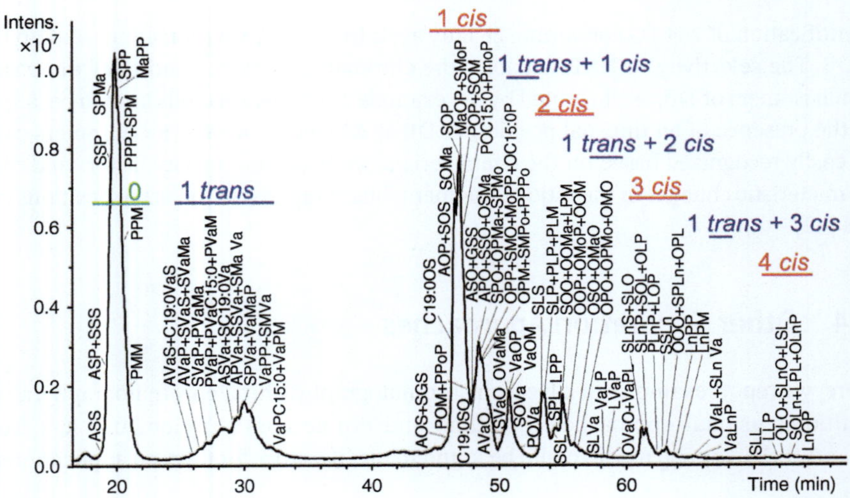

Figure 4.15 Silver ion HPLC/APCI-MS analysis of TG in fallow deer (Cervus elaphus) tissue extract using three ChromSpher Lipids columns (250 mm × 4.6 mm, 5 μm) connected in series. The separation is optimized for the resolution of *cis* and *trans* geometric isomers of double bonds. Source: Reprinted with permission from Lísa et al. [2].

chain; therefore, the retention behavior of *trans* isomers is closer to saturated lipids, while *cis* isomers have a higher retention (Figure 4.15). The main application range of this technique is in the analysis of TG, for example, in plant oils and animal fats or other nutrition-related samples, where the *trans* content is important information for consumers. The mobile phases in silver ion HPLC are as in NP chromatography, e.g.

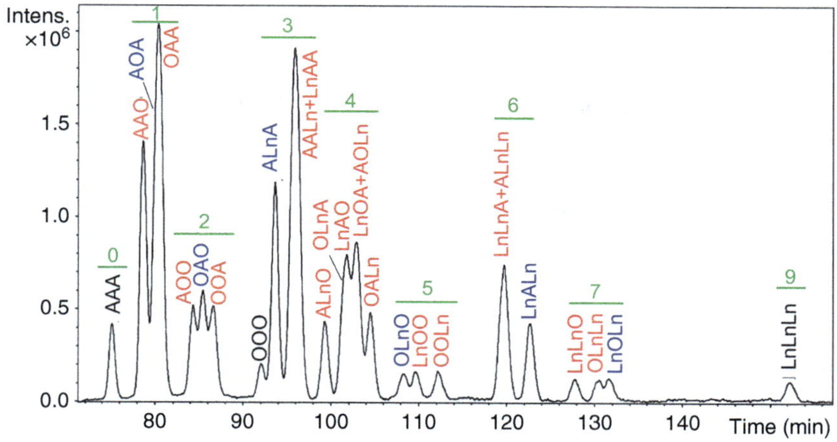

Figure 4.16 Chiral HPLC/APCI-MS analysis of synthesized triacylglycerol standards using two Lux Cellulose-1 columns (250 mm × 4.6 mm, 3 μm) connected in series. The numbers correspond to the number of double bonds. Enantiomers are highlighted in red, and regioisomers are highlighted in blue. Source: Reprinted and adapted with permission from Lísa and Holčapek [78].

hexane with a small addition of a polar modifier (typically acetonitrile with concentration less than 1.5% because of solubility issues) [2, 75, 76]. Some groups use mobile phases based on dichloromethane [77]. The leakage of silver ions into the mass spectrometer is not reported in the literature or known to the authors of this chapter.

4.4.2 Chiral Chromatography

The chromatographic resolution of lipid enantiomers is the most difficult task and necessarily requires chiral interactions for their separation. Theoretically, the chiral additive could be in the mobile phase, but this would be too expensive and probably not compatible with MS detection; therefore, the most common option for chiral separation is the use of chiral stationary phases. There are not as many examples in the literature, and they are mainly based on chiral stationary phases based on polysaccharide chemistry, such as cellulose-tris-(3,5-dimethylphenylcarbamate) [78, 79], 3,5-dimethyl-phenyl-carbamate modified β-cyclodextrin [80], and cellulose tris(3,5-dichlorophenylcarbamate) immobilized on silica [81]. The literature shows examples of chiral separation of TG [78–82], where the middle *sn*-2 carbon atom becomes a chiral center, when fatty acyls in *sn*-1 and *sn*-3 positions are different. Another complication in the chiral analysis of TG is the absence of commercially available standards; hence, synthetic procedures must be developed in the laboratory to verify the identification and retention order of individual enantiomers [78]. Figure 4.16 shows an example of chiral separation of the randomization mixture of AAA, OOO, and LnLnLn, which contains several pairs of enantiomers and regioisomers. This method also enables the resolution of chiral DG and MG (not shown here). Chiral separations of lipids are based on NP chromatographic systems; therefore, typical

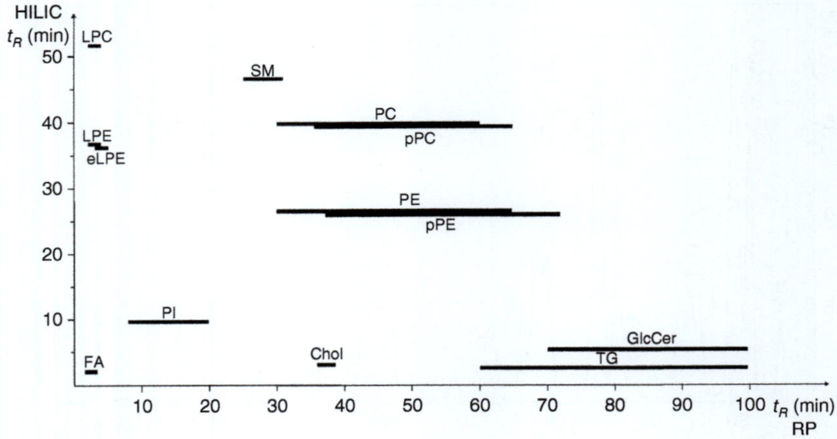

Figure 4.17 Orthogonality of offline 2D-HPLC/MS lipid analysis using HILIC and RP-HPLC methods. Source: Reprinted with permission from Lísa et al. [83].

mobile phases contain hexane or heptane with a smaller portion of polar additives, such as a very small amount of 2-propanol in hexane: gradient from 0.1% to 0.4% 2-propanol [78], from 0.2% to 1% 2-propanol [80], pure acetonitrile [81], or pure methanol in isocratic recycling configuration [79]. Such conditions are not compatible with ESI, so APCI has been used. Chiral HPLC separations of TG are rather long. It is likely that the analysis time will be significantly reduced by chiral UHPSFC/MS, but no publication is still available.

4.4.3 Multidimensional Approaches

The most demanding chromatographic applications for complex biological samples rely on the use of two- or multidimensional separation, which could be realized either in the offline or online mode. Both strategies have their own advantages and drawbacks. The offline approach is easier to implement because it is based on the collection of selected zones of the chromatogram (typical lipid class separation in the HILIC mode), solvent evaporation, redissolution in the solvent compatible with the second dimension, and subsequent injection, which is typically represented by RP-UHPLC [83]. Figure 4.17 shows the orthogonality of both separation mechanisms in the lipidomic analysis, which provides a quite good coverage of the separation space. The advantage of such a strategy is the possibility of a very detailed characterization of the lipidome because both dimensions could be independently optimized with tailored methods for individual classes. The drawback is a very long analysis time, which disqualifies such approach from applications focused on high throughput. On the other hand, online 2D requires technical experience to construct and optimize such a system because some specific considerations must be taken into account, primarily the compatibility of mobile phases in both dimensions. The most common combination is the use of RP and HILIC, where some groups prefer to use HILIC in the second dimension [84] while the other groups use the opposite configuration [85]. The illustrative example of 2D separation in the RP × HILIC configuration is shown in Figure 4.18. Another configuration suitable mainly for TG analysis

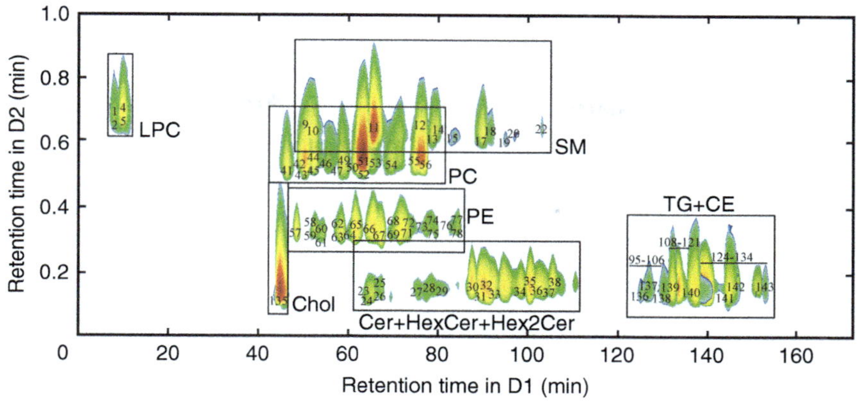

Figure 4.18 Comprehensive online 2D-HPLC/MS analysis of porcine brain lipidomic extract using RP-HPLC and HILIC methods. The annotation of peak numbers is described in the original publication. Source: Reprinted with permission from Holčapek et al. [84].

is the combination of silver ion chromatography and RP-UHPLC, which could be performed offline [76] or online [61]. The major technical problem in 2D online concept is the fact that chromatographic separation primarily means the dilution and band broadening of chromatographic zones, and in the case of 2D separation, these dilution effects occur in both dimensions, which causes the reduction of sensitivity, resulting in fewer detected peaks. There are extensive efforts in the chromatographic community to reduce this unwanted phenomenon using various concentration approaches [86, 87], but at present, online 2D does not appear to be competitive with well-optimized 1D separation coupled with MS. Another option in the multidimensional concept is the implementation of ion mobility, which offers a different type of separation mechanism based on the shape of molecules, as described in more detail in Chapter 6. Some groups use the concept of multidimensional chromatography and multidimensional MS coupling, which provides the most comprehensive level of structure information from multiple MS modalities, but requires technical skills and available instrumentation to construct such a system [65].

List of Abbreviations

APCI	atmospheric pressure chemical ionization
APPI	atmospheric pressure photoionization
CE	cholesterol ester
Cer	ceramide
CN	total carbon number
DB	double bond
DG	diacylglycerol
ECN	equivalent carbon number
EMA	European Medicines Agency
ESI	electrospray ionization

FAME	fatty acid methyl ester
FDA	Food and Drug Administration
GlcCer	glucosylceramide
HexCer	hexosylceramide
HILIC	hydrophilic interaction liquid chromatography
IS	internal standard
LacCer	lactosylceramide
LPC	lysophosphatidylcholine
LPE	lysophosphatidylethanolamine
LPG	lysophosphatidylglycerol
LPI	lysophosphatidylinositol
MG	monoacylglycerol
MS	mass spectrometry
NARP	nonaqueous reversed phase
NIST	National Institute of Standards and Technology
NP	normal-phase
PA	phosphatidic acid
PC	phosphatidylcholine
PE	phosphatidylethanolamine
PG	phosphatidylglycerol
PI	phosphatidylinositol
PS	phosphatidylserine
RP	reversed-phase
$scCO_2$	supercritical carbon dioxide
SFC	supercritical fluid chromatography
SM	sphingomyelin
TG	triacylglycerol
UHPLC	ultrahigh-performance liquid chromatography
UHPSFC	ultrahigh-performance supercritical fluid chromatography

References

1 Ecker, J., Scherer, M., Schmitz, G., and Liebisch, G. (2012). A rapid GC-MS method for quantification of positional and geometric isomers of fatty acid methyl esters. *J. Chromatogr. B* 897: 98–104.

2 Lísa, M., Netušilová, K., Franěk, L. et al. (2011). Characterization of fatty acid and triacylglycerol composition in animal fats using silver-ion and non-aqueous reversed-phase high-performance liquid chromatography/mass spectrometry and gas chromatography/flame ionization detection. *J. Chromatogr. A* 1218 (42): 7499–7510.

3 Ruiz-Samblas, C., Gonzalez-Casado, A., and Cuadros-Rodriguez, L. (2015). Triacylglycerols determination by high-temperature gas chromatography in the analysis of vegetable oils and foods: a review of the past 10 years. *Crit. Rev. Food Sci. Nutr.* 55 (11): 1618–1631.

4 Holčapek, M., Liebisch, G., and Ekroos, K. (2018). Lipidomic analysis. *Anal. Chem.* 90 (7): 4249–4257.
5 Lange, M., Ni, Z.X., Criscuolo, A., and Fedorova, M. (2019). Liquid chromatography techniques in lipidomics research. *Chromatographia* 82 (1): 77–100.
6 Holčapek, M. and Byrdwell, W.C. (2017). *Handbook of Advanced Chromatography/ Mass Spectrometry Techniques*, 1e. Academic Press and AOCS Press, 520 pages.
7 Čajka, T. and Fiehn, O. (2016). Toward merging untargeted and targeted methods in mass spectrometry-based metabolomics and lipidomics. *Anal. Chem.* 88 (1): 524–545.
8 Wolrab, D., Chocholoušková, M., Jirásko, R. et al. (2020). Validation of lipidomic analysis of human plasma and serum by supercritical fluid chromatography-mass spectrometry and hydrophilic interaction liquid chromatography-mass spectrometry. *Anal. Bioanal. Chem.* 412 (10): 2375–2388.
9 Liebisch, G., Fahy, E., Aoki, J. et al. (2020). Update on LIPID MAPS classification, nomenclature, and shorthand notation for MS-derived lipid structures. *J. Lipid Res.* 61 (12): 1539–1555.
10 Holčapek, M., Cífková, E., Červená, B. et al. (2015). Determination of nonpolar and polar lipid classes in human plasma, erythrocytes and plasma lipoprotein fractions using ultrahigh-performance liquid chromatography-mass spectrometry. *J. Chromatogr. A* 1377: 85–91.
11 Abreu, S., Solgadi, A., and Chaminade, P. (2017). Optimization of normal phase chromatographic conditions for lipid analysis and comparison of associated detection techniques. *J. Chromatogr. A* 1514: 54–71.
12 Christie, W.W. (1985). Rapid separation and quantification of lipid classes by high-performance liquid-chromatography and mass (light-scattering) detection. *J. Lipid Res.* 26 (4): 507–512.
13 McLaren, D.G., Miller, P.L., Lassman, M.E. et al. (2011). An ultraperformance liquid chromatography method for the normal-phase separation of lipids. *Anal. Biochem.* 414 (2): 266–272.
14 McCalley, D.V. (2018). A study of column equilibration time in hydrophilic interaction chromatography. *J. Chromatogr. A* 1554: 61–70.
15 U.S. Department of Health and Human Services Food and Drug Administration (2018). Draft Guidance for Industry: Bioanalytical Method Validation. https://www.fda.gov/files/drugs/published/Bioanalytical-Method-Validation-Guidance-for-Industry.pdf (accessed 19 July 2022).
16 European Medicines Agency (2015). Guidelines on bioanalytical method validation. https://www.ema.europa.eu/en/bioanalytical-method-validation (accessed 19 July 2022).
17 Cífková, E., Hájek, R., Lísa, M., and Holčapek, M. (2016). Hydrophilic interaction liquid chromatography-mass spectrometry of (lyso)phosphatidic acids, (lyso) phosphatidylserines and other lipid classes. *J. Chromatogr. A* 1439: 65–73.
18 Isaac, G., Wilson, I.D., and Plumb, R.S. (2022). Application of hybrid surface technology for improving sensitivity and peak shape of phosphorylated lipids such as phosphatidic acid and phosphatidylserine. *J. Chromatogr. A* 1669: 462921.

19 Hájek, R., Jirásko, R., Lísa, M. et al. (2017). Hydrophilic interaction liquid chromatography-mass spectrometry characterization of gangliosides in biological samples. *Anal. Chem.* 89 (22): 12425–12432.

20 Hájek, R., Lísa, M., Khalikova, M. et al. (2018). HILIC/ESI-MS determination of gangliosides and other polar lipid classes in renal cell carcinoma and surrounding normal tissues. *Anal. Bioanal. Chem.* 410 (25): 6585–6594.

21 Hořejši, K., Jirásko, R., Chocholoušková, M. et al. (2021). Comprehensive identification of glycosphingolipids in human plasma using hydrophilic interaction liquid chromatography-electrospray ionization mass spectrometry. *Metabolites* 11 (3): 140.

22 Okazaki, Y., Kamide, Y., Hirai, M.Y., and Saito, K. (2013). Plant lipidomics based on hydrophilic interaction chromatography coupled to ion trap time-of-flight mass spectrometry. *Metabolomics* 9 (1): 121–131.

23 Hines, K.M., Waalkes, A., Penewit, K. et al. (2017). Characterization of the mechanisms of daptomycin resistance among Gram-positive bacterial pathogens by multidimensional lipidomics. *Msphere* 2 (6): 492–517.

24 Alves, E., Melo, T., Simoes, C. et al. (2013). Photodynamic oxidation of *Staphylococcus warneri* membrane phospholipids: new insights based on lipidomics. *Rapid Commun. Mass Spectrom.* 27 (14): 1607–1618.

25 Zhang, Y.F., Zhang, M., Dong, L.P. et al. (2022). Lipidomics screening of polyunsaturated phospholipid molecular species in crab (*Portunus trituberculatus*) muscular tissue: a nontarget approach by HILIC-MS. *Eur. J. Lipid Sci. Technol.* 124 (3): 2100097.

26 Cífková, E., Holčapek, M., Lísa, M. et al. (2015). Lipidomic differentiation between human kidney tumors and surrounding normal tissues using HILIC-HPLC/ESI-MS and multivariate data analysis. *J. Chromatogr. B* 1000: 14–21.

27 Cífková, E., Brumarová, R., Ovčačíková, M. et al. (2022). Lipidomic and metabolomic analysis reveals changes in biochemical pathways for non-small cell lung cancer tissues. *Biochim. Biophys. Acta* 1867 (2): 159082.

28 Calvano, C.D., Ventura, G., Sardanelli, A.M.M. et al. (2019). Searching for potential lipid biomarkers of Parkinson's disease in Parkin-mutant human skin fibroblasts by HILIC-ESI-MS/MS: preliminary findings. *Int. J. Mol. Sci.* 20 (13): 3341.

29 Cífková, E., Lísa, M., Hrstka, R. et al. (2017). Correlation of lipidomic composition of cell lines and tissues of breast cancer patients using hydrophilic interaction liquid chromatography/electrospray ionization mass spectrometry and multivariate data analysis. *Rapid Commun. Mass Spectrom.* 31 (3): 253–263.

30 Lange, M. and Fedorova, M. (2020). Evaluation of lipid quantification accuracy using HILIC and RPLC MS on the example of NIST SRM 1950 metabolites in human plasma. *Anal. Bioanal. Chem.* 412 (15): 3573–3584.

31 Peterka, O., Jirásko, R., Chocholoušková, M. et al. (2020). Lipidomic characterization of exosomes isolated from human plasma using various mass spectrometry techniques. *Biochim. Biophys. Acta* 1865 (5): 158634.

32 Alves, E., Melo, T., Barros, M.P. et al. (2019). Lipidomic profiling of the olive (*Olea europaea* L.) fruit towards its valorisation as a functional food: in-depth

identification of triacylglycerols and polar lipids in Portuguese olives. *Molecules* 24 (14): 2555.
33 Akbal, L. and Hopfgartner, G. (2020). Hyphenation of packed column supercritical fluid chromatography with mass spectrometry: where are we and what are the remaining challenges? *Anal. Bioanal. Chem.* 412 (25): 6667–6677.
34 van de Velde, B., Guillarme, D., and Kohler, I. (2020). Supercritical fluid chromatography – mass spectrometry in metabolomics: past, present, and future perspectives. *J. Chromatogr. B* 1161: 122444.
35 Perrenoud, A.G.G., Veuthey, J.L., and Guillarme, D. (2012). Comparison of ultra-high performance supercritical fluid chromatography and ultra-high performance liquid chromatography for the analysis of pharmaceutical compounds. *J. Chromatogr. A* 1266: 158–167.
36 Wolrab, D., Peterka, O., Chocholoušková, M., and Holčapek, M. (2022). Ultrahigh-performance supercritical fluid chromatography/mass spectrometry in the lipidomic analysis. *TrAC, Trends Anal. Chem.* 149: 116546.
37 Wolrab, D., Jirásko, R., Cífková, E. et al. (2022). Lipidomic profiling of human serum enables detection of pancreatic cancer. *Nat. Commun.* 13 (1): 124.
38 Wolrab, D., Jirásko, R., Peterka, O. et al. (2021). Plasma lipidomic profiles of kidney, breast and prostate cancer patients differ from healthy controls. *Sci. Rep.* 11 (1): 20322.
39 Chocholoušková, M., Wolrab, D., Jirásko, R. et al. (2021). Intra-laboratory comparison of four analytical platforms for lipidomic quantitation using hydrophilic interaction liquid chromatography or supercritical fluid chromatography coupled to quadrupole – time-of-flight mass spectrometry. *Talanta* 231: 122367.
40 Wolrab, D., Chocholoušková, M., Jirásko, R. et al. (2020). Determination of one year stability of lipid plasma profile and comparison of blood collection tubes using UHPSFC/MS and HILIC-UHPLC/MS. *Anal. Chim. Acta* 1137: 74–84.
41 Holčapek, M., Cífková, E., Lísa, M., et al. A method of diagnosing pancreatic cancer based on lipidomic analysis of a body fluid. European patent EP 3514545 (granted), filed 22 January 2018.
42 Holčapek, M., Wolrab, D., Jirásko, R., and Cífková, E.. A method of diagnosing cancer based on lipidomic analysis of a body fluid. EP18174963.1 (pending), filed 29 May 2018.
43 Lísa, M. and Holčapek, M. (2015). High-throughput and comprehensive lipidomic analysis using ultrahigh-performance supercritical fluid chromatography—mass spectrometry. *Anal. Chem.* 87 (14): 7187–7195.
44 Gazárková, T., Plachká, K., Švec, F., and Nováková, L. (2022). Current state of supercritical fluid chromatography-mass spectrometry. *TrAC, Trends Anal. Chem.* 149: 116544.
45 Takeda, H., Izumi, Y., Takahashi, M. et al. (2018). Widely-targeted quantitative lipidomics method by supercritical fluid chromatography triple quadrupole mass spectrometry. *J. Lipid Res.* 59 (7): 1283–1293.

46 Bamba, T., Lee, J.W., Matsubara, A., and Fukusaki, E. (2012). Metabolic profiling of lipids by supercritical fluid chromatography/mass spectrometry. *J. Chromatogr. A* 1250: 212–219.

47 Wolrab, D., Jirásko, R., Chocholoušková, M. et al. (2019). Oncolipidomics: mass spectrometric quantitation of lipids in cancer research. *TrAC, Trends Anal. Chem.* 120: 115480.

48 Vaňková, Z., Peterka, O., Chocholoušková, M. et al. (2022). Retention dependences support highly confident identification of lipid species in human plasma by reversed-phase UHPLC/MS. *Anal. Bioanal. Chem.* 414 (1): 319–331.

49 Ovčačíková, M., Lísa, M., Cífková, E., and Holčapek, M. (2016). Retention behavior of lipids in reversed-phase ultrahigh-performance liquid chromatography-electrospray ionization mass spectrometry. *J. Chromatogr. A* 1450: 76–85.

50 Sandra, K., Pereira, A.D., Vanhoenacker, G. et al. (2010). Comprehensive blood plasma lipidomics by liquid chromatography/quadrupole time-of-flight mass spectrometry. *J. Chromatogr. A* 1217 (25): 4087–4099.

51 Fauland, A., Kofeler, H., Trotzmuller, M. et al. (2011). A comprehensive method for lipid profiling by liquid chromatography-ion cyclotron resonance mass spectrometry. *J. Lipid Res.* 52 (12): 2314–2322.

52 Huynh, K., Barlow, C.K., Jayawardana, K.S. et al. (2019). High-throughput plasma lipidomics: detailed mapping of the associations with cardiometabolic risk factors. *Cell Chem. Biol.* 26 (1): 71–84.

53 Triebl, A., Burla, B., Selvalatchmanan, J. et al. (2020). Shared reference materials harmonize lipidomics across MS-based detection platforms and laboratories. *J. Lipid Res.* 61 (1): 105–115.

54 Damen, C.W.N., Isaac, G., Langridge, J. et al. (2014). Enhanced lipid isomer separation in human plasma using reversed-phase UPLC with ion-mobility/high-resolution MS detection. *J. Lipid Res.* 55 (8): 1772–1783.

55 Berkecz, R., Lísa, M., and Holčapek, M. (2017). Analysis of oxylipins in human plasma: comparison of ultrahigh-performance liquid chromatography and ultrahigh-performance supercritical fluid chromatography coupled to mass spectrometry. *J. Chromatogr. A* 1511: 107–121.

56 Chocholoušková, M., Jirásko, R., Vrána, D. et al. (2019). Reversed phase UHPLC/ESI-MS determination of oxylipins in human plasma: a case study of female breast cancer. *Anal. Bioanal. Chem.* 411 (6): 1239–1251.

57 Kofeler, H.C., Ahrends, R., Baker, E.S. et al. (2021). Recommendations for good practice in MS-based lipidomics. *J. Lipid Res.* 62: 100138.

58 Kofeler, H.C., Eichmann, T.O., Ahrends, R. et al. (2021). Quality control requirements for the correct annotation of lipidomics data. *Nat. Commun.* 12 (1): 47771.

59 Peterka, O., Jirásko, R., Vaňková, Z. et al. (2021). Simple and reproducible derivatization with benzoyl chloride: improvement of sensitivity for multiple lipid classes in RP-UHPLC/MS. *Anal. Chem.* 93 (41): 13835–13843.

60 Holčapek, M., Jandera, P., and Fischer, J. (2001). Analysis of acylglycerols and methyl esters of fatty acids in vegetable oils and in biodiesel. *Crit. Rev. Anal. Chem.* 31 (1): 53–56.

61 Dugo, P., Kumm, T., Chiofalo, B. et al. (2006). Separation of triacylglycerols in a complex lipidic matrix by using comprehensive two-dimensional liquid chromatography coupled with atmospheric pressure chemical ionization mass spectrometric detection. *J. Sep. Sci.* 29 (8): 1146–1154.

62 Lísa, M., Holčapek, M., Řezanka, T., and Kabátová, N. (2007). High-performance liquid chromatography-atmospheric pressure chemical ionization mass spectrometry and gas chromatography-flame ionization detection characterization of delta 5-polyenoic fatty acids in triacylglycerols from conifer seed oils. *J. Chromatogr. A* 1146 (1): 67–77.

63 Lísa, M. and Holčapek, M. (2008). Triacylglycerols profiling in plant oils important in food industry, dietetics and cosmetics using high-performance liquid chromatography-atmospheric pressure chemical ionization mass spectrometry. *J. Chromatogr. A* 1198: 115–130.

64 Holčapek, M., Lísa, M., Jandera, P., and Kabátová, N. (2005). Quantitation of triacylglycerols in plant oils using HPLC with APCI-MS, evaporative light-scattering, and UV detection. *J. Sep. Sci.* 28 (12): 1315–1333.

65 Byrdwell, W.C., Kotapati, H.K., Goldschmidt, R. et al. (2022). Three-dimensional liquid chromatography with parallel second dimensions and quadruple parallel mass spectrometry for adult/infant formula analysis. *J. Chromatogr. A* 1661: 462682.

66 Byrdwell, W.C. (2015). The updated bottom up solution applied to atmospheric pressure photoionization and electrospray ionization mass spectrometry. *J. Am. Oil Chem. Soc.* 92: 1533–1547.

67 Li, M., Zhou, Z.G., Nie, H.G. et al. (2011). Recent advances of chromatography and mass spectrometry in lipidomics. *Anal. Bioanal. Chem.* 399 (1): 243–249.

68 Holčapek, M., Jandera, P., Zderadička, P., and Hrubá, L. (2003). Characterization of triacylglycerol and diacylglycerol composition of plant oils using high-performance liquid chromatography-atmospheric pressure chemical ionization mass spectrometry. *J. Chromatogr. A* 1010 (2): 195–215.

69 Holčapek, M., Dvořáková, H., Lísa, M. et al. (2010). Regioisomeric analysis of triacylglycerols using silver-ion liquid chromatography atmospheric pressure chemical ionization mass spectrometry: comparison of five different mass analyzers. *J. Chromatogr. A* 1217 (52): 8186–8194.

70 Li, X.W., Collins, E.J., and Evans, J.J. (2006). Examining the collision-induced decomposition spectra of ammoniated triglycerides as a function of fatty acid chain length and degree of unsaturation. II. The PXP/YPY series. *Rapid Commun. Mass Spectrom.* 20 (2): 171–177.

71 Leskinen, H., Suomela, J.P., and Kallio, H. (2007). Quantification of triacylglycerol regioisomers in oils and fat using different mass spectrometric and liquid chromatographic methods. *Rapid Commun. Mass Spectrom.* 21 (14): 2361–2373.

72 Byrdwell, W.C. (2005). The bottom-up solution to the triacylglycerol lipidome using atmospheric pressure chemical ionization mass spectrometry. *Lipids* 40 (4): 383–417.

73 Larix decudua (2007). Kurt Stüber's Online Library. http://www.biolib.de/thome/band1/tafel_026.html (accessed 19 July 2022).

74 Momchilova, S. and Nikolova-Damyanova, B. (2003). Stationary phases for silver ion chromatography of lipids: preparation and properties. *J. Sep. Sci.* 26 (3, 4): 261–270.

75 Lísa, M., Velinská, H., and Holčapek, M. (2009). Regioisomeric characterization of triacylglycerols using silver-ion HPLC/MS and randomization synthesis of standards. *Anal. Chem.* 81 (10): 3903–3910.

76 Holčapek, M., Velinská, H., Lísa, M., and Česla, P. (2009). Orthogonality of silver-ion and non-aqueous reversed-phase HPLC/MS in the analysis of complex natural mixtures of triacylglycerols. *J. Sep. Sci.* 32 (21): 3672–3680.

77 Nikolova-Damyanova, B. (2009). Retention of lipids in silver ion high-performance liquid chromatography: facts and assumptions. *J. Chromatogr. A* 1216 (10): 1815–1824.

78 Lísa, M. and Holčapek, M. (2013). Characterization of triacylglycerol enantiomers using chiral HPLC/APCI-MS and synthesis of enantiomeric triacylglycerols. *Anal. Chem.* 85 (3): 1852–1859.

79 Kalpio, M., Nylund, M., Linderborg, K.M. et al. (2015). Enantioselective chromatography in analysis of triacylglycerols common in edible fats and oils. *Food Chem.* 172: 718–724.

80 Řezanka, T., Kolouchová, I., Nedbalová, L., and Sigler, K. (2018). Enantiomeric separation of triacylglycerols containing very long chain fatty acids. *J. Chromatogr. A* 1557: 9–19.

81 Nagai, T., Kinoshita, T., Kasamatsu, E. et al. (2020). Simultaneous quantification of mixed-acid triacylglycerol positional isomers and enantiomers in palm oil and lard by chiral high-performance liquid chromatography coupled with mass spectrometry. *Symmetry* 12 (9): 1385.

82 Masuda, K., Abe, K., and Murano, Y. (2021). A practical method for analysis of triacylglycerol isomers using supercritical fluid chromatography. *J. Am. Oil Chem. Soc.* 98 (1): 21–29.

83 Lísa, M., Cífková, E., and Holčapek, M. (2011). Lipidomic profiling of biological tissues using off-line two-dimensional high-performance liquid chromatography mass spectrometry. *J. Chromatogr. A* 1218 (31): 5146–5156.

84 Holčapek, M., Ovčačíkova, M., Lísa, M. et al. (2015). Continuous comprehensive two-dimensional liquid chromatography-electrospray ionization mass spectrometry of complex lipidomic samples. *Anal. Bioanal. Chem.* 407 (17): 5033–5043.

85 Donato, P., Micalizzi, G., Oteri, M. et al. (2018). Comprehensive lipid profiling in the Mediterranean mussel (*Mytilus galloprovincialis*) using hyphenated and multidimensional chromatography techniques coupled to mass spectrometry detection. *Anal. Bioanal. Chem.* 410 (14): 3297–3313.

86 Gargano, A.F.G., Duffin, M., Navarro, P., and Schoenmakers, P.J. (2016). Reducing dilution and analysis time in online comprehensive two-dimensional liquid chromatography by active modulation. *Anal. Chem.* 88 (3): 1785–1793.

87 Stoll, D.R., Harmes, D.C., Staples, G.O. et al. (2018). Development of comprehensive online two-dimensional liquid chromatography/mass spectrometry using hydrophilic interaction and reversed-phase separations for rapid and deep profiling of therapeutic antibodies. *Anal. Chem.* 90 (9): 5923–5929.

5

Mass Spectrometry Imaging of Lipids

Shane R. Ellis[1,2] *and Jens Soltwisch*[3]

[1] *University of Wollongong, Molecular Horizons and School of Chemistry and Molecular Bioscience, Wollongong, NSW, Australia*
[2] *Illawarra Health and Medical Research Institute, Wollongong, NSW, Australia*
[3] *University of Münster, Institute of Hygiene, Robert-Koch-Straße 41, 48149, Münster, Germany*

5.1 Introduction

Mass spectrometry imaging (MSI) is a label-free imaging technique capable of simultaneously imaging numerous analytes in a single experiment. Depending on sample preparation and experimental design, it is suitable for many analyte classes, including elements, metabolites, lipids, peptides, proteins, pharmaceuticals, and glycans. Lipids are one of the most suitable molecular classes for MSI analysis because of the high signal intensity readily obtained for several abundant lipid classes and the fact that lipids require arguably the most straightforward sample preparation (i.e. no washing or enzymatic digestion is required). Lipid imaging has been applied in numerous applications outlined below. The most popular general application area is mapping region-specific changes in lipid composition through heterogeneous tissues and studying the molecular processes associated with disease onset and progression.

Independent of the choice of desorption/ionization mechanism and mass spectrometry employed, the basic approach of MSI remains the same. A focused surface probe such as a laser beam, an ion beam, a solvent droplet, or an electrospray is directed at the sample surface where it locally samples the analytes present within a pre-defined area. The sampled analytes are then ionized by one of many approaches and then detected by mass spectrometry. Each sampling position corresponds to a single pixel that is represented by a mass spectrum. Analyte distributions are then determined by either plotting the intensity of a selected ion as a function of position or using a variety of multivariate image analysis techniques that make use of the high dimensionality of MSI datasets [1]. Typical MSI experiments can now detect hundreds of lipid-related features in a single experiment. Combined with the high

Mass Spectrometry for Lipidomics: Methods and Applications, First Edition.
Edited by Michal Holčapek and Kim Ekroos.
© 2023 WILEY-VCH GmbH. Published 2023 by WILEY-VCH GmbH.

sensitivity and chemical specificity provided by modern mass spectrometry, MSI offers many advantages for lipid imaging that cannot be met using other imaging modalities.

5.2 Sample Preparation for Mass Spectrometry Imaging of Lipids

MSI analyses of lipids are primarily conducted on thin sections. These provide a flat surface that is convenient to analyze and enable the implementation of complementary imaging modalities such as optical microscopy. The samples may include whole-body sections or sections of specific organs derived from animal models, clinical biopsies, and tissue microarrays and plant- or fungus-derived tissue. In recent years, cell culture and single-cell analysis has gained increasing interest.

5.2.1 Tissue Samples

Great care has to be taken in the harvest and processing of tissue samples to conserve the morphological and chemical integrity [2–4]. This necessitates tissue fixation to minimize molecular degradation by enzymatic and metabolic activity and exposure to reactive oxygen species. Because chemical fixation is generally not well suited for lipid MSI, in the case of freshly harvested tissue, cryo-fixation is the method of choice [4, 5]. Here, the sample is flash frozen and fixed by carefully lowering it into or floating it on top of a cryogenic liquid, thereby quenching all metabolic activity as quickly as possible. While fixation is usually well controlled and completed directly after removing the tissue for the material derived from animal models, patient-derived material such as biopsies or excised tumor tissue may experience longer delays [6]. Fragile and small tissue samples may be embedded for cryo-fixation to retain the original morphology and structure. Embedding media compatible with mass spectrometry (MS) analysis include gelatin, agarose, and cellulose derivatives (carboxymethylcellulose CMC [marketed as M1 embedding medium] and hydroxyethylcellulose HEC), solutions, as well as dedicated polymer systems such as poly[*N*-(2-hydroxypropyl)methacrylamide] (pHPMA) [7–11]. Polymer-based media such as tissue-TEK OCT (optimal cutting temperature) optimized for preparing histological samples may spread analytes across the sample during sectioning and produce a sizable background signal and ion suppression effect during MSI analysis. Thus, their use requires careful optimization [12]. If OCT or other embedding media cannot be avoided, the chemical noise derived from embedding may be removed using dedicated washing protocols which cause minimal alterations of the lipid content and distributions within the tissue [13]. The chemical fixation of tissue intrinsically affects the molecular integrity of the sample and should be kept to a minimum whenever possible. Formaldehyde or similar cross-linking agents may act on amine groups of lipid classes such as phosphatidylethanolamine (PE) and phosphatidylserine (PS) and render them undetectable [14, 15].

5.2.2 Sectioning and Mounting

Most commonly, tissue cryo-sections for MSI are prepared at a thickness between 5 and 20 μm. While thicker sections are easier to handle, thin sections may provide higher spatial resolution, better compatibility with microscopy modalities, and reduce topography effects and surface charging that can be detrimental to analysis, particularly with axial-time-of-flight (TOF) instruments [16]. Specific parameters such as cutting temperature, blade geometry, and angle between the sample and blade must be optimized for the individual combination of sample and embedding medium. For example, for samples containing high amounts of readily diffusible lipids such as triacylglycerols (TAGs), the cutting temperature should be low enough to prevent contamination of the blade and spreading of these compounds during sectioning. Using conventional thaw mounting techniques, sections can be mounted on histological glass slides or the conductive surface of indium tin oxide (ITO)-coated glass slides if the intended mass spectrometer requires a conductive surface. For brittle or frail samples, tape-transfer mounting techniques can also be advantageous [3]. Vandenbosch et al. demonstrated the use of double-sided tape to mount decalcified bone samples without losing the spatial integrity for lipid MALDI-MSI analysis, and Yoon et al. optimized the method for TOF-secondary ion mass spectrometry (SIMS) analysis of soft (brain) and hard (corn seed) tissue [3, 17]. The cryo-sectioned and mounted samples should be either desiccated and measured immediately or stored frozen (typically at −80 °C) for short- to mid-term storage.

5.2.3 Cell Culture

In contrast to tissue samples, cell culture can be grown directly on glass or ITO-coated slides. Especially when grown to subconfluence, the membranes of isolated cells may rupture during sample preparation, leading to diffusion of membrane-bound lipids and leakage of the cytoplasm. Several groups have presented protocols on the preparation of cells for MALDI-MSI that include a short formalin fixation, washing, drying, and optional staining steps [18, 19]. While the short chemical fixation effectively conserves the cellular morphology without significantly decreasing the PE or PS signal intensity, the employed formaldehyde permeates the membrane, leading to leakage and washout of the cytosol. Alternatively, freeze-drying and frozen-hydrated techniques based on freeze-fracture or cryo-sectioning that conserve the contents of the cytosol have been presented for SIMS analysis [20, 21]. Especially, the latter two, however, require elaborate and highly specialized equipment and are not straightforwardly compatible with analysis at atmospheric pressure or the application of a matrix for matrix-assisted laser desorption/ionization (MALDI) analysis.

5.2.4 Pre-processing

In MSI of lipids, the signal intensity for specific lipids is highly dependent on the biological matrix at the respective microvolume or pixel. The local concentration of salt, for example, can substantially influence the formation of adducts with alkali metal cations. The samples can be washed with aqueous solutions of alkali metal salts with varying organic counterions such as acetate, citrate, or formate to favor the formation of the desired adduct, and in some cases increase the overall sensitivity [22, 23]. The preferential formation of specific alkali metal cations can also be utilized to generate ions that yield greater structural information upon MS/MS [24–26]. Washes with volatile ammonium salts can be used to favor the formation of protonated ions [23]. To produce specific metal cation adducts such as gold, sodium, copper, or silver, the tissue section can also be treated with nanoparticles and salts or sputtered with thin layers of the respective element [27–29]. Dufresne et al., e.g. demonstrate the detection of intact cholesterol and other olefins not generally ionized by conventional MALDI matrices as silver adducts directly from brain tissue [30].

5.2.5 Handling and Storage

Whole organs intended for MSI of lipids should be stored frozen at −80 °C with or without the embedding medium. The use of vacuum-sealed containers may minimize the excessive build-up of frost or development of freezer-burn during long-term storage. Whenever possible, tissue sections should be prepared fresh to prevent degradation on the newly exposed surfaces. Lukowski et al. reported a decrease in lipid annotations in the first 24 hours after sectioning of 35–45% at room temperature and 15–20% after storage at −80 °C [31]. For short- to mid-term storage, the tissue sections can be kept at −80 °C under a protective atmosphere of N_2 or in a vacuum-sealed container to prevent build-up of frost as well as oxidation. The frozen sections should be thawed and desiccated under vacuum or in a dry atmosphere to prevent formation of frost or dew.

5.2.6 Formalin-Fixed Paraffin-Embedded Tissue

Tissue repositories around the world archive an innumerable amount of tissue samples of numerous origins. Most of these samples are conserved using formalin fixation paraffin embedding (FFPE) to allow storage and sectioning at room temperature. During their preparation, FFPE tissues undergo several washing steps with non-polar solvents that remove the majority of lipids. In some cases, a few remaining lipids can be detected and localized following paraffin removal by xylene washes [32]. However, the interpretation of lipid MSI data from FFPE tissue is hampered by the severe disturbance of lipid content that occurs during sample preparation, storage, and processing [33].

5.3 Desorption/Ionization Techniques used for MSI of Lipids

5.3.1 Matrix-Assisted Laser Desorption/Ionization (MALDI)

MALDI is arguably the most popular and commercially developed technique deployed for MSI of lipids. In typical MALDI, analyte molecules are embedded into a large excess of a crystalline chemical matrix, most often small organic molecules, and irradiated with nanosecond-long laser pulses generally at 337, 349, or 355 nm. The optical properties of the matrix and laser wavelength are matched such that the laser pulse is absorbed by the matrix, leading to an explosive disintegration of the crystal lattice. Analyte molecules, largely transparent to the employed laser light, are co-desorbed in the rapid process and transferred to the gasphase with a low thermal burden and minimal fragmentation [34]. Ionization mechanisms in MALDI are still under lively discussion and may involve different pathways, including photoactivated gas-phase charge-transfer processes and charge separation of pre-formed ions [35–37]. For sample preparation in conventional MALDI analysis of extracts and standards, the analyte and matrix are mixed in a solution and deposited onto a surface, resulting in analyte–matrix co-crystallization. Upon drying, more polar compounds are built into defects within the matrix crystal lattice [38]. Because of a mismatch in solubility, less polar analyte molecules such as lipids are more likely to cover the surface of matrix microcrystals [39]. Matrix application for MALDI-MSI is more complicated as a matrix must be deposited in a manner that minimizes analyte delocalization. The microcrystalline layer must be thin and homogeneous, and the crystal size should be smaller than the intended pixel size [40]. Most commonly for MSI applications, the matrix is applied by pneumatic spraying. Here, a fine mist of matrix solution is deposited onto the sample in cycles, leading to iterative microextraction within each droplet and fast evaporation of the solvent [41]. The properties of the resulting matrix layer such as analyte extraction, sample thickness, crystal size, and homogeneity are governed by spray parameters such as choice of solvent system, flow rate, distances between the sprayer and the sample, number of spray cycles, and spray temperature [42]. Matrix application by sublimation is also well suited for MALDI-MSI of lipids and brings the advantages of generating smaller (submicron) crystal sizes and further minimizes delocalization because of the solvent-free nature of the approach, making it often the method of choice for high spatial resolution analyses [43]. For this, a reservoir of the matrix and the sample are placed inside a vacuum. Heating the matrix powder leads to sublimation and re-deposition on the surface of the cooled sample, forming a microcrystalline and porous layer. Migration into the matrix layer for lipids is facilitated by their inherent fluidity and driven by capillary forces, surface wetting, and diffusion [39]. Analyte incorporation can be improved by "recrystallization" methods that include heat treatment and interaction with solvent vapor [44].

Table 5.1 lists the most popular matrices for MALDI-MSI of lipids and their preferred field of application and polarity. The matrix choice has to be adapted to the individual sample, lipids of interest, and instrumentation [45, 46]. While the use of more volatile matrices such as 2,6-dihydroxyacetophenone (DHAP) is restricted in high-vacuum instruments [47], matrices such as α-cyano-4-hydroxycinnamic acid (CHCA) tend to produce sizable chemical backgrounds because of the formation of clusters at elevated and atmospheric pressure conditions.

From a hardware perspective, the pixel size in MALDI-MSI is limited by the size of the laser ablation crater that depends on the focused spot size and the required laser fluence. While commercially available instruments can routinely reach a pixel

Table 5.1 Popular matrices for MALDI-MSI of lipids.

Substance	Abbreviation	Preferred polarity	Vacuum stability
2,5-Dihydroxybenzoic acid	DHB	Positive	High
α-Cyano-4-hydroxycinnamic acid	CHCA/HCCA	Positive	High
1,5-Diaminonaphtalene	DAN	Positive/Negative	Medium
2,5-Dihydroxyacetophenone	2,5-DHA/DHAP	Positive/Negative	Medium
2,6-Dihydroxyacetophenone	2,6-DHA	Positive/Negative	Low
2,4,6-Trihydroxyacetophenone	THAP	Positive/Negative	Low
Norharmane	NRM/NORH	Negative	High
9-aminoacridine	9-AA	Negative	Medium
N-(1-naphthyl) ethylenediamine dihydrochloride	NEDC	Negative	Medium

size of 10–15 µm, more specialized applications have reported pixels as small as 600 nm [48]. MALDI can detect many different lipid species, with phospholipids (PLs) and sphingolipids generally giving the highest signal intensities. The types of ions detected with MALDI across both positive- and negative-ion modes are similar to other MSI approaches and described in Section 5.7.1. Demonstrating the suitability of MALDI for lipid detection, Bowman et al. tentatively assign 702 individual lipid ion species in the positive-ion mode from a total of 2643 peaks based on accurate mass alone, using the ultra-high resolving power of a 21T Fourier transform ion cyclotron resonance mass spectrometer (FTICR-MS) and a mass accuracy of 150 ppb [49].

The sensitivity for certain lipid classes can be improved using post-ionization approaches. In a technique termed MALDI-2, a second laser pulse interacts with the evolving MALDI-plume, producing many additional matrix ions via resonant multiphoton ionization [50]. Under the right ion source pressure conditions (>2 mbar), subsequent gas-phase reactions initiated by the ionized matrix distribute the charge among a wide variety of lipid classes and boost signal intensities up to several orders of magnitude [51]. Bowman et al. report a ~sixfold increase in the number of tentatively assigned lipids in positive-ion mode analysis of rat liver tissue at pixel sizes between 6 and 20 µm when using MALDI-2 [52]. Applying this approach to imaging lipids in human multiple sclerosis tissue at pixel sizes of 6 µm using oversampling 147 lipids identified at the sum-composition level by accurate mass measurements were successfully imaged, including cholesterol ester species that localized to lipid droplets with diameters of ~10–30 µm. Other methods such as plasma-based post-ionization can also yield significant increases in sensitivity and lipid coverage but have not yet been explored to the same extent as MALDI-2 [53]. The increasing sensitivity provided by ever-improving instrumentation and post-ionization approaches such as MALDI-2 and technical advancements in the miniaturization of laser spot size allow for MALDI-MSI with a pixel size in the submicron range

[18, 48, 54]. This opens the door to the analysis of intact lipids on a subcellular level as demonstrated in Figure 5.1a,b.

With a number of platforms for MALDI-MSI commercially available, the technique has been used in a large number of applications across numerous tissue types [57, 58]. Next to the targeted spatial analysis of a specific lipid species or lipid class, an untargeted approach can be used to identify potential lipid biomarkers. An example for this procedure was presented by Paine et al., utilizing the improvements in acquisition speed to record three-dimensional data of medulloblastoma in a mouse model from a total of 49 sagittal sections (Figure 5.1c). This enabled the identification of specific lipid species such as PE(16:0_24:1) or PIP2(18:0_20:4) with decreasing or increasing signal intensities between metastasizing and non-metastasizing tumors [55]. As a non-mammalian example, Khalil et al. used atmospheric pressure

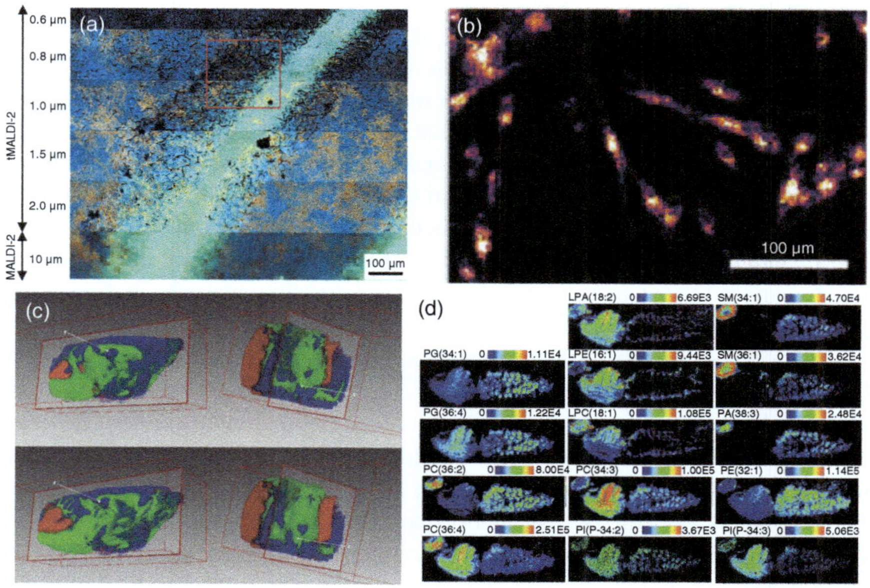

Figure 5.1 (a) Overlay portraying the distribution of blue, m/z = 577.519, $[DAG(34:1)]^+$; orange, m/z = 784.525, PE(36:1), $[M+K]^+$; and green, m/z = 828.692, HexCer(42:1-OH), $[M+H]^+$ in mouse cerebellum tissue. The top five panels were recorded with the transmission mode -MALDI-2 at the indicated pixel size. The bottom panel was recorded in top illumination geometry at a pixel size of 10.0 μm. (b) Ion intensity distribution of $[PC(36:2)+H]^+$ in Vero-B4 cell cultures measured by *t*-MALDI-2-MSI using DHAP. (c) 3-D reconstructions of 49 aligned sagittal sections from a ND2:SmoA1 transgenic mouse brain containing a non-metastasizing cerebellum tumor using three representative channels: m/z 790.5 in blue, m/z 888.6 in green, and m/z 885.5 in red. Visualization of two sagittal (left) and two coronal (right) virtual sections. (d) Positive-ion AP-SMALDI-MS images obtained from a whole-body section of *Anopheles stephensi*. Each image represents the sum of intensities of the corresponding $[M+H]^+$, $[M+Na]^+$, and $[M+K]^+$ adducts. Source: (a) Adapted with permission of Niehaus et al. [48], Springer Nature, (b) Adapted with permission of Bien et al. [18], American Chemical Society, (c) Paine et al. [55]/Springer Nature/CC BY 4.0, (d) Adapted with permission of Khalil et al. [56], American Chemical Society.

MALDI-MSI to investigate phospholipid distribution in the whole-body section of *Anopheles stephensi* mosquitoes (Figure 5.1d) [56]. In the positive-ion mode, a wide range of lipid species from a number of phospho- and sphingolipid classes displayed specific distributions throughout the insect's body.

5.3.2 Secondary Ion Mass Spectrometry SIMS

SIMS was one of the earliest techniques used for MSI and is often applied to lipid imaging in tissues and cells [21, 59]. Among all MSI techniques, SIMS offers the highest spatial resolution, which is routinely in the low micrometer regime or better. As such, SIMS has found numerous applications for mapping lipid distributions and compositions of individual cells. Ion generation by SIMS is achieved by bombarding the sample with a high-energy (~10–70 keV) ion beam. The beam consists of either atomic metal ions or clusters and is focused through a series of lenses to spot sizes as small as 100 nm in the case of atomic or small cluster beams. As the high-energy projectile strikes the surface, a collision cascade in the samples top monolayers is induced, leading to the sputtering of neutrals, electrons, and ions from the sample. The ions are then detected by a mass spectrometer, typically using TOF. SIMS is primarily a surface analysis method in contrast to MALDI and electrospray ionization (ESI)-based methods that likely produce ions from analytes originating from within the volume of tissue sections. The primary drawback of SIMS for lipid imaging is that the higher energies involved in the sputtering and ionization process can lead to extensive fragmentation. Using traditional ion beam fragmentation can be so severe that intact species are not detected.

Primary ion beams based on liquid metal ion sources have been most widely used for SIMS and include In^+, Au_3^+, and Bi_3^+ beams. Small cluster sources such as Au_3^+ and Bi_3^+ were developed to help increase the yield of intact biomolecular ions [60]; however, fragmentation remains extensive with low yields of intact lipids, and the primary signals include the phosphocholine headgroup at *m/z* 184, $[Chol+H-H_2O]^+$, and free fatty acid (FFA) fragments. Nonetheless, the ability to focus these beams to spot sizes of 100 nm or less presents a powerful approach for high-resolution lipid imaging. For example, an In^+ ion beam was used to study the lipid changes associated with fusion pore formation during *Tetrahymena* mating [61]. Using the characteristic headgroup fragments at *m/z* 184 for the phosphocholine headgroup and *m/z* 126 for the 2-aminoethylphosphonolipid headgroup, the authors concluded that lipids with smaller headgroups were enriched at the fusion site and thereby demonstrated the unique subcellular imaging capabilities of SIMS. Intact ion yields can be improved by surface treatment, including gold coating [62] and the use of MALDI-like matrices [63].

To further increase the intact ion yields for SIMS, cluster beams such as C_{60}^+ were developed [64, 65]. These deposit more of their energy into the top few monolayers, leading to increased sputter yields, less sub-surface damage, and an overall gentler sputtering/ionization process. However, they cannot generally be focused to the small spot sizes achieved using liquid metal ion beams, with spatial resolutions of 300 nm reported for C_{60}^+ SIMS [66]. Furthermore, despite the softer sputtering process, fragment ions can still dominate the spectra using C_{60}^+. Gas cluster ion beams (GCIBs) appear to be best suited for detecting and imaging intact lipid species with SIMS. GCIB sources consist of ionized clusters containing several thousand atoms or molecules such as Ar_n, $(H_2O)_n$, and $(CO_2)_n$ [67]. Although GCIBs can currently be focused toward spot sizes of only ~1 μm or larger, the increased yield of intact lipid signals is substantial, including for larger lipid species such as cardiolipins (CL) and gangliosides (GL) [68]. For example, Angerer et al. have shown that a 20 keV Ar_{4000}^+ beam could produce an up to 50-fold increase in secondary ion yields for intact species such as phosphatidylinositol (PI) and GM1 GLs compared to a 40 keV C_{60}^+ beam [69]. Tian et al. used a 70 keV CO_2 ($n > 10000$) primary ion beam to image intact lipid species such as PE and CL within HT22 cells with a spatial resolution of 1.6 μm (Figure 5.2) [70]. Other selected examples demonstrating the applicability of GCIB–SIMS to lipid imaging includes lipid heterogeneity throughout human breast cancer tissue [71], imaging peroxidized PE lipids in ferroptotic H9c2 cardiomyocytes and neurons following traumatic brain injury [72], phospholipids in human basal cell carcinoma [73], various lipid species in flatworms [74], and lipid accumulation in infarcted mouse heart tissue [75]. The benefits of cluster beams and the advantage offered by operating them as continuous beams have led to improved SIMS-based mass spectrometers that can incorporate continuous ion beams and provide improved mass accuracy/resolution and MS/MS capabilities. Interested readers are referred to Refs. [76–78].

A further advantage of cluster beams is the reduced surface and subsurface damage that enables 3D imaging and depth profiling of tissues and cells. Here, a cluster beam such as C_{60}^+ or GCIB is used to sputter several monolayers, after which the freshly exposed surface can be interrogated using SIMS-MSI. Such methods can have a depth resolution as low as several tens of nanometers. The examples of this include the investigations of lipids in the inner and outer membrane of Gram-negative bacteria [79] and the 3D MSI of cells and tissues [80].

Nano-SIMS is another MSI method that uses a diatonic compound (DC) beam such as Cs^+ or O_2^- and can provide spatial resolutions as low as 50 nm [81]. This method results in extensive fragmentation producing mainly atomic and diatomic fragmented ions and is often coupled with stable isotope labeling to target certain molecules via the isotopic enrichment of related atomic/diatomic signals. For example, using ^{15}N-labeled sphingolipids (detected as $^{15}CN^-$) and ^{18}O-labeled cholesterol (detected as $^{18}O^-$) incorporated into fibroblast cells, Frisz et al. demonstrated that areas rich in sphingolipids were not enriched in cholesterol, which instead was distributed evenly throughout the plasma membrane [82]. Another example of nano-SIMS applied to lipid imaging is the use of deuterium-labeled triacylglycerol-rich lipoproteins to study lipid incorporation into capillary endothelial cells and cardiomyocytes [83].

5.3.3 MSI Methods Using Electrospray Ionization

5.3.3.1 Desorption Electrospray Ionization

Desorption electrospray ionization (DESI) is an ambient MSI method that involves the exposure of the sample (e.g. tissue section) to charged microdroplets generated by ESI [84]. These charged, high-velocity microdroplets impinge the sample and extract the analytes [85]. The droplets scatter off the surface toward the inlet capillary of the mass spectrometer. Ionization occurs via ESI-like processes as the charged microdroplets undergo desolvation. Thus, DESI analysis does not require external matrices and allows samples to be analyzed under ambient conditions. Spray solvents consisting of $MeOH{:}H_2O$ or $ACN{:}H_2O$ mixtures are most commonly used for

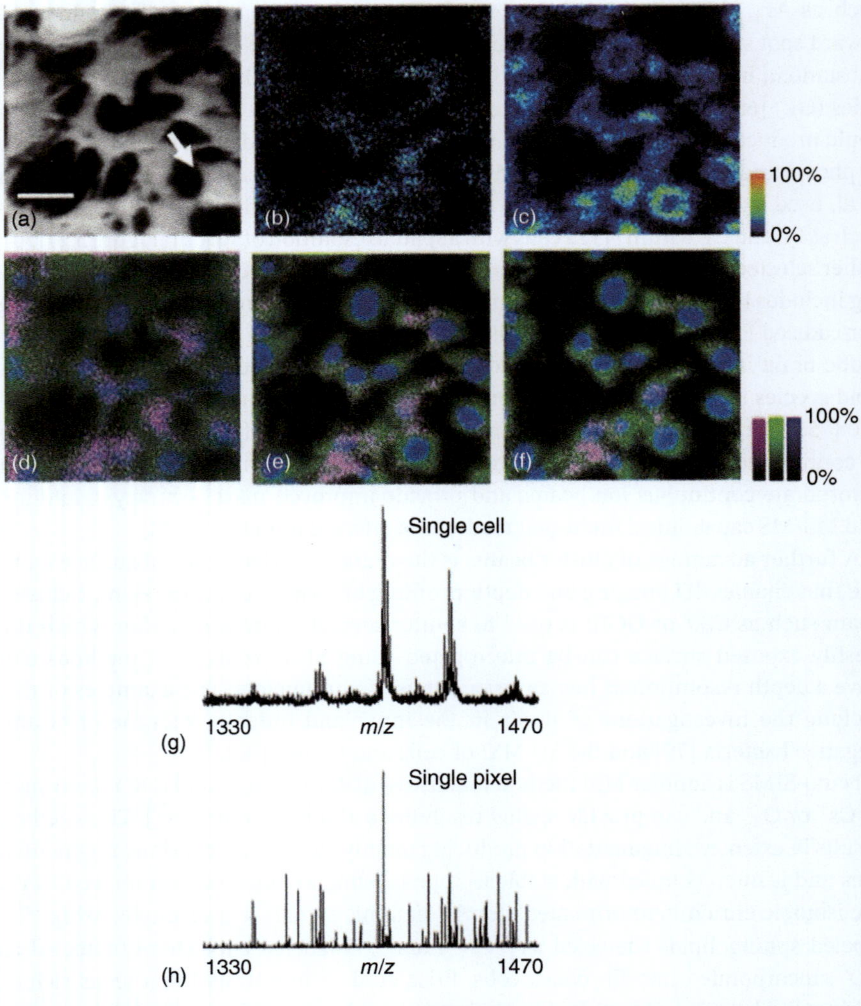

Figure 5.2 GCIB-SIMS-MSI of single Ht22 cells at 1 μm pixel size using a 70 keV $(CO_2)_{10000}^+$ primary ion beam. Before analysis, the cells were treated with (1-ethyl-3-(3-dimethylaminopropyl)carbodiimide hydrochloride) and phospholipase C. (a) Total-ion current image from the first analysis layer showing the cell locations (scale bar = 50 μm). (b and c) SIMS-MSI data form the second analysis layer hosing distribution of (b) $[CL(68:2)-H]^-$ and (c) $[PI(38:4)-H]^-$. (D–F) shows distributions of $[PI(38:4)-H]^-$ (green), $[CL(68:2)-H]^-$ (magenta), and deoxyribosediphosphate (*m/z* 257.0, blue) from the () first (0–200 nm), (e) second (200–400 nm), and (f) third (400–600 nm) analysis layers (depth indicated from the initial sample surface). (g) Mass spectrum showing the cardiolipin mass range from the cell marked with an arrow in (a). (h) Representative single-pixel spectrum from the same indicated cell. Source: Tian et al. [70].

DESI and are suitable for positive- and negative-ion mode analysis. However, these can disturb the underlying tissue structure, prohibiting informative histological staining after DESI. Use of 1:1 *N,N*-dimethylformamide:EtOH spray solvents has been shown to preserve the tissue structure and generate rich lipid spectra [86]. The spot size of the electrospray largely determines the spatial resolution of DESI-MSI on the sample surface with pixels as low as 20 μm being achieved for tissue imaging [87]. However, pixel sizes of 50–150 μm are more common.

DESI-MSI is well suited for imaging a wide range of lipid species from tissues, including many phospholipids and sphingolipids [88, 89]. For example, one study demonstrated that DESI detects many phospholipid classes from tissue surfaces that are also detected by liquid chromatography mass spectrometry (LC-MS) [90]. Another study used DESI-MSI to map lipid changes throughout rat sciatic nerve tissue with lipid identifications supported by LC-MS/MS data [91]. Many lipid species, including phospholipids (PLs), TAGs, diacylglycerols (DAGs), glycosphingolipids (GSLs), sulfatides, and ceramide-1-phosphates, were detected and imaged with distinct lipid profiles observed across fibers, connective tissue, and adipose tissue. DESI also generated higher signals for FFAs than MALDI, which has been explored in a variety of studies. As one example, Sato et al. investigated the distribution of polyunsaturated fatty acids (PUFAs) such as FA(22:5) and FA(22:6) along with PUFA metabolites including 12-hydroxyeicosapentaenoic acid (12-HEPE), 15-hydroxydocosahexaenoic acid (15-HDoHE), Protectin D1, and protectin D1 and leukotriene B5 (LTB5) within plaques derived from apolipoprotein E-deficient mice supplemented with either FA(22:5) or FA(22:6) diets [92].

DESI-MS has been applied to study lipid distributions in many tissue types, including cancerous tissues such as brain [93–95], breast [96], ovarian [97–99], and colorectal [100, 101] where it can also classify the nature of the diseased tissue. For example, DESI-MSI can differentiate ovarian high-grade carcinomas and borderline ovarian tumors [97] in addition to breast cancer subtypes [96]. DESI-MSI in three dimensions has been applied to study cancer tissue such as glioblastoma [102] and colorectal cancers [103]. Henderson et al. combined both positive- and negative-ion mode DESI-MSI to reveal 3D lipid distributions throughout xenograft glioblastoma tumors from mice [102], revealing distinct lipid within hypoxic and normoxic regions with acylcarnitines localizing to the hypoxic regions and PI(38:4) higher in viable tissue.

5.3.3.2 Laser Ablation Electrospray Ionization and IR-Matrix-Assisted Laser Desorption-Electrospray Ionization

Laser ablation electrospray ionization (LAESI) [104] and infrared-matrix-assisted laser desorption-electrospray ionization (IR-MALDESI) [105] are two similar ambient-based approaches using an infrared laser to desorb analytes from the sample surface into a plume of charged droplets generated by an ESI emitter. Desorption is initiated by absorption of the 2.94 μm laser pulse by water, while ionization occurs via ESI-like processes for analytes captured by the charged droplets. For tissue imaging experiments, a thin film of amorphous ice is formed on the surface by cooling the sample and acts as the energy-absorbing matrix. The spatial resolution is determined by the size of the laser spot on the sample and is typically 100–200 μm. However, recent implementations have reported spatial resolutions for MSI experiments of 50 μm [106].

LAESI/IR-MALDIESI has been applied to the imaging of lipids and metabolites from a variety of samples, including plant material [107, 108], ovarian tissue [109], zebrafish [110], dog liver [111], mouse brain [112], and mouse skin tissue [113]. The latter study demonstrated the 3D analysis of lipids in skin tissue by utilizing the ability to sequentially probe deeper into the sample with each successive laser pulse. Monitoring signals as a function of laser shots thus provides insights into the distribution of analytes as a function of depth. A depth resolution of 7 μm was achieved along with a lateral resolution of 50 μm and allowed 3D imaging of whole skin without the need for sectioning of skin samples. Numerous lipid species, including PLs, sphingolipids, TAGs, DAGs, and cholesterol, were detected. As a selected example, sphingosine-1-phosphate was found with higher signal intensity in the dermis compared to the epidermis and hypodermis, while cholesterol was higher in the epidermis and TAGs in the hypodermis [113]. In addition, unsaturated lipids that may be poorly ionized using typical ESI spay solutions can be enhanced by using dopants such as silver [114].

5.3.3.3 Nanospray Desorption Electrospray Ionization

Nanospray desorption electrospray ionization (nano-DESI) is another ambient MSI method for imaging lipids from tissue sections [115]. It involves the formation of a liquid microjunction between two capillaries on the sample surface. The solvent flow forming the microjunction extracts analytes from the sample and is aspirated into a nano-ESI capillary for ionization and transfer into the inlet capillary. As per other ESI-based methods, nano-DESI is well suited for detecting many lipid classes well ionized by ESI and spatial resolutions as low as ~10 μm reported. For example, Yin et al. demonstrated the localization of lipid signals, including a variety of phosphatidylcholine (PC) and oxidized PC species to individual islets at a spatial resolution of 11 μm [116].

A comparison of lipid coverage from mouse lung tissue compared to that obtained following lipid extraction and LC-MS/MS revealed that nano-DESI could detect 265 lipid signals across the positive- and negative-ion modes from 20 lipid subclasses using 9 : 1 MeOH:H_2O (v/v) as the solvent [117]. This corresponds to roughly half of the signals detected following Folch extraction and LC-MS/MS and confirms the suitability of nano-DESI for many lipid species. TAGs were detected significantly better using LC-MS/MS compared to nano-DESI. TAG detection using nano-DESI-MSI can be improved by using less polar solvents such as 5 : 3.5 : 1.5 (v/v/v) MeOH:CAN:toluene [118]. The addition of dopants such as silver to the solvent can also aid in detecting additional lipid classes. For example, the use of silver dopant promoted the formation of $[M+Ag]^+$ ions of prostaglandins and has been applied for imaging prostaglandins such as PGE_2, PGF2α, dimethyl-PGE_2, PGA_1, and PGK_2 within the mouse uterine tissue from four day pregnant mice. The sensitivity of $[M+Ag]^+$ ions was ~30-fold higher than that obtained when using the $[M-H]^-$ ions. Prostaglandins were primarily localized to the luminal epithelium and glandular epithelium regions of the tissue.

5.4 Combining Ion Mobility of Lipids with MSI

Ion mobility provides a powerful approach to resolve isobaric and isomeric lipid signals as well as reduce background interferences. The application of ion mobility to lipidomics is described in Chapter 6 and its application to MSI reviewed in Refs. [119, 120]. Below, we outline several examples where ion mobility has benefitted MSI studies on lipids.

Combining trapped-ion mobility spectrometry (TIMS) with MALDI-MSI has enabled the resolution of several isomeric lipid species such as ions tentatively assigned to protonated PC(O-32:1), PC(P-32:0), and the ceramide (Cer) Cer(t40;1) detected at m/z 718.58 [121]. Each of these mobility-resolved species exhibited distinct localization within mouse pup tissue. The use of TIMS in this study also provided a 2.5-fold increase in peak capacity. MALDI coupled with TIMS can also separate isobaric lipids such as $[PC(16:0\_20:4)+H]^+$ and $[PC(16:0\_18:1)+Na]^+$ [122] as well as help resolve the increased lipid signals detected using MALDI-2 [123]. For example, using MALDI-2 combined with TIMS detection of 8 mobility-resolved peaks between m/z 810–811 was demonstrated from rat testes tissue imaged with a pixel size of 10 μm.

Ion mobility has also been coupled with a variety of ambient MSI techniques such as DESI [124, 125], nano-DESI [126], and IR-MALDESI [127]. A unique feature of these ESI-based MSI methods is the ability to generate multiply charged ions of lipids such as CLs and GLs that then occupy the same m/z range as singly charged PLs and sphinoglipids. High-field asymmetric waveform ion mobility spectrometry (FAIMS) combined with DESI-MS has shown to resolve doubly charged CL from other phospholipids generated from both rat brain tissue and oncocytic thyroid tumor tissue [125]. Crucially, the addition of FAIMS also increased the S/N of CL lipids and enabled the detection of 71 CL species, 23 more than detected without FAIMS. In another study, traveling-wave ion mobility spectrometry (TWIMS) combined with DESI-MSI was able to resolve signals arising from doubly and triply charged polysilylated GL lipids from other abundant signals arising from phospholipids [124].

Although ion mobility does not usually allow one to identify lipids based on collision-cross section (CCS) measurements alone (in the absence of analyzing synthetic standards), its ability to increase the peak capacity and S/N and resolve isobaric and isomeric signals makes it a powerful tool that will undoubtedly be increasingly applied in MSI studies. CCS libraries will also likely help annotate and identify detected lipid species [128–131].

5.5 On Tissue Chemical Derivatization for MSI

Many lipid species are not readily ionized using conventional MSI approaches, leaving large swathes of the lipidome invisible in MSI studies. Although post-ionization approaches can dramatically improve the sensitivity and lipid coverage for many species [52, 53, 132], on-tissue chemical derivatization (OTCD) is another approach that can enhance the detection sensitivity for many targeted classes. OTCD involves the reaction or analytes containing targeted functional groups with a derivatization reagent that covalently modifies the analyte and converts it into a more readily ionizable species – often by adding a fixed positive charge via a quaternary nitrogen. OTCD has been comprehensively reviewed recently [132, 133].

Most often, OTCD is performed by depositing the derivatization reagent onto the surface of a tissue section before its analysis by MSI. Given the low ionization efficiencies of sterols, several studies have applied OTCD to enable their analysis by MALDI-MSI in a variety of tissues using Girard T reagent that derivatizes ketone groups [134–136]. For example, Shimma et al. detected and localized increased testosterone levels in the testes of mice treated with human chorionic gonadotropin [134]. A related approach using an intermediate enzymatic conversion has been reported for the MALDI-MSI of cholesterol in mouse brain tissue derived from a Niemann–Pick type C1 disease model and during development from birth to 10 weeks [137]. This method first employed the reaction of cholesterol with cholesterol oxidase that oxidizes the 3β-hydroxy group to a 3-oxo group, which then undergoes OTCD using Girard P-hydrazine. Lysophosphatidic acid (LPA) and sphingosine-1-phosphate lipids, two species often found at very low abundance, have been successfully studied in brain tissue using MALDI-MSI and OTCD [138]. This approach uses a zinc complex known as Phos-TAG that reacts with phosphate monoesters and was applied to study the region-specific accumulation of lysophosphatidic acid and sphingosine-1-phosphate (S1P) in both Sgpl1$^{fl/fl/Nes}$ and Ppap2b$^{fl/fl/Nes}$ mice that are deficient in S1P lyase and LPP3/PAP2B enzymes, respectively. FFAs have also been studied using MALDI-MSI and OTCD [139].

It is also possible to induce derivatization *in situ* within the charged microdroplets produced during ESI. This has the advantage of not requiring additional sample treatment before MSI. For example, betaine aldehyde, a reagent that reacts with hydroxyl groups, has been used to enable DESI-MSI of cholesterol in rat brain tissue [140]. Another example is the use of dication ion-pairing compounds to facilitate the positive-ion mode detection of lipids typically better detected in the negative-ion mode such as acidic phospholipids such as PS and PI and FFAs [141].

5.6 Quantification in MSI

Signal intensities of lipids detected during MSI can vary dramatically depending on the lipid class and the chemical and morphological environment in which they are present. As such, a lipid species present at the same concentration in two regions of a tissue section can yield different ion intensities that limit the quantitative interpretation of the data. Acquisition of quantitative MSI data requires using internal standards (ISs) applied homogenously to the sample to allow for per-pixel signal normalization and determination of absolute concentration per pixel [142, 143]. Typically, as is the case with extract-based lipidomics workflows, at least one internal standard per lipid class is required. Calibration curves are often created by spotting a dilution series over a control tissue or tissue homogenate that attempts to replicate the samples chemical environment. Alternatively, mimetic tissue models doped with different concentrations of internal standards can also be used [144]. For example, calibration curves generated using brain tissue homogenates spiked with isotopically labeled PC IS have been used to quantitatively image PC lipids throughout mouse brain tissue [145].

The application of IS for signal normalization and attempts to correct for region-specific ionization efficiencies and analyte extraction [146] can be made by depositing it either below or on top of the tissue section [142], although which approach best reflects the conditions of extraction into the matrix layer (in the case of MALDI) or solvent (e.g. in the case of DESI and nano-DESI) is unclear. For example, deuterated internal standard deposited onto a glass slide before mounting the tissue section has been reported for quantitative imaging of acetyl-L-carnitine from brain tissue [137]. D_7-cholesterol applied on top of a tissue section using an automated sprayer has been utilized for quantitative-MSI (Q-MSI) of cholesterol in diseased brain tissue [137]. Alternatively, doping of the extraction solvent used for nano-DESI with non-endogenous PC(25:0) and PC(43:6) has been used for quantitative imaging of PC lipids in rat brain tissue (Figure 5.3) [147]. A similar

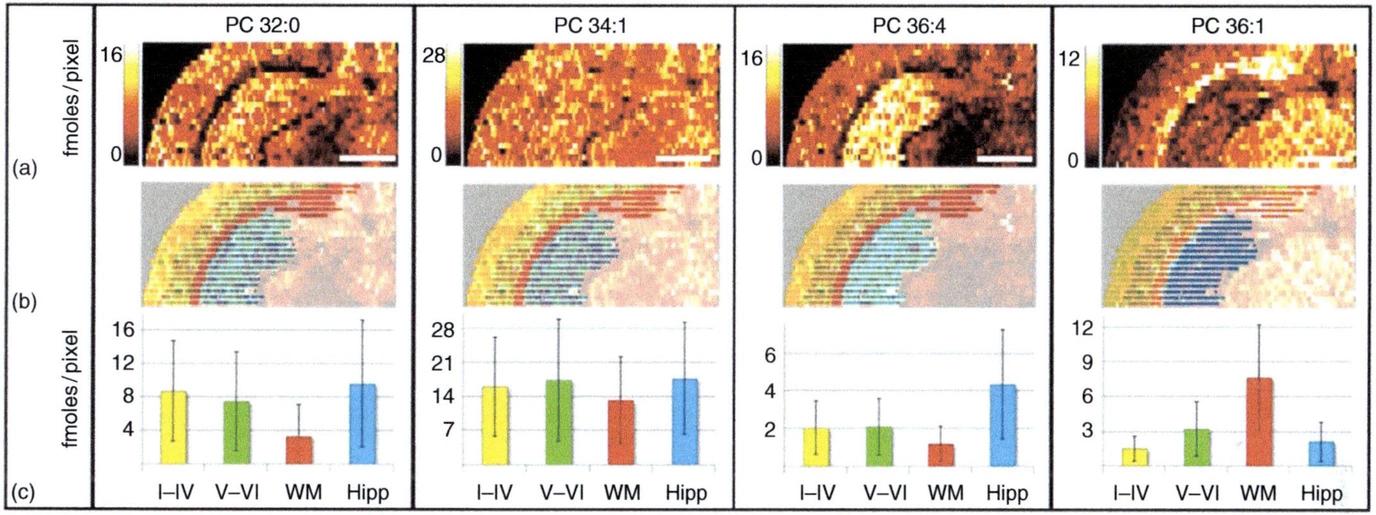

Figure 5.3 Quantitative nano-DESI-MSI if PC lipids in rat brain tissue. (a) Shows quantitative ion images of potassiated PC(32:0). PC(34:1), PC(36:4), and PC (36:1) (left to right). Signal intensities are normalized to the internal standard $[PC(43:6)+K]^+$. (b) Regions of interest color coded as yellow, neocortical layers I–IV (I–IV); green, neocortical layers V–VI (V–VI); red, white matter (WM); and blue, hippocampus (Hipp). (c) Average amounts of each PC lipids in each brain region are represented as fmol/pixel (pixel size = $67 \times 200\,\mu m^2$) that are color coded as described in (b). Source: Reprinted with permission of Lanekoff et al. [147], American Chemical Society.

nano-DESI approach using isotopically labeled IS has been reported for Q-MSI of arachidonic acid and prostaglandins mouse uterine tissue [148]. It should be noted that how accurately the extraction and ionization of a standard reflect that of endogenous molecules is not yet entirely clear, nor is the ability of MSI to quantify accurately on the single-pixel level. However, several Q-MSI studies have demonstrated that the MSI-determined amounts in different tissue regions are consistent with ~20% of values measured by LC-MS/MS, pointing to the general validity of the approach [143].

5.7 Lipid Identification for MSI

5.7.1 Types of Ions Generated by MSI

As MSI is performed on complex biological samples, such as tissue sections, spectra can become more complex compared to those acquired by analysis of lipid extracts because of the formation of multiple adducts for each lipid. These can complicate the spectra and increase the probability of unresolved isobaric overlaps that primarily arise from endogenous salts, leading to simultaneous detection of $[M+H]^+$, $[M+Na]^+$, and $[M+K]^+$ ions. This is particularly noticeable for some PLs, GSLs, and TAGs that are detected in the positive-ion mode but may also complicate negative-ion mode spectra where lipids such as CL can be detected as $[M\text{-}2H+Na]^-$/$[M\text{-}2H+K]^-$ ions, in addition to the more common $[M-H]^-$. Proper consideration and identification of different adducts formed are essential to correctly identify lipids detected during MSI experiments.

Different adducts from the same lipid species may give rise to different ion distributions that reflect Na^+/K^+ ratios throughout the tissue. For example, decreased levels of $[M+K]^+$ ions and increases in $[M+Na]^+$ ions of PC lipids have been observed using MALDI-MSI of brain tissue following traumatic brain injury [149] and ischemic stroke [150, 151] and attributed to loss of Na/K-ATPase. It is critical that these effects are considered and changing adduct ratios not incorrectly assigned as alterations in lipid distribution. One approach to circumvent the influence of salt distributions is to wash the sample with aqueous buffer solution, typically ammonium formate or ammonium acetate, that removes salts from the tissue and favors the formation of $[M+H]^+$/$[M-H]^-$ ions [22, 23].

The polarity in which the mass spectrometer is operated significantly influences the lipid species detected. Many lipid species are preferentially ionized in one polarity. Neutral and basic lipids (e.g. PC, sphingomyelin (SM), TAGs, and some GSLs) are usually best detected in the positive-ion mode. In contrast, acidic lipids such as PS, PI, GL, CL, FFA, and bile acids are better detected in the negative-ion mode in the form of deprotonated species. Therefore, acquiring both positive- and negative-ion mode MSI data from the sample to maximize lipid coverage can be advantageous. Examples of this include the sequential acquisition of dual-polarity data using MALDI [152, 153] and DESI [154] or fast polarity switching during MSI experiments using MALDI [155], IR-MALDESI [109], and DESI [156].

5.7.2 In-source Fragmentation Considerations

Careful consideration of in-source fragmentation is critical for accurate data interpretation and lipid assignments. While in-source fragmentation is also an issue for ESI analysis [157, 158], it can become even more significant for MSI where the extent of in-source fragmentation can be larger for methods such as MALDI and especially SIMS. SIMS analysis of tissue and cells often yields high abundance fragment signals corresponding to the phosphocholine headgroup at *m/z* 184 and FFAs. Other examples of in-source fragmentation that may be encountered during MSI include headgroup losses from phospholipids that give rise to either phosphatidic acid (PA) or $[DAG+H/Na/K-H_2O]^+$ ions and the formation of dimethyl-PE (DMPE) ions that arise from the loss of CH_3 from PC lipids following anion adduction and are isomeric with PE [159]. Figure 5.4 summarizes the in-source fragments observed during the MALDI analysis of 17 phospholipids and sphingolipid standards. Note that in the case of MALDI [160], the extent of in-source fragmentation can be influenced by the laser energy and the choice of matrix.

While it is generally advisable to minimize in-source fragmentation, it may also be exploited to aid lipid identification. For example, Angerer et al. used a 40 keV cluster ion beam consisting of 15% CO_2 in argon for the SIMS-MSI analysis of *Phagocata gracilis* flatworms, resulting in the generation of both intact lipids signals and their in-source fragments [161]. The co-localization of fragments with their precursor lipids allowed fragment/precursor assignments to facilitate annotation of lipids species to the molecular lipid species level.

5.7.3 MSI Lipid Identification Using Accurate Mass

The procedure for identifying lipids detected in MSI follows the same approach used for shotgun lipidomics (see Chapter 3). Sum-composition identification acquired using high mass resolution mass analyzers such as Orbitrap, FTICR, and orthogonal TOF analyzers is commonly performed in MSI studies. Sum-composition identification typically requires mass accuracies ≤3 ppm and can be aided by online annotation platforms such as Metaspace [162, 163]. However, it is important to manually curate automated identifications to minimize false identifications such as those inconsistent with lipid ionization or biosynthesis pathways.

An essential requirement of accurate sum-composition identification is the resolution of peaks from isobaric interferences [164]. In many MSI studies, mass

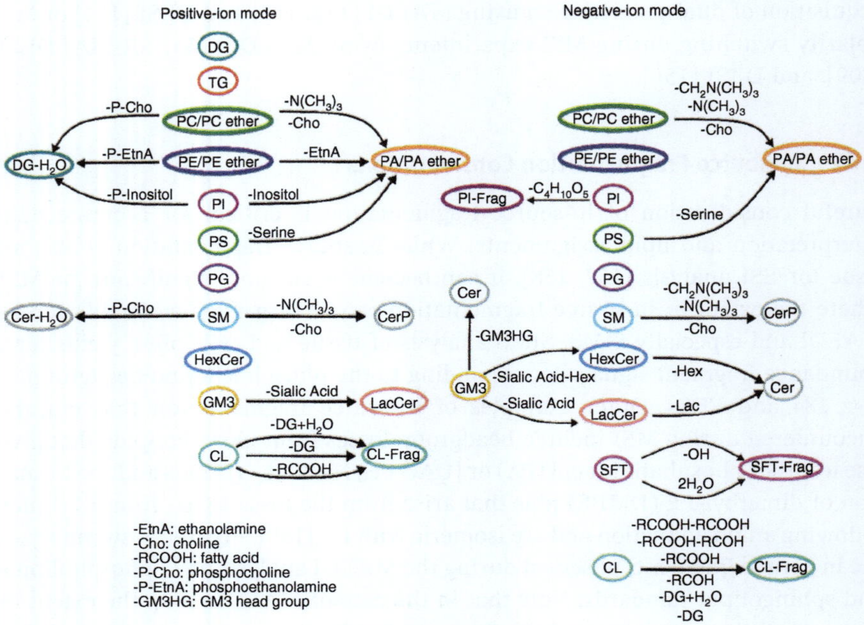

Figure 5.4 Summary of common in-source fragmentation pathways that may occur during MALDI-MS analysis of lipids. Similar processes can also occur for other MSI techniques. Source: Reprinted with permission from reference Garate et al. [160]. Copyright (2020), American Chemical Society.

resolutions >100 000 are obtained, which are sufficient to resolve many isobaric peaks. For example, the recent coupling of SIMS with Orbitrap mass spectrometry enabled SIMS-MSI of lipids at mass resolutions of 240 000 (@ *m/z* 200) with pixel sizes <2 μm using a 20 keV argon GCIB [76]. While such resolutions in the lipid *m/z*-region are sufficient in many cases, a higher resolution can be required [165]. For example, a mass resolution of >150 000 @ *m/z* 750 is needed to resolve common isotopologues such as a $^{13}C_2$-containing peak with the monoisotopic peak of the same lipid containing one less double bond [166]. Even higher mass resolving powers (>300 000) are needed to resolve the difference between $^{12}C_2$ and $^{23}Na^1H$, such as that needed to resolve $[PC(36:1)+Na]^+$ and $[PC(38:4+H)]^+$ ions. Mass resolutions as high as 10^6 have been reported for MSI using FTICR coupled with DESI [167], MALDI [49], and LAESI [107]. For example, using 21 T FTICR with a mass resolution >800 000 in the phospholipid mass range, it was revealed that peak splits of <2 mDa are commonly observed during tissue imaging experiments (e.g. $[PE(O\text{-}38:7)^{13}C_1\text{-}H]^-$ and $[PG(34:1)\text{-}H]^-$). Such small mass differences cannot typically be resolved using conventional instrumentation and require additional methods such MS/MS (see below) to resolve and identify.

5.7.4 Deploying MS/MS for Lipid Identification in MSI

Identification beyond the sum-composition requires MS/MS to characterize lipids to the molecular species level (i.e. identifying a PI containing 18:0 and 20:4 fatty acyls). MS/MS spectra can be obtained manually from the tissue following MSI acquisition for the identification of ions of interest. MS-MSI can also be performed whereby selected peaks are fragmented and the ion distributions of fragment ions used for MSI. Prentice et al. have demonstrated the acquisition of multiple MS/MS spectra from each laser shot using MALDI-axial-TOF instrument by rapidly switching the timed ion selector and enabling detection of fragments supporting the identification of potassiated PC(32:0), PC(36:1), and PC (40:8) during a single MALDI-MSI acquisition. Fisher et al. described a new tandem-TOF-SIMS instrument allowing simultaneous acquisition of both MS^1 and MS/MS spectra from the same ion packets [168]. This system has been used to localize vitamin E within neuronal cells and *Mycobacterium marinum*-infected zebrafish [169]. MS/MS also has the advantage of allowing differential imaging of lipids that cannot be resolved at the MS^1 level. This has been deployed for nano-DESI-MSI, whereby a targeted list of 92 *m/z* values was sequentially fragmented within each pixel [170]. As one example, detection of characteristic fragments allowed the imaging and identification of $[PE(P\text{-}16{:}0/22{:}6)+Na]^+$ and $[PC(32{:}1)+K]^+$ lipids within mouse uterine tissue that would otherwise require a mass resolving power >3 500 000.

Broadband MS/MS data can also be acquired during MSI acquisitions using data-dependent acquisition (DDA) approaches [171, 172]. While these do not allow for MS/MS-imaging (as there are no spatially repetitive MS/MS data), they allow large-scale identification of detected ions. For example, using a hybrid ion trap/Orbitrap instrument, MALDI-MSI and accurate mass data can be acquired using the Orbitrap while DDA-MS/MS are acquired in parallel using the ion trap. This method has been demonstrated for rat brain imaging at a spatial resolution of 40 μm whereby automated lipid identifications utilizing both accurate mass MS^1 data and MS/MS are performed using $ALEX^{123}$ software [172]. Across the positive- and negative-ion mode, the spatial distribution of 100 molecular lipid species was revealed in addition to their high confidence identification using both accurate mass (MS^1) and MS/MS. For example, the addition of MS/MS enabled identifying isomeric PS(18:0_20:1) and PS(18:1_20:0) located primarily within the white matter (WM).

5.7.5 Isomer-Resolved MSI

MSI combined with conventional collision-induced dissociation (CID) MS/MS does not allow the resolution of many isomeric lipids such as those varying in the stereospecific number (*sn*) of acyl chain on the glycerol backbone or lipids varying in the double-bond (db) position of acyl chain double bonds. As different isomeric variants can reflect different biosynthetic processes and/or give rise to different functional properties (e.g. membrane fluidity), developing methods for isomer-resolved MSI has become a significant area of research in recent years.

The coupling of ozone-induced dissociation (OzID) with MALDI-MSI has facilitated imaging of both *sn*- and db-isomers of PC throughout biological tissues [26]. OzID relies on the gas-phase reaction of mass-selected lipids with ozone. The products of this reaction allow unambiguous assignment of db-positional isomers. For *sn*-isomers, CID is first performed to generate the $[M+Na-183]^+$ ion, which is then reacted with ozone in an MS^3 experiment to yield *sn*-specific fragments. The recent coupling of this OzID with MALDI-MSI on a Waters Synapt G2Si mass spectrometer using the high-pressure ion mobility region as the reaction chamber facilitates the rates of five pixels/second for both db- and *sn*-isomers [173]. By fragmenting a population of selected precursor ions before the ion mobility region, isomer-specific fragments can be generated simultaneously for db- and *sn*-isomers. Further, sequential ozonolysis on CID/OzID product ions ($CID/OzID^2$) reveals db-positions specific to the *sn*-1 location. The technique was deployed to map PC db-isomer distributions throughout human prostate cancer tissue [174, 175]. In one study by Young et al., the distribution of PC(34:1*n*-9) was correlated with epithelial cells from potential premalignant regions, whereas PC(34:1*n*-7) correlated with immune cell infiltration and inflammation [175]. The isomer-specific distributions were rationalized as arising from the different ordering of desaturation (SCD-1) and elongation (EVOLV5/EVOLV6) reactions throughout the tissue. In addition to OzID, electron-induced dissociation (EID) on mass-selected PC ions is another gas-phase method enabling imaging of db- and *sn*-isomers from tissue [176]. EID involves the reaction of ionized lipids with energetic (2–70 eV) electrons, whose interaction leads to rich MS/MS spectra containing both even and odd electron fragment ions, some of which are diagnostic of db- and *sn*-position. Gas-phase charge inversion methods involving the conversion of cationized PC lipids into demethylated anions have also been used to study *sn*-isomer populations in brain tissue using MALDI-FTICR [177]. Subsequent CID of the $[PC-CH_3]^-$ produces conventional acyl chain-specific fragments, whose ratios can provide insights into the relative population of different *sn*-isomers.

Derivatization of lipids before analysis is another approach for isomer-resolved MSI. On-tissue Paternò–Büchi (PB) reactions are an example of this and were first coupled with MSI using a MALDI-MSI approach and benzaldehyde as the reactive reagent [178]. Following deposition of the PB reagent, ultraviolet (UV) activation, mass selection, and CID of PB-derivatized lipids diagnostic fragments allowing differentiation of db-isomers are formed. PB reactions have been applied to numerous PLs including PCs as well as hexosylceramides. For example, PS(18:1_18:1)*n*-9 was elevated in the gray matter of mouse brain tissue relative to the *n*-7 variant. Benzophenone is another PB reagent used for MALDI-MSI of db-isomers in both brain tissue and the parasite *Schistosoma mansoni* [179]. Unlike benzaldehyde, the PB reaction is induced upon UV laser irradiation used to initiate MALDI. Benzophenone has also been used to promote PB reactions for DESI-MSI analysis of FA(18:1) db-isomers brain tumor tissue from mice [180]. Furthermore, a variety of alternative derivatization methods that allow generating of products yielding db-specific fragments upon CID have recently been reported, including hydroperoxides for nano-DESI-MSI [181] and surface epoxidation for DESI [182] and IR-MALDESI [183].

Ultraviolet photodissociation (UVPD) can also be used for isomer-resolved MSI and involves the irradiation of mass-selected lipids with a 193 nm laser pulse. To date, only DESI-MSI has been coupled with UVPD [184], and it has been applied to study both PC isomers in brain tissue, in addition to region-specific db-isomer populations throughout human lymph node tissue containing thyroid cancer metastasis [184]. UVPD has also been used to study FFA db-isomers using a charge inversion approach between FFA and 1,8-ethyl DC [185]. Changing populations of *n*-9 and *n*-7 FA18:1 were correlated with metastatic, estrogen receptor, and progesterone status of ovarian cancer tissue.

5.8 Conclusions

Lipid imaging continues to be one of the most common applications using MSI technologies and has provided new insights into the distribution of lipids and their disease-specific alterations throughout tissues and other biological systems. The relative ease of detection of some abundant lipid classes also makes lipid species the analyte of choice for evaluating and developing new MSI methods and capabilities. With ever-improving sensitivity, lipid coverage, spatial resolution, and lipid identification capabilities, MSI is expected to play an increasingly important role in studying lipid metabolism throughout biology and for the classification of diseased tissues based on region-specific alterations in lipid composition.

Acknowledgments

S.R.E. acknowledges funding from the Australian Research Council Future Fellowship Scheme (grant number FT190100082).

References

1 Verbeeck, N., Caprioli, R.M., and Van de Plas, R. (2020). Unsupervised machine learning for exploratory data analysis in imaging mass spectrometry. *Mass Spectrom. Rev.* 39: 245–291.
2 Heeren, R.M.A., Kükrer-Kaletaş, B., Taban, I.M. et al. (2008). Quality of surface: the influence of sample preparation on MS-based biomolecular tissue imaging with MALDI-MS and (Me-)SIMS. *Appl. Surf. Sci.* 255: 1289–1297.
3 Yoon, S. and Lee, T.G. (2018). Biological tissue sample preparation for time-of-flight secondary ion mass spectrometry (TOF–SIMS) imaging. *Nano Converg.* 5: 24.

4 Goodwin, R.J.A. (2012). Sample preparation for mass spectrometry imaging: small mistakes can lead to big consequences. *J. Proteomics* 75: 4893–4911.

5 Patterson, N.H., Thomas, A., and Chaurand, P. (2014). Monitoring time-dependent degradation of phospholipids in sectioned tissues by MALDI imaging mass spectrometry. *J. Mass Spectrom.* 49: 622–627.

6 Dill, A.L., Eberlin, L.S., Costa, A.B. et al. (2011). Data quality in tissue analysis using desorption electrospray ionization. *Anal. Bioanal. Chem.* 401: 1949.

7 Altelaar, A.F.M., van Minnen, J., Jiménez, C.R. et al. (2005). Direct molecular imaging of *Lymnaea stagnalis* nervous tissue at subcellular spatial resolution by mass spectrometry. *Anal. Chem.* 77: 735–741.

8 Kruse, R. and Sweedler, J.V. (2003). Spatial profiling invertebrate ganglia using MALDI MS. *J. Am. Soc. Mass Spectrom.* 14: 752–759.

9 Abe, T., Niizuma, K., Kanoke, A. et al. (2018). Metabolomic analysis of mouse brain after a transient middle cerebral artery occlusion by mass spectrometry imaging. *Neurol. Med.Chir.* 58: 384–392.

10 Strohalm, M., Strohalm, J., Kaftan, F. et al. (2011). Poly[*N*-(2-hydroxypropyl) methacrylamide]-based tissue-embedding medium compatible with MALDI mass spectrometry imaging experiments. *Anal. Chem.* 83: 5458–5462.

11 Scott, A.J., Chandler, C.E., Ellis, S.R. et al. (2019). Maintenance of deep lung architecture and automated airway segmentation for 3D mass spectrometry imaging. *Sci. Rep.* 9: 20160.

12 Buchberger, A.R., DeLaney, K., Johnson, J., and Li, L. (2018). Mass spectrometry imaging: a review of emerging advancements and future insights. *Anal. Chem.* 90: 240–265.

13 Truong, J.X.M., Spotbeen, X., White, J. et al. (2021). Removal of optimal cutting temperature (OCT) compound from embedded tissue for MALDI imaging of lipids. *Anal. Bioanal. Chem.* 413: 2695–2708.

14 Vos, D.R.N., Bowman, A.P., Heeren, R.M.A. et al. (2019). Class-specific depletion of lipid ion signals in tissues upon formalin fixation. *Int. J. Mass Spectrom.* 446: 116212.

15 Carter, C.L., Jones, J.W., Farese, A.M. et al. (2016). Inflation-fixation method for lipidomic mapping of lung biopsies by matrix assisted laser desorption/ionization–mass spectrometry imaging. *Anal. Chem.* 88: 4788–4794.

16 Shimma, S. and Sugiura, Y. (2014). Effective sample preparations in imaging mass spectrometry. *Mass Spectrom.* 3: S0029–S0029.

17 Vandenbosch, M., Nauta, S.P., Svirkova, A. et al. (2021). Sample preparation of bone tissue for MALDI-MSI for forensic and (pre)clinical applications. *Anal. Bioanal. Chem.* 413: 2683–2694.

18 Bien, T., Bessler, S., Dreisewerd, K., and Soltwisch, J. (2021). Transmission-mode MALDI mass spectrometry imaging of single cells: optimizing sample preparation protocols. *Anal. Chem.* 93: 4513–4520.

19 Gilmore, I.S., Heiles, S., and Pieterse, C.L. (2019). Metabolic imaging at the single-cell scale: recent advances in mass spectrometry imaging. *Annu. Rev. Anal. Chem.* 12: 201–224.

20 Lanekoff, I., Kurczy, M.E., Adams, K.L. et al. (2011). An in situ fracture device to image lipids in single cells using TOF–SIMS. *Surf. Interface Anal.* 43: 257–260.

21 Passarelli, M.K. and Winograd, N. (2011). Lipid imaging with time-of-flight secondary ion mass spectrometry (TOF-SIMS). *Biochim. Biophys. Acta, Mol. Cell. Biol. Lipids* 1811: 976–990.

22 Angel, P.M., Spraggins, J.M., Baldwin, H.S., and Caprioli, R. (2012). Enhanced sensitivity for high spatial resolution lipid analysis by negative ion mode matrix assisted laser desorption ionization imaging mass spectrometry. *Anal. Chem.* 84: 1557–1564.

23 Wang, H.-Y.J., Liu, C.B., and Wu, H.-W. (2011). A simple desalting method for direct MALDI mass spectrometry profiling of tissue lipids. *J. Lipid Res.* 52: 840–849.

24 Griffiths, R.L., Sarsby, J., Guggenheim, E.J. et al. (2013). Formal lithium fixation improves direct analysis of lipids in tissue by mass spectrometry. *Anal. Chem.* 85: 7146–7153.

25 Hall, Z., Ament, Z., Wilson, C.H. et al. (2016). Myc expression drives aberrant lipid metabolism in lung cancer. *Cancer Res.* 76: 4608–4618.

26 Paine, M.R.L., Poad, B.L.J., Eijkel, G.B. et al. (2018). Mass spectrometry imaging with isomeric resolution enabled by ozone-induced dissociation. *Angew. Chem.* 57: 10530–10534.

27 Jackson, S.N., Baldwin, K., Muller, L. et al. (2014). Imaging of lipids in rat heart by MALDI-MS with silver nanoparticles. *Anal. Bioanal. Chem.* 406: 1377–1386.

28 Ràfols, P., Vilalta, D., Torres, S. et al. (2018). Assessing the potential of sputtered gold nanolayers in mass spectrometry imaging for metabolomics applications. *PLoS One* 13: e0208908.

29 Hansen, R.L., Dueñas, M.E., and Lee, Y.J. (2019). Sputter-coated metal screening for small molecule analysis and high-spatial resolution imaging in laser desorption ionization mass spectrometry. *J. Am. Soc. Mass Spectrom.* 30: 299–308.

30 Dufresne, M., Thomas, A., Breault-Turcot, J. et al. (2013). Silver-assisted laser desorption ionization for high spatial resolution imaging mass spectrometry of olefins from thin tissue sections. *Anal. Chem.* 85: 3318–3324.

31 Lukowski, J.K., Pamreddy, A., Velickovic, D. et al. (2020). Storage conditions of human kidney tissue sections affect spatial lipidomics analysis reproducibility. *J. Am. Soc. Mass Spectrom.* 31: 2538–2546.

32 Buck, A., Ly, A., Balluff, B. et al. (2015). High-resolution MALDI-FT-ICR MS imaging for the analysis of metabolites from formalin-fixed, paraffin-embedded clinical tissue samples. *J. Pathol.* 237: 123–132.

33 Isberg, O.G., Xiang, Y., Bodvarsdottir, S.K. et al. (2021). The effect of sample age on the metabolic information extracted from formalin-fixed and paraffin embedded tissue samples using desorption electrospray ionization mass spectrometry imaging. *J. Mass Spectrom. Adv. Clin. Lab* 22: 50–55.

34 Vertes, A., Gijbels, R., and Levine, R.D. (1990). Homogeneous bottleneck model of matrix-assisted ultraviolet laser desorption of large molecules. *Rapid Commun. Mass Spectrom.* 4: 228–233.

35 Bae, Y.J. and Kim, M.S. (2015). A thermal mechanism of ion formation in MALDI. *Annu. Rev. Anal. Chem.* 8: 41–60.

36 Knochenmuss, R. (2006). Ion formation mechanisms in UV-MALDI. *Analyst* 131: 966–986.

37 Jaskolla, T.W. and Karas, M. (2011). Compelling evidence for lucky survivor and gas phase protonation: the unified MALDI analyte protonation mechanism. *J. Am. Soc. Mass Spectrom.* 22: 976–988.

38 Glückmann, M., Pfenninger, A., Krüger, R. et al. (2001). Mechanisms in MALDI analysis: surface interaction or incorporation of analytes. *Int. J. Mass Spectrom.* 210, 211: 121–132.

39 Van Nuffel, S., Elie, N., Yang, E. et al. (2018). Insights into the MALDI process after matrix deposition by sublimation using 3D TOF-SIMS imaging. *Anal. Chem.* 90: 1907–1914.

40 Thomas, A. and Chaurand, P. (2014). Advances in tissue section preparation for MALDI imaging MS. *Bioanalysis* 6: 967–982.

41 Bouschen, W., Schulz, O., Eikel, D., and Spengler, B. (2010). Matrix vapor deposition/recrystallization and dedicated spray preparation for high-resolution scanning microprobe matrix-assisted laser desorption/ionization imaging mass spectrometry (SMALDI-MS) of tissue and single cells. *Rapid Commun. Mass Spectrom.* 24: 355–364.

42 Tressler, C., Tilley, S., Yang, E. et al. (2021). Factorial design to optimize matrix spraying parameters for MALDI mass spectrometry imaging. *J. Am. Soc. Mass Spectrom.* 32: 2728–2737.

43 Murphy, R.C., Hankin, J.A., Barkley, R.M., and Zemski Berry, K.A. (1811). MALDI imaging of lipids after matrix sublimation/deposition. *Biochim. Biophys. Acta, Mol. Cell. Biol. Lipids* 2011: 970–975.

44 Yang, J. and Caprioli, R.M. (2011). Matrix sublimation/recrystallization for imaging proteins by mass spectrometry at high spatial resolution. *Anal. Chem.* 83: 5728–5734.

45 Perry, W.J., Patterson, N.H., Prentice, B.M. et al. (2020). Uncovering matrix effects on lipid analyses in MALDI imaging mass spectrometry experiments. *J. Mass Spectrom.* 55: e4491.

46 Leopold, J., Popkova, Y., Engel, K.M., and Schiller, J. (2018). Recent developments of useful MALDI matrices for the mass spectrometric characterization of lipids. *Biomolecules* 8: 173.

47 Ogrinc Potočnik, N., Porta, T., Becker, M. et al. (2015). Use of advantageous, volatile matrices enabled by next-generation high-speed matrix-assisted laser desorption/ionization time-of-flight imaging employing a scanning laser beam. *Rapid Commun. Mass Spectrom.* 29: 2195–2203.

48 Niehaus, M., Soltwisch, J., Belov, M.E., and Dreisewerd, K. (2019). Transmission-mode MALDI-2 mass spectrometry imaging of cells and tissues at subcellular resolution. *Nat. Methods* 16: 925–931.

49 Bowman, A.P., Blakney, G.T., Hendrickson, C.L. et al. (2020). Ultra-high mass resolving power, mass accuracy, and dynamic range MALDI mass spectrometry imaging by 21-T FT-ICR MS. *Anal. Chem.* 92: 3133–3142.

50 Soltwisch, J., Kettling, H., Vens-Cappell, S. et al. (2015). Mass spectrometry imaging with laser-induced postionization. *Science* 348: 211–215.

51 Potthoff, A., Dreisewerd, K., and Soltwisch, J. (2020). Detailed characterization of the postionization efficiencies in MALDI-2 as a function of relevant input parameters. *J. Am. Soc. Mass Spectrom.* 31: 1844–1853.

52 Bowman, A.P., Bogie, J.F.J., Hendriks, J.J.A. et al. (2020). Evaluation of lipid coverage and high spatial resolution MALDI-imaging capabilities of oversampling combined with laser post-ionisation. *Anal. Bioanal. Chem.* 412: 2277–2289.

53 Elia, E.A., Niehaus, M., Steven, R.T. et al. (2020). Atmospheric pressure MALDI mass spectrometry imaging using in-line plasma induced postionization. *Anal. Chem.* 92: 15285–15290.

54 Kompauer, M., Heiles, S., and Spengler, B. (2017). Atmospheric pressure MALDI mass spectrometry imaging of tissues and cells at 1.4-mm lateral resolution. *Nat. Methods* 14: 90–96.

55 Paine, M.R.L., Liu, J., Huang, D. et al. (2019). Three-dimensional mass spectrometry imaging identifies lipid markers of medulloblastoma metastasis. *Sci. Rep.* 9: 2205.

56 Khalil, S.M., Römpp, A., Pretzel, J. et al. (2015). Phospholipid topography of whole-body sections of the *Anopheles stephensi* mosquito, characterized by high-resolution atmospheric-pressure scanning microprobe matrix-assisted laser desorption/ionization mass spectrometry imaging. *Anal. Chem.* 87: 11309–11316.

57 Zemski Berry, K.A., Hankin, J.A., Barkley, R.M. et al. (2011). MALDI imaging of lipid biochemistry in tissues by mass spectrometry. *Chem. Rev.* 111: 6491–6512.

58 Bowman, A.P., Heeren, R.M.A., and Ellis, S.R. (2019). Advances in mass spectrometry imaging enabling observation of localised lipid biochemistry within tissues. *Trends Anal. Chem.* 120, 115197.

59 Sämfors, S. and Fletcher, J.S. (2020). Lipid diversity in cells and tissue using imaging SIMS. *Annu. Rev. Anal. Chem.* 13: 249–271.

60 Touboul, D., Kollmer, F., Niehuis, E. et al. (2005). Improvement of biological time-of-flight-secondary ion mass spectrometry imaging with a bismuth cluster ion source. *J. Am. Soc. Mass Spectrom.* 16: 1608–1618.

61 Ostrowski, S.G., Bell, C.T.V., Winograd, N., and Ewing, A.G. (2004). Mass spectrometric imaging of highly curved membranes during *Tetrahymena* mating. *Science* 305: 71–73.

62 Altelaar, A.F.M., Klinkert, I., Jalink, K. et al. (2006). Gold-enhanced biomolecular surface imaging of cells and tissue by SIMS and MALDI mass spectrometry. *Anal. Chem.* 78: 734–742.

63 Svara, F.N., Kiss, A., Jaskolla, T.W. et al. (2011). High-reactivity matrices increase the sensitivity of matrix enhanced secondary ion mass spectrometry. *Anal. Chem.* 83: 8308–8313.

64 Wong, S.C.C., Hill, R., Blenkinsopp, P. et al. (2003). Development of a C_{60}^+ ion gun for static SIMS and chemical imaging. *Appl. Surf. Sci.* 203, 204: 219–222.

65 Bich, C., Touboul, D., and Brunelle, A. (2014). Cluster TOF–SIMS imaging as a tool for micrometric histology of lipids in tissue. *Mass Spectrom. Rev.* 33: 442–451.

66 Tian, H., Six, D.A., Krucker, T. et al. (2017). Subcellular chemical imaging of antibiotics in single bacteria using C_{60}-secondary ion mass spectrometry. *Anal. Chem.* 89: 5050–5057.

67 Winograd, N. (2018). Gas cluster ion beams for secondary ion mass spectrometry. *Annu. Rev. Anal. Chem.* 11: 29–48.

68 Tian, H., Sparvero, L.J., Anthonymuthu, T.S. et al. (2021). Successive high-resolution (H_2O)N-GCIB and C_{60}-SIMS imaging integrates multi-omics in different cell types in breast cancer tissue. *Anal. Chem.* 93: 8143–8151.

69 Angerer, T.B., Blenkinsopp, P., and Fletcher, J.S. (2015). High energy gas cluster ions for organic and biological analysis by time-of-flight secondary ion mass spectrometry. *Int. J. Mass Spectrom.* 377: 591–598.

70 Tian, H., Sparvero, L.J., Blenkinsopp, P. et al. (2019). Secondary-ion mass spectrometry images cardiolipins and phosphatidylethanolamines at the subcellular level. *Angew. Chem.* 58: 3156–3161.

71 Angerer, T.B., Magnusson, Y., Landberg, G., and Fletcher, J.S. (2016). Lipid heterogeneity resulting from fatty acid processing in the human breast cancer microenvironment identified by GCIB-TOF-SIMS imaging. *Anal. Chem.* 88: 11946–11954.

72 Sparvero, L.J., Tian, H., Amoscato, A.A. et al. (2021). Direct mapping of phospholipid ferroptotic death signals in cells and tissues by gas cluster ion beam secondary ion mass spectrometry (GCIB-SIMS). *Angew. Chem. Int. Ed.* 60: 11784–11788.

73 Dimovska Nilsson, K., Neittaanmäki, N., Zaar, O. et al. (2020). TOF-SIMS imaging reveals tumor heterogeneity and inflammatory response markers in the microenvironment of basal cell carcinoma. *Biointerphases* 15: 041012.

74 Angerer, T.B., Chakravarty, N., Taylor, M.J. et al. (2019). Insights into the histology of planarian flatworm *Phagocata gracilis* based on location specific, intact lipid information provided by GCIB-ToF-SIMS imaging. *Biochim. Biophys. Acta, Mol. Cell. Biol. Lipids* 1864: 733–743.

75 Sämfors, S., Ståhlman, M., Klevstig, M. et al. (2019). Localised lipid accumulation detected in infarcted mouse heart tissue using TOF-SIMS. *Int. J. Mass Spectrom.* 437: 77–86.

76 Passarelli, M.K., Pirkl, A., Moellers, R. et al. (2017). The 3D Orbisims – label-free metabolic imaging with subcellular lateral resolution and high mass-resolving power. *Nat. Methods* 14: 1175–1183.

77 Smith, D.F., Robinson, E.W., Tolmachev, A.V. et al. (2011). C_{60} secondary ion Fourier transform ion cyclotron resonance mass spectrometry. *Anal. Chem.* 83: 9552–9556.

78 Fletcher, J.S., Rabbani, S., Henderson, A. et al. (2008). A new dynamic in mass spectral imaging of single biological cells. *Anal. Chem.* 80: 9058–9064.

79 Dimovska Nilsson, K., Palm, M., Hood, J. et al. (2019). Chemical changes on, and through, the bacterial envelope in *Escherichia coli* mutants exhibiting impaired plasmid transfer identified using time-of-flight secondary ion mass spectrometry. *Anal. Chem.* 91: 11355–11361.

80 Fletcher, J.S. (2015). Latest applications of 3D TOF-SIMS bio-imaging. *Biointerphases* 10: 018902.

81 Nuñez, J., Renslow, R., Cliff, J.B., and Anderton, C.R. (2017). NanoSIMS for biological applications: current practices and analyses. *Biointerphases* 13: 03B301.

82 Frisz, J.F., Klitzing, H.A., Lou, K. et al. (2013). Sphingolipid domains in the plasma membranes of fibroblasts are not enriched with cholesterol. *J. Biol. Chem.* 288: 16855–16861.

83 He, C., Weston, T.A., Jung, R.S. et al. (2018). NanoSIMS analysis of intravascular lipolysis and lipid movement across capillaries and into cardiomyocytes. *Cell Metabol.* 27: 1055–1066.e1053.

84 Takáts, Z., Wiseman, J.M., Gologan, B., and Cooks, R.G. (2004). Mass spectrometry sampling under ambient conditions with desorption electrospray ionization. *Science* 306: 471–473.

85 Costa, A.B. and Graham Cooks, R. (2008). Simulated splashes: elucidating the mechanism of desorption electrospray ionization mass spectrometry. *Chem. Phys. Lett.* 464: 1–8.

86 Eberlin, L.S., Ferreira, C.R., Dill, A.L. et al. (2011). Nondestructive, histologically compatible tissue imaging by desorption electrospray ionization mass spectrometry. *ChemBioChem* 12: 2129–2132.

87 Tillner, J., Wu, V., Jones, E.A. et al. (2017). Faster, more reproducible DESI-MS for biological tissue imaging. *J. Am. Soc. Mass Spectrom.* 28: 2090–2098.

88 Eberlin, L.S., Ferreira, C.R., Dill, A.L. et al. (2011). Desorption electrospray ionization mass spectrometry for lipid characterization and biological tissue imaging. *Biochim. Biophys. Acta, Mol. Cell. Biol. Lipids* 1811: 946–960.

89 Ellis, S.R., Brown, S.H., in het Panhuis, M. et al. (2013). Surface analysis of lipids by mass spectrometry: more than just imaging. *Prog. Lipid Res.* 52: 329–353.

90 Abbassi-Ghadi, N., Jones, E.A., Gomez-Romero, M. et al. (2016). A comparison of DESI-MS and LC-MS for the lipidomic profiling of human cancer tissue. *J. Am. Soc. Mass Spectrom.* 27: 255–264.

91 Fernández, R., Carriel, V., Lage, S. et al. (2016). Deciphering the lipid architecture of the rat sciatic nerve using imaging mass spectrometry. *ACS Chem. Neurosci.* 7: 624–632.

92 Sato, T., Horikawa, M., Takei, S. et al. (2019). Preferential incorporation of administered eicosapentaenoic acid into thin-cap atherosclerotic plaques. *Atertio. Thromb. Vasc. Biol.* 39: 1802–1816.

93 Woolman, M., Katz, L., Gopinath, G. et al. (2021). Mass spectrometry imaging reveals a gradient of cancer-like metabolic states in the vicinity of cancer not seen in morphometric margins from microscopy. *Anal. Chem.* 93: 4408–4416.

94 Jarmusch, A.K., Pirro, V., Baird, Z. et al. (2016). Lipid and metabolite profiles of human brain tumors by desorption electrospray ionization-MS. *Proc. Natl. Acad. Sci. U.S.A.* 113: 1486.

95 Eberlin, L.S., Norton, I., Dill, A.L. et al. (2012). Classifying human brain tumors by lipid imaging with mass spectrometry. *Cancer Res.* 72: 645.

96 Santoro, A.L., Drummond, R.D., Silva, I.T. et al. (2020). In situ DESI-MSI lipidomic profiles of breast cancer molecular subtypes and precursor lesions. *Cancer Res.* 80: 1246.

97 Sans, M., Gharpure, K., Tibshirani, R. et al. (2017). Metabolic markers and statistical prediction of serous ovarian cancer aggressiveness by ambient ionization mass spectrometry imaging. *Cancer Res.* 77: 2903.

98 Dória, M.L., McKenzie, J.S., Mroz, A. et al. (2016). Epithelial ovarian carcinoma diagnosis by desorption electrospray ionization mass spectrometry imaging. *Sci. Rep.* 6: 39219.

99 Paine, M.R.L., Kim, J., Bennett, R.V. et al. (2016). Whole reproductive system non-negative matrix factorization mass spectrometry imaging of an early-stage ovarian cancer mouse model. *PLoS One* 11: e0154837.

100 Gerbig, S., Golf, O., Balog, J. et al. (2012). Analysis of colorectal adenocarcinoma tissue by desorption electrospray ionization mass spectrometric imaging. *Anal. Bioanal. Chem.* 403: 2315–2325.

101 Veselkov, K.A., Mirnezami, R., Strittmatter, N. et al. (2014). Chemo-informatic strategy for imaging mass spectrometry-based hyperspectral profiling of lipid signatures in colorectal cancer. *Proc. Natl. Acad. Sci. U.S.A.* 111: 1216.

102 Henderson, F., Jones, E., Denbigh, J. et al. (2020). 3D DESI-MS lipid imaging in a xenograft model of glioblastoma: a proof of principle. *Sci. Rep.* 10: 16512.

103 Inglese, P., McKenzie, J.S., Mroz, A. et al. (2017). Deep learning and 3D-DESI imaging reveal the hidden metabolic heterogeneity of cancer. *Chem. Sci.* 8: 3500–3511.

104 Nemes, P. and Vertes, A. (2007). Laser ablation electrospray ionization for atmospheric pressure, in vivo, and imaging mass spectrometry. *Anal. Chem.* 79: 8098–8106.

105 Robichaud, G., Barry, J.A., and Muddiman, D.C. (2014). IR-MALDESI mass spectrometry imaging of biological tissue sections using ice as a matrix. *J. Am. Soc. Mass Spectrom.* 25: 319–328.

106 Bokhart, M.T., Manni, J., Garrard, K.P. et al. (2017). IR-MALDESI mass spectrometry imaging at 50 micron spatial resolution. *J. Am. Soc. Mass Spectrom.* 28: 2099–2107.

107 Stopka, S.A., Samarah, L.Z., Shaw, J.B. et al. (2019). Ambient metabolic profiling and imaging of biological samples with ultrahigh molecular resolution using laser ablation electrospray ionization 21 Tesla FTICR mass spectrometry. *Anal. Chem.* 91: 5028–5035.

108 Bartels, B. and Svatoš, A. (2015). Spatially resolved in vivo plant metabolomics by laser ablation-based mass spectrometry imaging (MSI) techniques: LDI-MSI and LAESI. *Front. Plant Sci.* 6: 471.

109 Nazari, M. and Muddiman, D.C. (2016). Polarity switching mass spectrometry imaging of healthy and cancerous hen ovarian tissue sections by infrared matrix-assisted laser desorption electrospray ionization (IR-MALDESI). *Analyst* 141: 595–605.

110 Knuth, M.M., Stutts, W.L., Ritter, M.M. et al. (2021). Vitamin D deficiency promotes accumulation of bioactive lipids and increased endocannabinoid tone in zebrafish. *J. Lipid Res.* 62: 100142.

111 Barry, J.A., Groseclose, M.R., Robichaud, G. et al. (2015). Assessing drug and metabolite detection in liver tissue by UV-MALDI and IR-MALDESI mass spectrometry imaging coupled to FT-ICR MS. *Int. J. Mass Spectrom.* 377: 448–455.

112 Loziuk, P., Meier, F., Johnson, C. et al. (2016). Transomic analysis of forebrain sections in Sp_2 conditional knockout embryonic mice using IR-MALDESI imaging of lipids and LC–MS/MS label-free proteomics. *Anal. Bioanal. Chem.* 408: 3453–3474.

113 Bai, H., Linder, K.E., and Muddiman, D.C. (2021). Three-dimensional (3D) imaging of lipids in skin tissues with infrared matrix-assisted laser desorption electrospray ionization (MALDESI) mass spectrometry. *Anal. Bioanal. Chem.* 413: 2793–2801.

114 Meier, F., Garrard, K.P., and Muddiman, D.C. (2014). Silver dopants for targeted and untargeted direct analysis of unsaturated lipids via infrared matrix-assisted laser desorption electrospray ionization (IR-MALDESI). *Rapid Commun. Mass Spectrom.* 28: 2461–2470.

115 Lanekoff, I., Heath, B.S., Liyu, A. et al. (2012). Automated platform for high-resolution tissue imaging using nanospray desorption electrospray ionization mass spectrometry. *Anal. Chem.* 84: 8351–8356.

116 Yin, R., Kyle, J., Burnum-Johnson, K. et al. (2018). High spatial resolution imaging of mouse pancreatic islets using nanospray desorption electrospray ionization mass spectrometry. *Anal. Chem.* 90: 6548–6555.

117 Nguyen, S.N., Kyle, J.E., Dautel, S.E. et al. (2019). Lipid coverage in nanospray desorption electrospray ionization mass spectrometry imaging of mouse lung tissues. *Anal. Chem.* 91: 11629–11635.

118 Unsihuay, D., Qiu, J., Swaroop, S. et al. (2020). Imaging of triglycerides in tissues using nanospray desorption electrospray ionization (Nano-DESI) mass spectrometry. *Int. J. Mass Spectrom.* 448: 116269.

119 Rivera, E.S., Djambazova, K.V., Neumann, E.K. et al. (2020). Integrating ion mobility and imaging mass spectrometry for comprehensive analysis of biological tissues: a brief review and perspective. *J. Mass Spectrom.* 55: e4614.

120 Sans, M., Feider, C.L., and Eberlin, L.S. (2018). Advances in mass spectrometry imaging coupled to ion mobility spectrometry for enhanced imaging of biological tissues. *Curr. Opin. Chem. Biol.* 42: 138–146.

121 Djambazova, K.V., Klein, D.R., Migas, L.G. et al. (2020). Resolving the complexity of spatial lipidomics using MALDI TIMS imaging mass spectrometry. *Anal. Chem.* 92: 13290–13297.

122 Fu, T., Oetjen, J., Chapelle, M. et al. (2020). In situ isobaric lipid mapping by MALDI–ion mobility separation–mass spectrometry imaging. *J. Mass Spectrom.* 55: e4531.

123 Soltwisch, J., Heijs, B., Koch, A. et al. (2020). MALDI-2 on a trapped ion mobility quadrupole time-of-flight instrument for rapid mass spectrometry imaging and ion mobility separation of complex lipid profiles. *Anal. Chem.* 92: 8697–8703.

124 Škrášková, K., Claude, E., Jones, E.A. et al. (2016). Enhanced capabilities for imaging gangliosides in murine brain with matrix-assisted laser desorption/

ionization and desorption electrospray ionization mass spectrometry coupled to ion mobility separation. *Methods* 104: 69–78.

125 Feider, C.L., Elizondo, N., and Eberlin, L.S. (2016). Ambient ionization and FAIMS mass spectrometry for enhanced imaging of multiply charged molecular ions in biological tissues. *Anal. Chem.* 88: 11533–11541.

126 Unsihuay, D., Yin, R., Sanchez, D.M. et al. (2021). High-resolution imaging and identification of biomolecules using nano-DESI coupled to ion mobility spectrometry. *Anal. Chim. Acta* 1186: 339085.

127 Ekelöf, M., Dodds, J., Khodjaniyazova, S. et al. (2020). Coupling IR-MALDESI with drift tube ion mobility-mass spectrometry for high-throughput screening and imaging applications. *J. Am. Soc. Mass Spectrom.* 31: 642–650.

128 Zhou, Z., Tu, J., Xiong, X. et al. (2017). Lipidccs: prediction of collision cross-section values for lipids with high precision to support ion mobility–mass spectrometry-based lipidomics. *Anal. Chem.* 89: 9559–9566.

129 Leaptrot, K.L., May, J.C., Dodds, J.N., and McLean, J.A. (2019). Ion mobility conformational lipid atlas for high confidence lipidomics. *Nat. Commun.* 10: 985.

130 Picache, J.A., Rose, B.S., Balinski, A. et al. (2019). Collision cross section compendium to annotate and predict multi-omic compound identities. *Chem. Sci.* 10: 983–993.

131 Zhou, Z., Luo, M., Chen, X. et al. (2020). Ion mobility collision cross-section atlas for known and unknown metabolite annotation in untargeted metabolomics. *Nat. Commun.* 11: 4334.

132 Liu, C., Qi, K., Yao, L. et al. (2019). Imaging of polar and nonpolar species using compact desorption electrospray ionization/postphotoionization mass spectrometry. *Anal. Chem.* 91: 6616–6623.

133 Zhou, Q., Fülöp, A., and Hopf, C. (2021). Recent developments of novel matrices and on-tissue chemical derivatization reagents for MALDI-MSI. *Anal. Bioanal. Chem.* 413: 2599–2617.

134 Shimma, S., Kumada, H.-O., Taniguchi, H. et al. (2016). Microscopic visualization of testosterone in mouse testis by use of imaging mass spectrometry. *Anal. Bioanal. Chem.* 408: 7607–7615.

135 Cobice, D.F., Livingstone, D.E.W., Mackay, C.L. et al. (2016). Spatial localization and quantitation of androgens in mouse testis by mass spectrometry imaging. *Anal. Chem.* 88: 10362–10367.

136 Cobice, D.F., Mackay, C.L., Goodwin, R.J.A. et al. (2013). Mass spectrometry imaging for dissecting steroid intracrinology within target tissues. *Anal. Chem.* 85: 11576–11584.

137 Angelini, R., Yutuc, E., Wyatt, M.F. et al. (2021). Visualizing cholesterol in the brain by on-tissue derivatization and quantitative mass spectrometry imaging. *Anal. Chem.* 93: 4932–4943.

138 Iwama, T., Kano, K., Saigusa, D. et al. (2021). Development of an on-tissue derivatization method for MALDI mass spectrometry imaging of bioactive lipids containing phosphate monoester using phos-tag. *Anal. Chem.* 93: 3867–3875.

139 Wu, Q., Comi, T.J., Li, B. et al. (2016). On-tissue derivatization via electrospray deposition for matrix-assisted laser desorption/ionization mass spectrometry imaging of endogenous fatty acids in rat brain tissues. *Anal. Chem.* 88: 5988–5995.

140 Wu, C., Ifa, D.R., Manicke, N.E., and Cooks, R.G. (2009). Rapid, direct analysis of cholesterol by charge labeling in reactive desorption electrospray ionization. *Anal. Chem.* 81: 7618–7624.

141 Lostun, D., Perez, C.J., Licence, P. et al. (2015). Reactive DESI-MS imaging of biological tissues with dicationic ion-pairing compounds. *Anal. Chem.* 87: 3286–3293.

142 Tobias, F. and Hummon, A.B. (2020). Considerations for MALDI-based quantitative mass spectrometry imaging studies. *J. Proteome Res.* 19: 3620–3630.

143 Ellis, S.R., Bruinen, A.L., and Heeren, R.M.A. (2014). A critical evaluation of the current state-of-the-art in quantitative imaging mass spectrometry. *Anal. Bioanal. Chem.* 406: 1275–1289.

144 Groseclose, M.R. and Castellino, S. (2013). A mimetic tissue model for the quantification of drug distributions by MALDI imaging mass spectrometry. *Anal. Chem.* 85: 10099–10106.

145 Jadoul, L., Longuespée, R., Noël, A., and De Pauw, E. (2015). A spiked tissue-based approach for quantification of phosphatidylcholines in brain section by MALDI mass spectrometry imaging. *Anal. Bioanal. Chem.* 407: 2095–2106.

146 Eiersbrock, F.B., Orthen, J.M., and Soltwisch, J. (2020). Validation of MALDI-MS imaging data of selected membrane lipids in murine brain with and without laser postionization by quantitative nano-HPLC-MS using laser microdissection. *Anal. Bioanal. Chem.* 412: 6875–6886.

147 Lanekoff, I., Thomas, M., and Laskin, J. (2014). Shotgun approach for quantitative imaging of phospholipids using nanospray desorption electrospray ionization mass spectrometry. *Anal. Chem.* 86: 1872–1880.

148 Duncan, K.D., Fang, R., Yuan, J. et al. (2018). Quantitative mass spectrometry imaging of prostaglandins as silver ion adducts with nanospray desorption electrospray ionization. *Anal. Chem.* 90: 7246–7252.

149 Hankin, J.A., Farias, S.E., Barkley, R.M. et al. (2011). MALDI mass spectrometric imaging of lipids in rat brain injury models. *J. Am. Soc. Mass Spectrom.* 22.

150 Mulder, I.A., Ogrinc Potočnik, N., Broos, L.A.M. et al. (2019). Distinguishing core from Penumbra by lipid profiles using mass spectrometry imaging in a transgenic mouse model of ischemic stroke. *Sci. Rep.* 9: 1090.

151 Janfelt, C., Wellner, N., Leger, P.-L. et al. (2012). Visualization by mass spectrometry of 2-dimensional changes in rat brain lipids, including *N*-acylphosphatidylethanolamines, during neonatal brain ischemia. *FASEB J.* 26: 2667–2673.

152 Ellis, S.R., Cappell, J., Potočnik, N.O. et al. (2016). More from less: high-throughput dual polarity lipid imaging of biological tissues. *Analyst* 141: 3832–3841.

153 Kaya, I., Jennische, E., Lange, S., and Malmberg, P. (2018). Dual polarity MALDI imaging mass spectrometry on the same pixel points reveals spatial lipid localizations at high-spatial resolutions in rat small intestine. *Anal. Methods* 10: 2428–2435.

154 Dexter, A., Steven, R.T., Patel, A. et al. (2019). Imaging drugs, metabolites and biomarkers in rodent lung: a DESI MS strategy for the evaluation of drug-induced lipidosis. *Anal. Bioanal. Chem.* 411: 8023–8032.

155 Korte, A.R. and Lee, Y.J. (2013). Multiplex mass spectrometric imaging with polarity switching for concurrent acquisition of positive and negative ion images. *J. Am. Soc. Mass Spectrom.* 24: 949–955.

156 Lamont, L., Eijkel, G.B., Jones, E.A. et al. (2018). Targeted drug and metabolite imaging: desorption electrospray ionization combined with triple quadrupole mass spectrometry. *Anal. Chem.* 90: 13229–13235.

157 Gathungu, R.M., Larrea, P., Sniatynski, M.J. et al. (2018). Optimization of electrospray ionization source parameters for lipidomics to reduce misannotation of in-source fragments as precursor ions. *Anal. Chem.* 90: 13523–13532.

158 Hu, C., Luo, W., Xu, J., and Han, X. (2022). Recognition and avoidance of ion source-generated artifacts in lipidomics analysis. *Mass Spectrom. Rev.* 41: 15–31.

159 Ellis, S.R., Soltwisch, J., Paine, M.R.L. et al. (2017). Laser post-ionisation combined with a high resolving power orbitrap mass spectrometer for enhanced MALDI-MS imaging of lipids. *Chem. Commun.* 53: 7246–7249.

160 Garate, J., Lage, S., Martín-Saiz, L. et al. (2020). Influence of lipid fragmentation in the data analysis of imaging mass spectrometry experiments. *J. Am. Soc. Mass Spectrom.* 31: 517–526.

161 Angerer, T.B., Velickovic, D., Nicora, C.D. et al. (2019). Exploiting the semidestructive nature of gas cluster ion beam time-of-flight secondary ion mass spectrometry imaging for simultaneous localization and confident lipid annotations. *Anal. Chem.* 91: 15073–15080.

162 Palmer, A., Phapale, P., Chernyavsky, I. et al. (2017). FDR-controlled metabolite annotation for high-resolution imaging mass spectrometry. *Nat. Methods* 14: 57–60.

163 Alexandrov, T., Ovchinnikova, K., Palmer, A. et al. (2019). Metaspace: a community-populated knowledge base of spatial metabolomes in health and disease. *bioRxiv* 539478. https://doi.org/10.1101/539478.

164 Ryan, E. and Reid, G.E. (2016). Chemical derivatization and ultrahigh resolution and accurate mass spectrometry strategies for "shotgun" lipidome analysis. *Acc. Chem. Res.* 49: 1596–1604.

165 Bielow, C., Mastrobuoni, G., Orioli, M., and Kempa, S. (2017). On mass ambiguities in high-resolution shotgun lipidomics. *Anal. Chem.* 89: 2986–2994.

166 Almeida, R., Pauling, J.K., Sokol, E. et al. (2015). Comprehensive lipidome analysis by shotgun lipidomics on a hybrid quadrupole-orbitrap-linear ion trap mass spectrometer. *J. Am. Soc. Mass Spectrom.* 26: 133–148.

167 Kooijman, P.C., Nagornov, K.O., Kozhinov, A.N. et al. (2019). Increased throughput and ultra-high mass resolution in DESI FT-ICR MS imaging through new-generation external data acquisition system and advanced data processing approaches. *Sci. Rep.* 9: 8.

168 Fisher, G.L., Bruinen, A.L., Ogrinc Potočnik, N. et al. (2016). A new method and mass spectrometer design for TOF-SIMS parallel imaging MS/MS. *Anal. Chem.* 88: 6433–6440.

169 Bruinen, A.L., Fisher, G.L., Balez, R. et al. (2018). Identification and high-resolution imaging of A-tocopherol from human cells to whole animals by TOF-SIMS tandem mass spectrometry. *J. Am. Soc. Mass Spectrom.* 29: 1571–1581.

170 Lanekoff, I., Burnum-Johnson, K., Thomas, M. et al. (2013). High-speed tandem mass spectrometric in situ imaging by nanospray desorption electrospray ionization mass spectrometry. *Anal. Chem.* 85: 9596–9603.

171 Hansen, R.L. and Lee, Y.J. (2017). Overlapping MALDI-mass spectrometry imaging for in-parallel MS and MS/MS data acquisition without sacrificing spatial resolution. *J. Am. Soc. Mass Spectrom.* 28: 1910–1918.

172 Ellis, S.R., Paine, M.R.L., Eijkel, G.B. et al. (2018). Automated, parallel mass spectrometry imaging and structural identification of lipids. *Nat. Methods* 15: 515–518.

173 Claes, B.S.R., Bowman, A.P., Poad, B.L.J. et al. (2021). Mass spectrometry imaging of lipids with isomer resolution using high-pressure ozone-induced dissociation. *Anal. Chem.* 93: 9826–9834.

174 Young, R.S.E., Bowman, A.P., Williams, E.D. et al. (2021). Apocryphal Fads2 activity promotes fatty acid diversification in cancer. *Cell Rep.* 34: 108738.

175 Young, R.S.E., Claes, B.S.R., Bowman, A.P. et al. (2021). Isomer-resolved imaging of prostate cancer tissues reveals specific lipid unsaturation profiles associated with lymphocytes and abnormal prostate epithelia. *Front. Endocrinol.* 12.

176 Born, M.-E.N. and Prentice, B.M. (2020). Structural elucidation of phosphatidylcholines from tissue using electron induced dissociation. *Int. J. Mass Spectrom.* 452: 116338.

177 Specker, J.T., Van Orden, S.L., Ridgeway, M.E., and Prentice, B.M. (2020). Identification of phosphatidylcholine isomers in imaging mass spectrometry using gas-phase charge inversion ion/ion reactions. *Anal. Chem.* 92: 13192–13201.

178 Bednařík, A., Bölsker, S., Soltwisch, J., and Dreisewerd, K. (2018). An on-tissue Paternò–Büchi reaction for localization of carbon–carbon double bonds in phospholipids and glycolipids by matrix-assisted laser-desorption–ionization mass-spectrometry imaging. *Angew. Chem. Int. Ed.* 57: 12092–12096.

179 Wäldchen, F., Spengler, B., and Heiles, S. (2019). Reactive matrix-assisted laser desorption/ionization mass spectrometry imaging using an intrinsically photoreactive Paternò–Büchi matrix for double-bond localization in isomeric phospholipids. *J. Am. Chem. Soc.* 141: 11816–11820.

180 Zhang, J., Guo, C., Huo, X. et al. (2021). Unsaturated lipid isomeric imaging based on the Paternò–Büchi reaction in the solid phase in ambient conditions. *Talanta* 235: 122816.

181 Unsihuay, D., Su, P., Hu, H. et al. (2021). Imaging and analysis of isomeric unsaturated lipids through online photochemical derivatization of carbon–carbon double bonds. *Angew. Chem. Int. Ed.* 60: 7559–7563.

182 Kuo, T.-H., Chung, H.-H., Chang, H.-Y. et al. (2019). Deep lipidomics and molecular imaging of unsaturated lipid isomers: a universal strategy initiated by MCPBA epoxidation. *Anal. Chem.* 91: 11905–11915.

183 Tu, A., Garrard, K.P., Said, N., and Muddiman, D.C. (2021). In situ detection of fatty acid C=C positional isomers by coupling on-tissue MCPBA epoxidation with infrared matrix-assisted laser desorption electrospray ionization mass spectrometry. *Rapid Commun. Mass Spectrom.* 35: e9119.

184 Klein, D.R., Feider, C.L., Garza, K.Y. et al. (2018). Desorption electrospray ionization coupled with ultraviolet photodissociation for characterization of phospholipid isomers in tissue sections. *Anal. Chem.* 90: 10100–10104.

185 Feider, C.L., Macias, L.A., Brodbelt, J.S., and Eberlin, L.S. (2020). Double bond characterization of free fatty acids directly from biological tissues by ultraviolet photodissociation. *Anal. Chem.* 92: 8386–8395.

6

Ion Mobility Spectrometry

Kaylie I. Kirkwood, Melanie T. Odenkirk, and Erin S. Baker

North Carolina State University, Department of Chemistry, Raleigh, NC 27695, USA
Kaylie I. Kirkwood and Melanie T. Odenkirk were Co-first authors.

6.1 Ion Mobility Spectrometry

6.1.1 Introduction

Mass spectrometry (MS)-based analyses have enabled highly comprehensive lipidomic studies, especially with recent advancements in complex sample extractions, front-end chromatography separation, fragmentation strategies, lipid standard availability, database construction, and bioinformatics tools [1–3]. However, there are still numerous analytical challenges remaining in the field of lipidomics. These challenges include the highly isomeric and isobaric nature of lipids which result in many species having the same masses, suppression of low-abundance lipid signals because of their broad endogenous concentration ranges, disparities in ionization efficiency for the diverse lipid species and classes, and difficulties in data analysis and lipid annotation [4, 5]. Thus, advanced analytical techniques such as those coupling ion mobility spectrometry (IMS) to MS platforms have been explored to enhance lipidomic measurements [6–9]. Here, we introduce the basic concepts of IMS, evaluate the capabilities and limitations of common IMS platforms, and explore novel applications utilizing IMS in multidimensional LC-IMS-MS/MS evaluations, imaging, and shotgun lipidomics.

IMS is an analytical technique that separates gas-phase ions based on their size, shape, and charge state [10, 11]. The common core principle of IMS is the separation of ions in an inert buffer gas under the influence of an electric field similar to electrophoresis. Thus, by just altering the electric field and buffer gas flow parameters, numerous different IMS techniques have been created. Several of the most common techniques include drift tube ion mobility spectrometry (DTIMS), traveling-wave ion mobility spectrometry (TWIMS), field asymmetric ion mobility spectrometry (FAIMS), trapped ion mobility spectrometry (TIMS), and differential

Mass Spectrometry for Lipidomics: Methods and Applications, First Edition.
Edited by Michal Holčapek and Kim Ekroos.
© 2023 WILEY-VCH GmbH. Published 2023 by WILEY-VCH GmbH.

mobility analyzer (DMA). The principles, advantages, and limitations of each IMS technique will be discussed in Section 6.1.2 of this chapter, except for DMA which is predominantly used for large analytes such as aerosols and antibodies [12, 13]. While standalone IMS devices have routinely been used for decades to detect illegal and dangerous substances such as explosives, growing interest in utilizing IMS for routine lipidomic analyses increased following the release of the first commercial IMS-MS platform in 2006 (Waters Synapt HDMS) [14]. Since IMS separations are rapid and typically occur in a millisecond timescale, they have been paired with numerous MS platforms. These IMS-MS measurements have both mobility and mass information for each detected ion, thereby improving the molecular characterizations and the selectivity of analyses without increasing the measurement time [10]. To date, time-of-flight mass analyzers are most commonly coupled with IMS used due to the complementary analysis times as IMS evaluations occur in milliseconds and time-of-flight (TOF) measurements microseconds (Figure 6.1) [15–17]. Furthermore, IMS separations need ions, so they have been showcased with any ionization sources that work for MS and interfaced with front-end separations such as liquid chromatography (LC) and gas chromatography (GC). The chromatography-IMS-MS analyses thus offer multidimensional characterization for each detected ion.

For lipidomic studies, IMS approaches offer many benefits including isomer separations, signal filtering, and structural characterization capabilities, all of which will be discussed further with specific examples in Section 6.1.4. While MS, fragmentation, and chromatography separations provide many advantages in separating and identifying lipid species, they fail to distinguish many lipid isomers. In these cases, IMS may be employed as a complementary separation dimension based on size and shape rather than the polarity or mass of the ion [10]. This can be especially beneficial for rapid separations where chromatography cannot be used, such as in

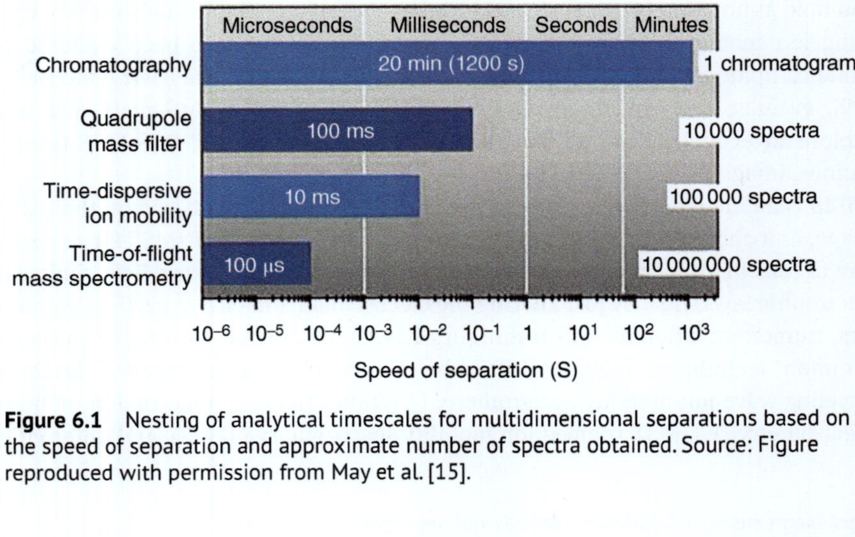

Figure 6.1 Nesting of analytical timescales for multidimensional separations based on the speed of separation and approximate number of spectra obtained. Source: Figure reproduced with permission from May et al. [15].

imaging and shotgun lipidomic experiments [18, 19]. When it comes to the annotation of both unknown and known lipids, IMS is also advantageous as the experimentally derived ion-neutral collision cross section (CCS) values can be compared to database and literature values to increase the identification confidence. The LIPID MAPS Structural Database has incorporated CCS values via the CCS Compendium originating from the McLean lab [20], and multiple lipidomic software platforms have leveraged experimentally derived and *in silico* CCS values as annotation parameters as well [21, 22]. *In silico* CCS predictions can further assist in the identification of unknown features and have shown excellent agreement with experimental CCS values [23–26]. Furthermore, mass versus mobility trendlines can aid in the classification of unknowns, as ions from the same biomolecular class fall along specific trendlines. Since IMS-MS conformational ordering is based on the relative gas-phase size of a given m/z space, where the slopes are in the order of lipids > peptides > carbohydrates > nucleotides (Figure 6.2), biomolecule class and subclass information can also be attained with IMS and MS measurements [27–29]. Computational tools are also often combined with IMS techniques and have recently been employed to infer theoretical structural information from experimental CCS values. This can be extremely useful in biological matrices where analyte concentrations are generally too low for traditional structural characterization approaches such as NMR [30].

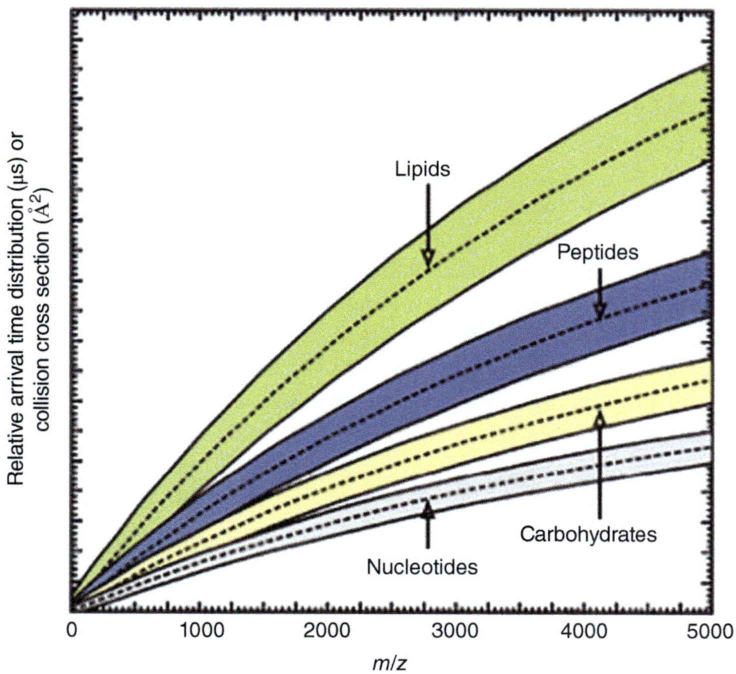

Figure 6.2 Conceptual depiction of IMS-MS conformational ordering of various biomolecular classes. Source: Figure Reproduced with permission from Fenn et al. [27].

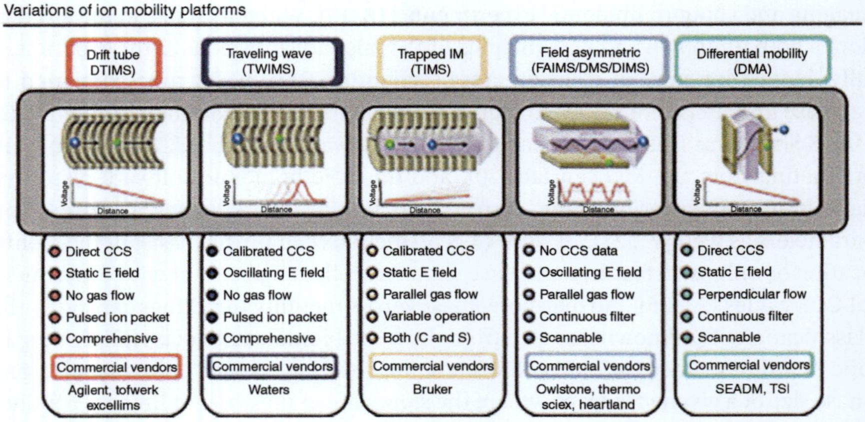

Figure 6.3 Various IMS platforms with general diagrams of the applied electric field and gas dynamics. Information on each platform's capabilities, objectives, and commercial manufacturers is illustrated below the diagrams. Source: Reproduced with permission from Dodds et al. [10].

6.1.2 Ion Mobility Spectrometry Techniques and Platforms

Multiple IMS techniques and platforms exist, which only differ in how the electric field and buffer gas flow are applied (Figure 6.3) [10]. Each technique has unique strengths, weaknesses, and traditional uses which will be explored here and further summarized in Table 6.1. Recent novel IMS techniques will also be discussed in Section 6.1.3.

6.1.2.1 Drift Tube Ion Mobility Spectrometry (DTIMS)

DTIMS is described as the classic, most conceptually simplistic IMS platform. For IMS platforms operating at low electric fields and under ideal pressure and temperature conditions like DTIMS, the arrival time of an ion is directly proportional to the size of the ion per charge state. Thus, by changing the electric field and performing separate measurements, the mobility of an ion (or K) can be directly related to the ion's velocity (v_d) as it moves through the buffer gas under an electric field (E), as illustrated in Eq. (6.1).

$$K = \frac{v_d}{E} \tag{6.1}$$

The Mason–Schamp equation (Eq. (6.2)) can then be used with DTIMS to calculate the analyte's rotationally averaged ion-neutral CCS (or Ω) from the reduced mobility (K_0) or the measured mobility at a standard temperature and pressure [31, 32]. Here, z is the charge of the ion, e is the charge of an electron, N_0 is the buffer gas density, μ is the reduced mass of the ion-neutral buffer gas pair, k_B is Boltzmann's

Table 6.1 Summary of benefits, limitations, and common uses in lipidomics for various IMS platforms.

	DTIMS	TWIMS	TIMS	FAIMS
Benefits	• CCS can be accurately calculated either directly or through calibration • Wide range of mobility coverage • Relatively high R_p at high pressures	• CCS can be calculated using calibration • Wide range of mobility coverage • Scalable to longer path lengths (higher R_p)	• CCS can be calculated using calibration • Tunable resolving power • Wide range of mobility coverage or targeted separations	• Adaptable to any mass analyzer • Targeted separations increase the S/N ratio • Works at atmospheric pressure
Limitations	• Relatively low duty cycle • Relatively low R_p at low pressure	• Requires CCS calibration • May experience ion heating leading to conformation changes	• Requires CCS calibration	• No CCS or structural information • Requires prior mobility (CV) determination
Common uses in lipidomics	• Comprehensive, untargeted analysis • Isomer separations • Structural analysis • Lipid class CCS trendlines	• Comprehensive, untargeted analysis • Isomer separations (with cyclic or SLIM devices) • Lipid class CCS trendlines	• Isomer separations • Tandem IMS	• Signal filtering for targeted analysis • Isomer separations • Lipid class CV trendlines

constant, T is the temperature, and Ω is the momentum transfer integral commonly termed CCS.

$$\Omega = \frac{3ze}{16N_0}\left(\frac{2\pi}{\mu k_B T}\right)^{1/2}\frac{1}{K_0} \tag{6.2}$$

Because of these relationships, DTIMS is the only IMS instrument (apart from DMA) where CCS values can be directly calculated from an ion's mobility (K), whereas other platforms require prior calibration using ions with CCS values previously characterized using DTIMS instruments. DTIMS is therefore a powerful and commonly used platform for small and large molecules [29, 33, 34]. The most common commercial DTIMS-MS platform is the Agilent 6560 IM-QTOF, and other commercial vendors of DTIMS instruments include TofWerk and Excellims [10].

In DTIMS experiments, ions are introduced into a drift tube under the influence of a weak uniform electric field, typically tens of V/cm, which propels the ions in the direction of the mass analyzer. There, the analytes are introduced to a drift tube filled with a buffer gas, typically nitrogen or helium, which has no directional flow. This results in a series of ion collisions with the buffer gas as ions progress through the drift cell. The time an ion takes to traverse the drift tube, known as drift time, is directly linked to the ion's mobility, *K*, and therefore its size (CCS). Larger, more extended ions experience more collisions with the buffer gas than compact ions; thus, larger analytes have a higher drift time and larger CCS value [29]. DTIMS experiments are performed under the low field limit, where the ratio of E/N is small due to the weak electric field. Therefore, the ability to directly calculate CCS arises from the assumption that the drift velocity is small relative to the thermal velocity of collision gas molecules, resulting in effective collisions that reduce mobility with respect to analyte size and shape [35].

While DTIMS can directly provide CCS values via a multifield or stepped-field method where data are collected over multiple time periods, each with an increased electric field strength, DTIMS experiments can also be performed in a CCS-calibrated mode known as the single-field method [36]. This allows drift time measurements to be made on the chromatographic timescale while still giving highly accurate and reproducible CCS values [37]. An interlaboratory study has demonstrated high reproducibility of CCS values that average 0.5% and 0.3% RSD for single-field and stepped-field approaches, respectively [37]. Depending on operating pressure, DTIMS also affords a relatively high resolving power (R_p) of up to 100 CCS/ΔCCS [11, 38]. However, the conventional operation of DTIMS at low pressures typically only achieves R_p of 50–60 [39]. DTIMS and TWIMS are time-dispersive instruments; therefore, both instruments generate a drift or arrival time spectrum with all ions traveling along a similar path under the same conditions. This is a comprehensive approach, whereby analysis is conducted without specific molecular targets, analogous to untargeted MS experiments [15]. As DTIMS devices analyze single ion pulses and may contain ion funnels with small apertures, they can suffer from low ion transmission and limitations in duty cycle, or the percentage of ions detected relative to those generated by the ionization source, which can be as low as 6% [10]. An increasingly common method to improve the duty cycle and DTIMS measurement sensitivity utilizes multiplexing strategies to pulse multiple ion packets into the drift tube at defined intervals within a single acquisition scan. Subsequent signals can be deconvoluted using transformation schemes such as Hadamard transform to correct their arrival times, increasing the duty cycle to up to 50% [40, 41]. Multiplexing IMS experiments are further discussed in Section 6.1.3.4.

6.1.2.2 Traveling-Wave Ion Mobility Spectrometry (TWIMS)

TWIMS platforms are schematically similar to DTIMS devices where an applied voltage drives ion motion through a stationary buffer gas surrounded by a series of ring electrodes [42]. TWIMS also employs the same time-dispersive, comprehensive approach as DTIMS [15]. However, TWIMS devices provide an oscillating electrodynamic field instead of a uniform electric field to produce a set of traveling voltage waves to push the ions through the buffer gas. A combination of radio frequency (RF) and direct current (DC) voltages is leveraged, where RF confinement radially focuses the ion packet to limit ion diffusion, and application of DC voltage to each electrode propels the ions axially in the direction of the mass analyzer by creating a wave in which the ions "surf" on [43]. Here, mobility separations are based on how each ion experiences the traveling waves and is measured as an arrival time, where higher mobility ions are carried by the wave and smaller, low-mobility ions can keep up with the waves, more frequently leading to shorter arrival times [44, 45].

The commercialization of a TWIMS-MS instrument (Synapt HDMS, currently G2-Si) in 2006 by Waters Corporation began the popularization of IMS-MS for routine analyses, and TWIMS remains a popular IMS technique. Currently, TWIMS and DTIMS platforms are the most common IMS-MS instruments for small-molecule analyses [16]. TWIMS devices operate under the low-field limit, indicating that they can be utilized to calculate the CCS values. However, due to the oscillating electric field, the direct relationship between K and CCS is not applicable. This necessitates the use of calibrant ions with well-characterized CCS values to calculate the analyte's CCS values from their arrival times. While polyalanine was traditionally used for TWIMS calibration, the importance of using calibrant ions with similar physical and chemical properties to the analytes of interest has been demonstrated. For example, the use of peptide calibrant ions when calculating lipid CCS values has been shown to introduce a significant error [46–48]. A benefit of TWIMS devices is the low amount of ion loss (i.e. higher duty cycle and sensitivity) relative to DTIMS as a result of the RF confinement. Another benefit is the low-voltage requirement due to constant wave heights; therefore, TWIMS devices are easily coupled to the existing instruments and scalable to longer path lengths for increased resolution. Traditional path lengths have relatively low R_p compared to DTIMS; however, newer designs such as the cyclic IMS platform from Waters Corporation and the Structures for Lossless Manipulations (SLIM) device recently commercialized by MOBILion Systems can give an extremely high R_p of >400 [49–52]. Further elaboration on cyclic IMS and SLIM separations is presented in Section 6.1.3.

6.1.2.3 Trapped Ion Mobility Spectrometry (TIMS)

TIMS is a relatively new form of IMS, which was first commercialized by Bruker Daltonics in 2017 as a timsTOF platform. Unlike DTIMS and TWIMS which have stationary buffer gases, TIMS devices leverage an opposing electric field and buffer gas flow to trap and accumulate ions [53]. Larger ions require a higher field strength to counterbalance the drag force from the buffer gas; therefore, they are trapped closer to the exit funnel (further along the electric field gradient) than smaller ions. Once the chosen accumulation time has been reached, the field strength is slowly decreased to eject ions of specific mobilities through the exit funnel to the mass analyzer from largest to smallest size [54, 55]. Thus, rather than the previously discussed comprehensive methods where all ions can be observed using the same experimental conditions, TIMS platforms take a scanning or fingerprinting approach similar to a quadrupole that requires changing the experimental parameters to elute ions of specified mobilities [56]. TIMS is similar to TWIMS with regard to CCS calculations, as it is also below the low-field limit, but K is not empirically related to CCS; thus, it is calibrated with ions of known CCS prior to collecting the experimental data. TIMS platforms offer tunable selectivity based on the experimental objective, where slower scanning (increasing ramp time and narrowing mobility range) offers higher selectivity with up to 200 R_p [57]. However, the higher R_p values lead to a decreased duty cycle and increased timescale of IMS measurements to the point where it can no longer be coupled to chromatographic separations. Thus, faster scanning rates give lower R_p but may be better suited for untargeted measurements [10].

6.1.2.4 Field Asymmetric Ion Mobility Spectrometry (FAIMS)

FAIMS, as well as differential mobility spectrometry (DMS) and differential ion mobility spectrometry (DIMS), are small atmospheric pressure (AP) IMS devices that differ only in the geometry of their electrodes. FAIMS and similar devices (referred to from hereon as FAIMS) are typically placed directly after the ionization source rather than within the vacuum region of the instrument [58]. Here, they are utilized as mobility filters often following chromatographic separations, analogous to quadrupole mass filters used to increase the selectivity and peak capacity by filtering out interferences and separating analytes of interest. FAIMS devices are composed of two electrodes across which an electric field is applied with buffer gas flow toward the mass analyzer [59]. Both dispersion and compensation voltages (CVs) are used to achieve mobility separations, where the dispersion voltage is an alternating asymmetric waveform with short durations of high-field portions and longer durations of low-field portions. Thus, an equal (voltage × time) product is rendered for each part of the waveform. The mobility of ions changes under high- (>5000 V/s) and low-field (<200 V/s) conditions, which causes the ions to drift radially through the electrode [11]. The CV is applied and manipulated to refocus, select, and filter ions [60]. For a given CV, only ions of a certain mobility are repelled from the electrodes, while dispersion of the remaining ions eventually leads to contact with the electrodes and neutralization [61]. The signal-to-noise (S/N) ratio of an analyte of interest can be increased by FAIMS separations as these devices continuously collect data, meaning they do not experience a loss in duty cycle as DTIMS, TWIMS, and TIMS devices would from collecting data from pulses of ions [10]. The main limitation of FAIMS devices is that they cannot be used to calculate CCS values. The operating field strength of these devices is beyond the low-field limit; therefore, the CV values cannot be correlated with the ion structure [11]. Furthermore, the ion structure itself may change within the FAIMS mobility region during the oscillations between low and high fields [60]. Therefore, FAIMS devices are commonly used in targeted analyses to filter interferences and separate analytes of interest; however, they can be used in untargeted analyses by scanning a range of CVs. Common commercially available platforms include the SelexION DMS device from SCIEX and the FAIMS Pro interface from Thermo Fisher Scientific. Additional commercial vendors of FAIMS devices include Owlstone Medical and Heartland MS [10].

6.1.3 Ion Mobility Resolving Power (R_p) Advancements

The spatial separation afforded by TIMS, FAIMS, and DMA allows for selective filtering of specific analytes at R_p of CCS/ΔCCS >200 [39]. While beneficial for targeted workflows, the scannable nature of these platforms is not necessarily conducive to chromatographic separations or for the simultaneous assessment of numerous analytes as would be ideal in untargeted workflows. Temporal separation instruments (DTIMS and TWIMS) afford the inclusion of all ions ideal for untargeted analysis but with limited R_p capabilities that hinder analyte separation. Given the abundance of isomers and isobars within the lipidome, there have been several recent initiatives to facilitate enhanced mobility-based separations. Separation efficiency is dependent on the drift gas composition, temperature, pressure, and path length; therefore, efforts to increase R_p have focused on the augmentation of these variables. For example, AP-DTIMS has demonstrated an R_p nearly double that of a traditional DTIMS instrument operating at ~4 Torr [62]. Conversely, elongation of path length has been developed in inventive system designs, which include the cyclic-IMS (cIM) [49], SLIM [63], and tandem IM (IMS–IMS) [64] instrumentation (Figure 6.4). Data post-processing strategies for increasing resolution and duty cycle have also been explored to improve the performance of the existing, commercially available instrumentation [65]. However, even with IMS R_p advancements achieving over 1000, there are still isomeric pairs within the lipidome arising from enantiomers that yield identical structures, which are indistinguishable in IMS [66]. Dopants and drift gas modifiers have thus been used to alter analyte adducts and modify molecule–ion collisions to further enhance the separation space differentiable with IMS [67, 68]. Herein, we detail some recent IMS R_p advancements and efforts to increase separation capabilities with IMS platforms. While a number of these techniques are currently in the development phase with limited exploration in omic workflows, they have enormous potential for lipidomics applications.

6.1.3.1 Cyclic IMS (cIM)

In early TWIMS separations, R_p averaged ~40, thereby challenging the separations of lipid isomers and isobars [42, 44]. However, enhancing R_p is non-trivial as there is a square root relationship between R_p and changeable parameters. For efforts to increase the path length, practicality limitations of a minimal instrument footprint resulted in creative mobility cell orientations to effectively increase the distance without overtaking the lab space. The first commercial launch of an IMS instrument meeting this criterion was the 2019 release of a cIM from Waters Corporation [49]. In this design, printed circuit boards (PCBs) are used as ion optics that appear orthogonally before and after the middle component, a 0.98 m closed loop of PCBs where IMS separation occurs (Figure 6.4a) [49, 64]. With cIM, ions are guided through the three-component system by a series of RF and DC voltages that create pseudopotential barriers in the z- and x-directions [49]. In the y-direction of the cIM component, the RF electrodes employ a repeating traveling-wave pattern similar to traditional TWIMS devices, where ions can "surf" to achieve size-based separation. Following a single pass in the cIM system, the R_p increased to ~80 due to the longer path length than the commercialized linear TWIMS platforms [49]. The path length was further extended by having ions continue to traverse the cIM in multiple passes with 100 passes on this system demonstrating ~750 R_p, thereby allowing for the resolution of reverse sequence peptides [49]. The ion optics running adjacent to the cIM cell also readily allow users to implement a combination of mobility selection, storage, tandem IMS, and ion activation in both single and multipass modes [49]. Therefore, users can have a highly specialized workflow for isolating lipid species and providing comprehensive information regarding lipid structure. Thus far, cIM have focused on standard separations. However, the improvements to IMS metrics including R_p are expected to transfer readily to lipidomic applications.

6.1.3.2 Standard Lossless Ion Manipulation (SLIM)

SLIM offers an alternative geometry of PCB arrangements to elongate the IMS path length. Iterations of development by Smith and coworkers have explored an adaptable architecture of PCBs by varying orientations and electric field applications. For example, a SLIM instrument spanning multiple meters was previously developed with a drift tube design that extended the entire path length [69–71]. While advantageous for direct CCS measurements, this platform is limited in terms of practicality and safety considerations as extremely high voltage is needed at the beginning lenses (>10 000 V) to create the voltage drop needed in DTIMS. To minimize the instrument footprint and increase the safety, Smith and coworkers were able to create a TWIMS-based 13-m serpentine path that allows ions to make U-turns (Figure 6.4b) [63, 64]. This system has previously demonstrated R_p values exceeding 200 [52] and was recently commercially released by MOBILion Systems as a standalone component for integration with MS instrumentation. Additionally, the MOBIE system in conjunction with Agilent offers the same 13 m SLIM system with a qTOF mass spectrometer. A prototype of the MOBIE system has demonstrated the

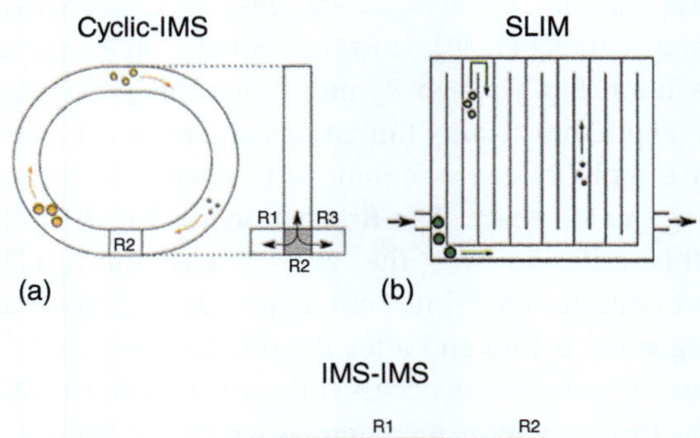

Figure 6.4 Geometries of advanced IMS instruments. (a) cyclic-IMS, (b) SLIM, and (c) Tandem IM separations. Source: Eldrid et al. [64].

separation of lipid standards including the alpha/beta conformers of GD1 that were near-baseline resolved and a pair of triacylglycerol (TG) double-bond (db)-position isomers ~80% resolved with R_p above 250 [52]. Both these standard pairs were previously indistinguishable in mixtures in DTIMS separations [52]. Similar to cIM, multipass experiments have also been performed with a SLIM SUPER system that has effectively increased instrument R_p capabilities to ~1860 [66, 72].

6.1.3.3 Tandem IMS

Integration of multiple IMS devices through tandem IMS has also been used to enhance R_p and the limit of detection (LOD) of analytes [64]. To accomplish this, gating devices are implemented between IMS cells such that tandem IMS systems can be operated to allow either full ion transmission, select filtering mobility windows, or serve as an ion activation cell for fragmentation pre- and post-mobility separation. A multi-FAIMS system was previously developed to allow for subsequent ion trapping and separation, which decreased the LOD [73]. Tandem DTIMS instruments developed by Clemmer and coworkers showed R_p capabilities of ~500 (Figure 6.4c) [64, 74]. High- and low-field IMS platforms have also been integrated, where FAIMS has been coupled to a DTIMS system to scan through mobility windows, effectively enhancing the sensitivity of DTIMS separations [75]. To date, commercial vendors offer few instruments with tandem IMS capabilities. Therefore, the utility of these systems for lipidomics is currently limited by the exclusivity of these platforms to those that can build in-house systems. However, there are some noteworthy exceptions. Bruker Daltonics developed a tandem tims TOF Pro that increases fragmentation capabilities and synchronizes TIMS and MS/MS selection, thereby combining the strengths of IMS with those of a qTOF [53, 54]. Lipidomic measurements have thus been performed on this platform leveraging a parallel accumulation–serial fragmentation (PASEF) strategy and 4D measurements with retention time, CCS, *m/z*, and fragment information [53]. Additionally, tandem IMS is accessible through multipass experiments on both the cyclic-IMS and SLIM systems.

6.1.3.4 IMS Data Deconvolution Software Strategies

SLIM and cIM systems are creatively engineered IMS platforms that effectively increase the path length while minimizing the instrument footprint. However, the subsequent increase in timescale required for these elongated paths can far exceed the millisecond requirements for IMS to remain nested between front-end separations and MS. Therefore, vendors have explored enhancing IMS efficiency and resolution capabilities of current technologies by implementing novel data processing strategies. In conventional DTIMS, each IMS separation lasts ~60 ms following trap accumulation of only ~4–10 ms, so biases do not occur. This results in an instrument duty cycle of ~7–17% (Figure 6.5a) [65, 76]. To improve sensitivity, multiplexing algorithms have been encoded through a series of stop-go binary sequences to open and close the entrance ion gate, thereby permitting multiple IMS experiments to occur simultaneously (Figure 6.5b) [65]. To deconvolute the spectra, a number of algorithms including a Fourier and Hadamard transformation have been used to produce one demultiplexed data file that sums the observed

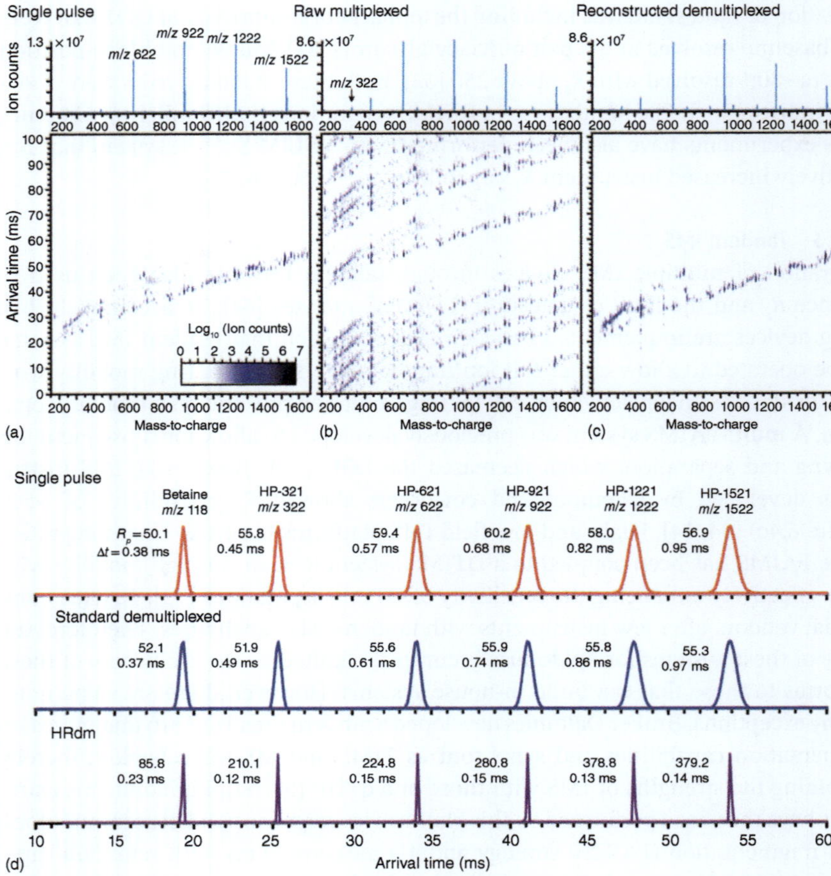

Figure 6.5 HRdm processing effects on DTIMS data. (a) IMS-MS data for single-pulse (conventional) DTIMS, (b) raw multiplexed data of sequentially collected IMS data, and (c) deconvolution of the multiplexed data to attain drift times. (d) The peak shape of example Agilent tune mix ions for single-pulse (red), standard demultiplexing (blue), and HRdm (purple) processing. Source: Figure reproduced with permission from May et al. [65].

signals and maps them to the correct drift time (Figure 6.5c) [65, 77]. Furthermore, the resulting spectra yield data with more points across the peak and increased sensitivity [41, 78].

Agilent Technologies recently developed a high-resolution demultiplexing (HRdm) data processing strategy that uses 3-, 4-, and recently 5-bit multiplexing modes to enhance DTIMS resolution [65]. To deconvolute the multipulse sequences, the free PNNL Preprocessor [79] software performs feature finding to identify peaks followed by the summation of signals over the domain to create one demultiplexed IMS spectrum [65]. With the Agilent HRdm software, the demultiplexed data are reprocessed with a proprietary high-resolution algorithm to diminish the points across the peak and enhance the resolution of the Agilent 6560 data [65]. For reference, Figure 6.5d depicts the peak shape of a single-pulse, demultiplexed, and

HRdm experiment [65]. Importantly, a number of data quality metrics have been scrutinized following the point reduction processing of HRdm. Investigations of this technique have demonstrated conserved drift times that allow for the direct and indirect measurement of CCS values, preserved quantitation capabilities, and provided R_p of >200. Additionally, the HRdm 2.0 software offers various modes of processing, which modulate the data reduction and R_p capabilities. Thus far, the applications of HRdm for lipidomics are limited given the initial release of this algorithm in 2020. While promising, the infancy of this approach leaves room to explore the robustness of the existing preliminary investigations to other molecules, isomer types, and biological samples. Further optimization of this processing strategy is expected to focus on greater sample complexity and enhancing processed data to give researchers the best output for complex applications. Additionally, the processing techniques employed herein have potential application to other IMS separations. Multiplexing, for example, can be implemented with all workflows with the exception of highly multipassed systems as these groups have the potential to overlap during the IMS separation [80].

6.1.3.5 Drift Gas Dopants and Modifiers

Given that path length is unchangeable in commercialized IMS instrumentation, and some isomeric species remain indistinguishable even with ultra-high R_p, researchers have also explored both drift gas dopants and modifiers to facilitate analyte mobility separations. The objective when using drift gas dopants is to move the analyte(s) of interest from the chemical noise and/or facilitate separations through selective dopant–analyte interactions [67]. Dopants are typically introduced at or before ionization to form dopant–analyte clusters. Some common dopant examples include alkali ions, ammonia, acetone, 5-nonanone, nicotinamide, triethyl phosphate (TEP), and chlorinated hydrocarbons. Conversely, modifiers are gases added to the drift region in large quantities (often more than 0.1% volume), which do not affect the mechanism of ion formation but instead impact the ion–molecular collision interactions [67]. The commonly explored drift gas modifiers to increase the resolution have included polar vapors (e.g. water or alcohols) and light gases (i.e. helium or hydrogen). Additionally, the drift gas composition itself can be varied (e.g. from He to N_2 or Ar) to alter analyte collisions and observed drift time based on ion size [81]. While N_2 and He are among the most common drift gases for small-molecule IMS separation, drift gas choice influences separation efficiency and other IMS metrics [81]. Therefore, it is important to disclose this information in publications and to choose adequate reference values that best match your operating system [82]. In this section, we detail applications of drift gas dopants and modifiers employed in lipidomic applications to facilitate separations.

Lipids are commonly identified in both negative and positive ionization modes as multiple adduct forms. Phosphatidylcholine (PC) lipids, for example, often form both a protonated and alkali metal adduct in the positive mode, resulting in multiple corresponding m/z and CCS values for one molecule. This is significant in complex biological spectra as metal adducts shift drift times, modify CCS values, and change the associated mass versus mobility trends. Alkali dopants also offer increased ionization of more acidic lipids in the positive ionization mode, and the drift time shifts can help differentiate lipid species. Furthermore, lipid adduct types have been shown to facilitate the distinction of isomeric and isobaric lipid species. For example, ceramide *R* and *S* isomers show differences in sodium ion binding such that the *S* enantiomer of a standard pair elutes prior to the *R* enantiomer [7]. Novel alkali metals have also been explored to facilitate lipid separation from a complex background. Cesium, for example, was used in matrix-assisted laser desorption/ionization (MALDI)-IMS and promoted the identification of an additional 22 phospholipid species largely within neutral and acidic classes [83]. Selective binding of transition metals to double bonds has also been leveraged to separate regioisomers given the greater difference in CCS of Ag^+ isomers compared to conventional H^+ and alkali metal ions [6]. Silver ion adduction and chromatography have therefore been implemented with DMS and DTIMS separations to separate PC *sn*-isomers [6, 84].

Conversely, researchers have attempted to change the drift gas composition to facilitate separations through the addition of lightweight or polar gases. For polar modifier addition, the asymmetric waveform of FAIMS allows for a dynamic formation of weak complexes between a polar buffer gas molecule and the analyte(s) of interest in low E field. In high-field conditions, however, this buffer gas–analyte complex dissociates because of the increasing ion temperature relative to the atmosphere [85]. CO_2–analyte complexes have been explored for enhancing small-molecule separation that was further benefitted by the observed increase in signal intensity [86, 87]. FAIMS separation efficiencies can also be increased by using high fractions of light gases (i.e. helium or hydrogen) [64]. A ratio of 65–70% He with nitrogen demonstrated ultra-high resolution that was able to separate three out of the four main isomeric species present in glycerolipid and phospholipid categories [88, 89]. To our knowledge, limited examples of drift gas modifiers are available for lipid isomers on other IMS platforms. However, these platforms have been implemented with modifiers to separate isomer types often observed with lipids. A more extensive review of dopants, drift gas modifiers, and analyte separation for a variety of IMS platforms is presented by Waraksa and coworkers [67]. It should also be noted that while drift gas modifiers can facilitate analyte separations, it is extremely difficult to measure reproducible CCS values in gas mixtures, and potential contamination issues often occur when switching between different drift gas compositions if drift cell bake outs are not performed routinely.

6.1.4 Benefits of IMS for Lipidomics

Isomeric and isobaric species are prolific within the lipidome, originating from fatty acyl (FA) position, functional group orientation (e.g. bis(monoacylglycerol)phosphate [BMP] versus phosphatidylglycerol [PG]), *sn*-position, double-bond position and orientation, regioisomers, and even species in different classes and subclasses with the same atoms but different head group compositions. Since IMS offers multiple analytical benefits including orthogonality to chromatographic and MS analyses, the reduction of spectral complexity of biological samples, and the measurement

Table 6.2 Benefits of IMS for lipidomics.

Analytical use of ion mobility	Description	Additional requirements	Example application areas
1. Chemical separation	Partition signal from chemical noise and increase the peak capacity of analysis	None	Imaging and shotgun lipidomics, chemical space reduction, and discovery of low-level lipid ions
2. Analyte identification and characterization	Use CCS values to characterize unknowns by correlation	Reference values from databases/libraries Normalized drift times, measured reduced mobilities, and/or calculated CCS values	Lipid identification
3. Structural analysis	Utilize experimental CCS values to infer structural information	Computational methods to link theoretical structure to CCS values	Fundamental understanding of IMS separations gas-phase chemical arrangement insight

Source: Adapted from May et al. [90].

of CCS to support molecular identification and infer structural information, its use in lipidomic studies keeps on increasing (Table 6.2) [90]. This section will further detail the IMS benefits of (i) chemical separation, (ii) analyte identification and characterization, and (iii) structural analysis for lipidomic assays.

6.1.4.1 Chemical Space Separation with IMS

Biomolecule classes such as oligonucleotides, lipids, metabolites, and proteins all share similar compositions of C, H, N, P, O atoms; however, each differs in its monomeric atomic structural arrangements that are then polymerized to form complex structures [91]. As such, each of these classes exhibits a unique structural density. Given the correlation of analyte size and mass, the separation of analytes by IMS-MS results in the formation of distinct trendlines when comparing the observed mass-to-mobility relationships, compensation voltage (CV), and/or CCS values (Figure 6.2). For complex sample types, the IMS size separation is particularly advantageous to filter biomolecule classes prior to MS analyses. This capability has resulted in an increase in the S/N ratio of lipids at lower abundances and enhanced peak capacity through the reduction of chemical noise interferences [92]. The linear trends of CCS and m/z further translate within biomolecular classes where variations in lipid backbone facilitate the separation of lipids by category (Figure 6.6a) [25, 92]. Additionally, within lipid categories, the fluctuations in the head group moiety such as those in phospholipids also showcase unique trends in both FAIMS CV versus m/z plots [88] and CCS and m/z plots (Figure 6.6b) [25, 92]. Further zooming into these mass–mobility trends has also demonstrated a correlation of fatty acyl

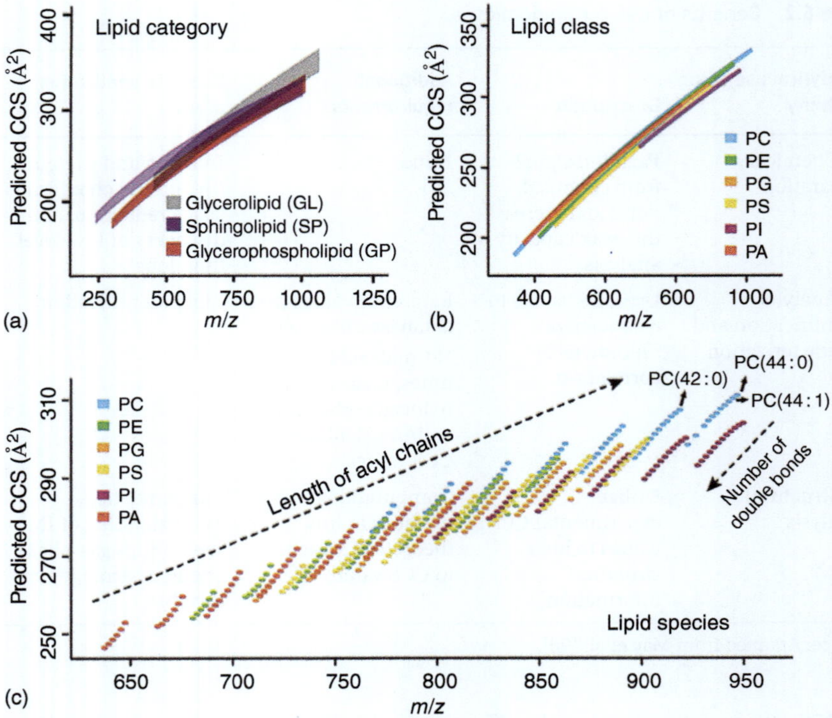

Figure 6.6 Mass versus mobility relationships for lipids. The separation of lipids by category (a), class (b), and summed fatty acyl composition (c) is facilitated by the relationship of CCS and/or mobility with observed *m/z*. Source: Figure adapted from Tu et al. [93].

information where lipids with the same head group and total carbon count exhibit a linear relationship (Figure 6.6c) [25, 92]. Thus, as the number of double bonds increases from 0 to 1 and so on, the observed CCS value decreases in a linear fashion [25, 92], and the saturated version of a lipid, i.e. PC(44:0), has the longest observed drift time and largest *m/z* value. As more unsaturated sites are added, both mass and drift time subsequently decrease. This relationship is incredibly powerful for postulating putative identifications of unknown spectral features.

6.1.4.2 Lipid Identification and Characterization with CCS

The integration of IMS and MS for lipidomic analyses has proven extremely useful for facilitating the separation of chemical space. However, the abundance of lipid isomers and the correlation of mass with size limit the characterization capabilities of the entire lipidome solely through these two dimensions, even with the integration of additional separation dimensions such as LC. Therefore, the amount of lipid speciation possible can be variable depending on the separation capabilities and co-existing isomers (Figure 6.7a) [25]. IMS analyses for numerous lipid isomer pair standards have noted R_p of several hundreds to distinguish variations in functional

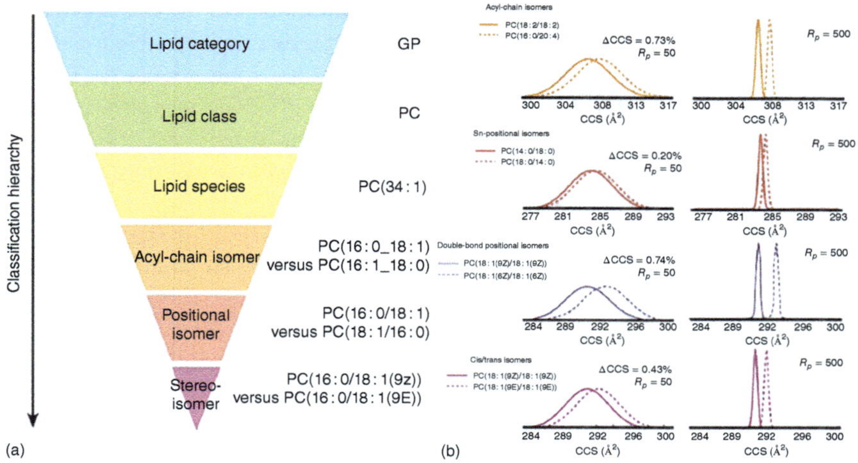

Figure 6.7 IMS separation capabilities for lipid isomers and the resulting effects on lipid speciation. Source: Figure reproduced with permission from Tu et al. [93].

group position, acyl chain position, chain length, and double-bond geometry and orientation (Figure 6.7b) [25]. This has however been accomplished. For instance, FAIMS platforms have demonstrated the successful separation of isomer types arising from fatty acyl differences [89]. Similarly, multiple lipid isomer types including PG and BMP isomers, which differ in their head group placement in the *sn*-3 (PG) or *sn*-2 (BMP) position, have been effectively resolved with TIMS [94]. Advancements in temporal IMS systems such as SLIM have shown effective separation of cis/trans and double-bond-positional isomers through increased separation path length [95]. However, biological sample complexity can preclude the separation efficiency that has previously been showcased with lipid isomer standards, demonstrating that size-based separation alone may not be enough to resolve species and make identifications in real-world samples. However, as CCS values are an intrinsic property of each molecule, they can be determined using low-field IMS systems and provide an additional descriptor for making identifications to enhance annotation confidence and facilitate isomer distinction within complex biological samples. Thus, the more CCS values collected for lipids, the better our confidence and annotation capabilities will be.

Databases of experimental CCS and mobility values have been released to support the identification of biomolecules. Notably, the CCS Compendium out of the McLean laboratory at Vanderbilt University houses 3800 experimental CCS values across 80 molecular classes determined from a DTIMS system operating under nitrogen gas [20]. Additionally, AllCCS [96] and LipidCCS [25] by the Zhou lab and DeepCCS [97] offer a means of computationally predicting lipid CCS values under nitrogen gas for a number of positive- and negative-mode adducts. CCSbase is another database containing over 14 000 computationally predicted and experimentally derived CCS values from a variety of IMS platforms and sources [98]. Other computational algorithms such as ISiCLE [99] also offer CCS prediction capabilities under helium gas. Taken together, the extensive culmination of CCS values in databases offers researchers a wealth of information that is readily accessible for analyte identification. Experimentally, CCS values are also of great importance for separating isomers and comparing data to reference values. CCS values have also been used as a filter to set tolerance windows to deconvolute spectra by observed drift time that has previously been demonstrated to reduce both false positive and negative identifications [100]. Vendor-neutral software platforms such as Skyline are also beginning to incorporate CCS and ion mobility spectrum filtering for small and large molecules [101]. More details on the benefits of CCS are presented in Section 6.1.5.

6.1.4.3 CCS for Lipid Structural Analysis

Since CCS is a descriptor for a gas-phase structure of a molecule, it has also been used in conjunction with cryo-EM, NMR, and CD to compare to the solution phase and elucidate structural information [102, 103]. The most obvious application of CCS in structural analysis lies with large biomolecules such as proteins [103, 104]. However, the measurement of CCS in tandem with *in silico* modeling can also provide a fundamental understanding of lipid adduct formation with observed differences in CCS elucidating the structural variations driving mass versus mobility trends and helping infer molecular structure when standards are unavailable. Kim et al. performed molecular dynamics simulations to elucidate the structural occurrences of saturated and unsaturated PC cations that detailed the preferential gas-phase structure of PC lipids as globular or extended conformations at varying tail lengths and degrees of unsaturation [105]. Likewise, modeling has been employed to understand the structural data of fatty acid isomer separations [7]. Taken together, CCS measurements provide researchers a valuable reference that can be used to detail the benefits of IMS for lipidomic analysis that also translates to optimizing IMS separation efficiency of an isomeric pair by leveraging *in silico* predictions.

6.1.5 Lipidomic Applications with IMS

6.1.5.1 IMS in Imaging and Shotgun Lipidomics

Most untargeted IMS techniques exist in a nested timescale between LC and MS such that a comprehensive annotation of retention time, drift/arrival time, and m/z can often be collected simultaneously [15]. The caveat, however, of the LC-IMS-MS workflows is the time expense of LC as a majority of lipid gradients require 20–40 minutes per injection. This is confounded in lipidomics as lipids are commonly analyzed in both the positive and negative modes, thereby requiring approximately an hour of instrument time for each sample. Shotgun lipidomics has become a prominent, high-throughput lipidomic analysis technique where extracted lipidome aliquots are directly injected into the mass spectrometer [106]. Conversely, MS imaging (MSi) prioritizes the annotation of an analyte's spatial distribution in heterogeneous tissue and/or cell types, which is also incompatible with chromatographic separations [107]. As both these techniques solely collect MS information, the greatest weakness of both shotgun and MSi is the depth of lipid speciation achievable. For shotgun lipidomics, assigning MS/MS spectra can be impeded by the prevalence of shared structural motifs, the diverse biological abundances of lipids, and the propensity of isomeric and isobaric species. MSi lipid identifications are even more challenged by the limited sample preparation capabilities needed to isolate lipids from other biomolecular classes. Additionally, MS/MS data collection in MSi applications is non-trivial, and challenges occur when spatially aligning the alternating MS and MS/MS scans causing a majority of imaging experiments to be collected in the MS-only mode [107]. However, the timescale of IMS readily allows it to be integrated into both shotgun and imaging workflows. Given that these two lipidomic techniques suffer from similar obstacles, we have combined the discussion of how IMS can be beneficially integrated into both these applications.

IMS can facilitate the reduction of spectral complexity through the partitioning of interfering chemical signals. For MSi, this capability is especially beneficial given the diversity of biomolecular classes represented in tissue before any extraction. Figure 6.8a,b depicts an example spectrum of differentiating isobaric peptide and protein species from lipid signals based on unique mass versus mobility trends [108]. Additionally, DMS integration into the shotgun lipidomic analyses has facilitated the distinction of isobars arising from ether versus diacyl linkages in addition to PC and sphingomyelin (SM) lipids [109]. The mass versus mobility trendlines can also be used to identify charge states and biomolecule classes, as evidenced by Figure 6.8c, and the shotgun annotation of wax and sterol esters that were used to develop a meibum lipidome library [108, 110]. Reduced spectral complexity with IMS also enhances S/N ratios that can facilitate the annotation of low-level lipids. A desorption electrospray ionization (DESI) imaging experiment comparing lipidome coverage with and without FAIMS shows an increase in the S/N ratio of ~50% and the annotation of numerous cardiolipin species that were otherwise indifferentiable from background noise (Figure 6.8d) [108]. Additionally, MALDI-TIMS MS work has demonstrated improvements of peak capacity by 250% for imaging experiments by integrating IMS into the analyses [94]. The annotation of CCS also takes drift time separations a step further as this descriptor normalizes the separation and with m/z information can be used to filter data and increase confidence for analyte identification. Integration of CCS with m/z has been shown to facilitate lipid identifications by making mass accuracy criteria less stringent and providing another dimension to assess data. A shotgun lipidomics study by Paglia et al. demonstrated how the addition of a CCS molecular descriptor can limit both false-negative and false-positive lipid identifications [100]. SLIM has also aided in ganglioside isomer distinction given its heightened resolution relative to commercially available DTIMS and TWIMS systems [111]. Taken together, the integration of IMS into imaging and shotgun lipidomic workflows can facilitate accurate lipid identifications by reducing spectral complexity and enhancing the number of descriptors being investigated while still maintaining the benefits of high-throughput shotgun lipidomics and the spatial information of imaging MS workflows.

6.1.5.2 IMS-MS/MS and Novel Speciation Approaches

As mentioned previously, the orthogonal collection of LC, IMS, MS, and MS/MS information provides a multitude of descriptors to increase the analyte

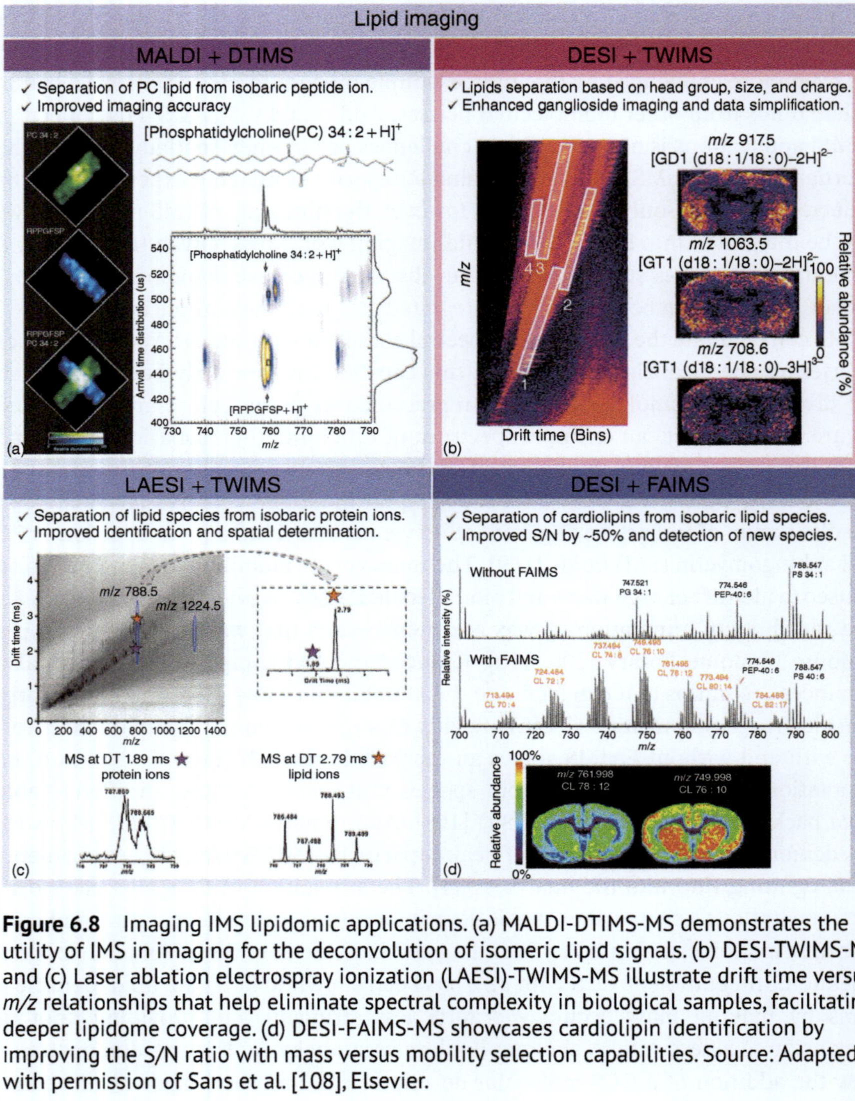

Figure 6.8 Imaging IMS lipidomic applications. (a) MALDI-DTIMS-MS demonstrates the utility of IMS in imaging for the deconvolution of isomeric lipid signals. (b) DESI-TWIMS-MS and (c) Laser ablation electrospray ionization (LAESI)-TWIMS-MS illustrate drift time versus *m/z* relationships that help eliminate spectral complexity in biological samples, facilitating deeper lipidome coverage. (d) DESI-FAIMS-MS showcases cardiolipin identification by improving the S/N ratio with mass versus mobility selection capabilities. Source: Adapted with permission of Sans et al. [108], Elsevier.

identification confidence. A sterol-omics study, for example, demonstrated that ~80% of derivatized isomers could be separated with LC and IMS together, while IMS or LC separations could only resolve 60% and 40% of isomers alone [112]. For other lipids such as phospholipids, sphingolipids, and glycerolipids, shared fatty acyl and head group moieties and overlapping mass regions preclude the confident assignment of fragments with either data independent acquisition (DIA) or data dependent acquisition (DDA) workflows, even with chromatography. In traditional LC-MS/MS workflows, DDA has become a common fragmentation method where ions are selected based on specific targets or abundance and then isolated and

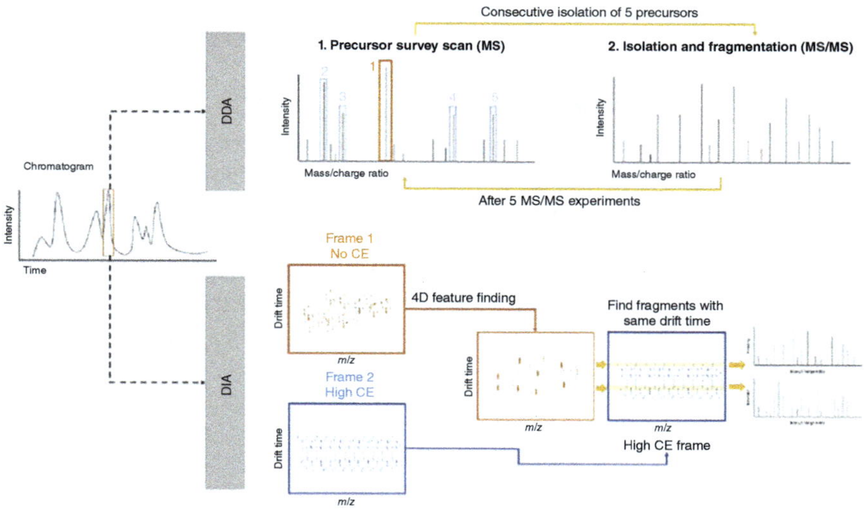

Figure 6.9 Example of MS/MS collection strategies. On top, DDA is used to selectively fragment ions based on their intensity for compound annotation. On bottom, DIA is used to fragment all ions regardless of intensity. By having the drift region prior to fragmentation, IMS-DIA allows for the separation of precursor signals by observed drift time to clean up the MS/MS spectra. Product ions can then be drift time aligned with precursor signals to map fragments to the correct precursor molecule. Source: Figure reproduced with permission from Nys et al. [113].

fragmented. Conversely, in DIA, all ions or specific *m/z* windows of ions are fragmented concurrently to produce extremely complex MS/MS spectra. With IMS integration prior to fragmentation, the drift time separation allows for the deconvolution of MS and MS/MS information for enhancing the confidence in identifications as the precursor and product ions are drift time aligned (Figure 6.9) [113]. To implement IMS-DIA workflows, a series of alternating scans of MS and MS/MS are typically collected as ions elute from the IMS cell. The resulting spectral clean-up leveraging IMS has made IMS-DIA a common practice for data collection. In the HDMS Waters system, a TWIMS can be operated in the MS^E mode such that co-eluting molecules are separated in the TWIMS cell and then fragmented using time-aligned parallel (TAP) fragmentation for cleaner MS/MS spectra [114, 115]. Additionally, the trapping capabilities of the tims TIMS cell in a Bruker timsTOF allow for a number of isolation, accumulation, and/or fragmentation options using their PASEF TIMS operation [53]. To optimize fragmentation efficiency on an Agilent DTIMS system, All Ions DIA can be employed similar to the TWIMS HDMS on a Waters platform [116]. Agilent DTIMS systems have also demonstrated the utility of ramping collision energy for collision induced dissociation (CID) such that ions with later drift times and therefore greater size experience collisions with more energy to facilitate fragmentation [117, 118]. Instrument modifications have also been used to allow for quadrupole ion selection on the Agilent system, further enhancing the sensitivity and S/N ratio in a fragmentation strategy similar to DDA [119].

IMS platforms have also been integrated with several fragmentation and/or derivatization strategies to enhance lipid speciation capabilities. Ozonolysis, for example, is a reaction-based annotation of double-bond location that has been implemented with IMS to facilitate the alignment of double-bond fragments for enhancing speciation [120]. Similarly, a Paterno–Büchi reaction that also cleaves double bonds was integrated with a supercritical fluid chromatography (SFC)-IMS separation on a Waters HDMS system where TAP fragmentation facilitated the assignment of fragments for over 500 glycerolipids and 30 sterols [121]. Electron impact excitation of ions from organics (EIEIO) is a novel fragmentation strategy that leverages an electron beam to fragment positive mode ions to identify *sn*-position and cis/trans isomers for specific lipid classes [122]. Recently, EIEIO fragmentation has been integrated with DMS and an isopropanol modifier to facilitate isomer separations [123]. Together, these workflows are significant steps toward annotating full lipid speciation. However, a major caveat of these techniques is that the resulting data are extensive, and software to facilitate data processing is limited. Therefore, these platforms have largely focused on proof-of-concept work with standards or example case studies that would be challenging to replicate for larger numbers of complex samples. As this data analysis becomes less manual, the integration of IMS with the novel lipid speciation strategies is expected to greatly expand annotation capabilities.

6.1.6 Conclusions and Outlook of IMS for Lipidomics

In this chapter, we have discussed the general principles and types of IMS, as well as its benefits, specific applications, and limitations in lipidomics applications. Specifically, IMS lipidomics benefits include enhanced separation, signal filtering, analyte identification, and structural characterization capabilities. IMS size-based separations can also be leveraged to distinguish isomeric or isobaric lipids, assist in the discovery of low-abundance lipids by filtering chemical noise, and allow separations in imaging and shotgun lipidomic applications. The ability to calculate CCS values directly or via calibration aids in lipid identification based on reference values, *in silico* predictions, and CCS versus m/z trends. Additionally, CCS values can give insight into the lipid structure in the gas phase when coupled with computational methods. Overall, IMS is a highly complementary separation technique to MS-based lipidomics which can also be readily coupled with front-end separations to give multidimensional data. The utility of IMS instrumentation in a broad range of applications has driven rapid innovation in instrument design as well as computational strategies. Technology developments in IMS have been made with the goals of increased R_p, ion transmission, ease of use, and data quality. Recent advancements discussed here include cIM and SLIM devices as well as drift gas dopants and modifiers to increase separation capacity. Additionally, data processing and annotation software are continually developed to increase the R_p and S/N ratio of existing instruments and better utilize CCS values or other IMS output values (drift/arrival time, mobility, FAIMS CV, etc.) to filter and annotate complex data. The limited software available for multidimensional data analysis is perhaps the greatest limitation of IMS integration into lipidomic experiments. While challenges with tools for data processing and annotation are not exclusive to IMS data and are a limitation for the greater lipidomics community, many lipidomics software platforms do not include the IMS dimension. Thus, processing IMS-MS data can be especially time consuming, even more so when coupled with LC and MS/MS dimensions. Additionally, CCS databases and libraries are becoming more readily available but still need substantial growth to fully utilize CCS as a reproducibly measured molecular descriptor. Despite these challenges, IMS is becoming an invaluable addition to the analytical toolbox in lipidomics and beyond for high-throughput lipid separation, identification, and characterization, and we expect IMS to be an essential component of many future lipidomic studies.

References

1 Züllig, T., Trötzmüller, M., and Köfeler, H.C. (2020). Lipidomics from sample preparation to data analysis: a primer. *Anal. Bioanal. Chem.* 412 (10): 2191–2209. https://doi.org/10.1007/s00216-019-02241-y.

2 Bowden, J.A., Heckert, A., Ulmer, C.Z. et al. (2017). Harmonizing lipidomics: NIST interlaboratory comparison exercise for lipidomics using SRM 1950-Metabolites in Frozen Human Plasma. *J. Lipid Res.* 58 (12): 2275–2288. https://doi.org/10.1194/jlr.M079012.

3 Niemelä, P.S., Castillo, S., Sysi-Aho, M., and Oresic, M. (2009). Bioinformatics and computational methods for lipidomics. *J. Chromatogr. B Analyt. Technol. Biomed. Life Sci.* 877 (26): 2855–2862. https://doi.org/10.1016/j.jchromb.2009.01.025.

4 Hancock, S.E., Poad, B.L.J., Batarseh, A. et al. (2017). Advances and unresolved challenges in the structural characterization of isomeric lipids. *Anal. Biochem.* 524: 45–55. https://doi.org/10.1016/j.ab.2016.09.014.

5 Liebisch, G., Ahrends, R., Arita, M. et al. (2019). Lipidomics needs more standardization. *Nat. Metab.* 1 (8): 745–747. https://doi.org/10.1038/s42255-019-0094-z.

6 Groessl, M., Graf, S., and Knochenmuss, R. (2015). High resolution ion mobility-mass spectrometry for separation and identification of isomeric lipids. *Analyst* 140 (20): 6904–6911. https://doi.org/10.1039/c5an00838g (accessed 19 July 2022).

7 Kyle, J.E., Zhang, X., Weitz, K.K. et al. (2016). Uncovering biologically significant lipid isomers with liquid chromatography, ion mobility spectrometry and mass spectrometry. *Analyst* 141 (5): 1649–1659. https://doi.org/10.1039/c5an02062j (accessed 19 July 2022).

8 Paglia, G., Kliman, M., Claude, E. et al. (2015). Applications of ion-mobility mass spectrometry for lipid analysis. *Anal. Bioanal. Chem.* 407 (17): 4995–5007. https://doi.org/10.1007/s00216-015-8664-8.

9 Kliman, M., May, J.C., and McLean, J.A. (2011). Lipid analysis and lipidomics by structurally selective ion mobility-mass spectrometry. *Biochim. Biophys. Acta* 1811 (11): 935–945. https://doi.org/10.1016/j.bbalip.2011.05.016.

10 Dodds, J.N. and Baker, E.S. (2019). Ion mobility spectrometry: fundamental concepts, instrumentation, applications, and the road ahead. *J. Am. Soc. Mass Spectrom.* 30 (11): 2185–2195. https://doi.org/10.1007/s13361-019-02288-2.

11 Lanucara, F., Holman, S.W., Gray, C.J., and Eyers, C.E. (2014). The power of ion mobility-mass spectrometry for structural characterization and the study of conformational dynamics. *Nat. Chem.* 6 (4): 281–294. https://doi.org/10.1038/nchem.1889.

12 Pease, L.F. 3rd, Elliott, J.T., Tsai, D.H. et al. (2008). Determination of protein aggregation with differential mobility analysis: application to IgG antibody. *Biotechnol. Bioeng.* 101 (6): 1214–1222. https://doi.org/10.1002/bit.22017.

13 de la Mora, J.F., de Juan, L., Eichler, T., and Rosell, J. (1998). Differential mobility analysis of molecular ions and nanometer particles. *TrAC, Trends Anal. Chem.* 17 (6): 328–339. https://doi.org/10.1016/S0165-9936(98)00039-9.

14 Pringle, S.D., Giles, K., Wildgoose, J.L. et al. (2007). An investigation of the mobility separation of some peptide and protein ions using a new hybrid quadrupole/travelling wave IMS/oa-ToF instrument. *Int. J. Mass Spectrom.* 261 (1): 1–12. https://doi.org/10.1016/j.ijms.2006.07.021.

15 May, J.C. and McLean, J.A. (2015). Ion mobility-mass spectrometry: time-dispersive instrumentation. *Anal. Chem.* 87 (3): 1422–1436. https://doi.org/10.1021/ac504720m.

16 Zhang, X., Quinn, K., Cruickshank-Quinn, C. et al. (2018). The application of ion mobility mass spectrometry to metabolomics. *Curr. Opin. Chem. Biol.* 42: 60–66. https://doi.org/10.1016/j.cbpa.2017.11.001.

17 Kanu, A. B.; Dwivedi, P.; Tam, M.; Matz, L.; Hill Jr, H. H. Ion mobility–mass spectrometry. *J. Mass Spectrom.* 2008, 43 (1), 1-22, https://doi.org/10.1002/jms.1383. https://doi.org/10.1002/jms.1383 (accessed 19 July 2022).

18 Kiss, A. and Heeren, R.M. (2011). Size, weight and position: ion mobility spectrometry and imaging MS combined. *Anal. Bioanal. Chem.* 399 (8): 2623–2634. https://doi.org/10.1007/s00216-010-4644-1.

19 Rose, B.S., Leaptrot, K.L., Harris, R.A. et al. (2021). High confidence shotgun lipidomics using structurally selective ion mobility-mass spectrometry. *Methods Mol. Biol.* 2306: 11–37. https://doi.org/10.1007/978-1-0716-1410-5_2.

20 Picache, J.A., Rose, B.S., Balinski, A. et al. (2019). Collision cross section compendium to annotate and predict multi-omic compound identities. *Chem. Sci.* 10 (4): 983–993. https://doi.org/10.1039/c8sc04396e (accessed 19 July 2022).

21 Zhou, Z., Shen, X., Chen, X. et al. (2019). LipidIMMS analyzer: integrating multi-dimensional information to support lipid identification in ion mobility–mass spectrometry based lipidomics. *Bioinformatics* 35 (4): 698–700. https://doi.org/10.1093/bioinformatics/bty661 (accessed 19 July 2022).

22 Tsugawa, H., Cajka, T., Kind, T. et al. (2015). MS-DIAL: data-independent MS/MS deconvolution for comprehensive metabolome analysis. *Nat. Methods* 12 (6): 523–526. https://doi.org/10.1038/nmeth.3393.

23 Ross, D.H., Cho, J.H., Zhang, R. et al. (2020). LiPydomics: a Python package for comprehensive prediction of lipid collision cross sections and retention times and analysis of ion mobility-mass spectrometry-based lipidomics data. *Anal. Chem.* 92 (22): 14967–14975. https://doi.org/10.1021/acs.analchem.0c02560.

24 Zhou, Z., Xiong, X., and Zhu, Z.-J. (2017). MetCCS predictor: a web server for predicting collision cross-section values of metabolites in ion mobility-mass spectrometry based metabolomics. *Bioinformatics* 33 (14): 2235–2237. https://doi.org/10.1093/bioinformatics/btx140 (accessed 19 July 2022).

25 Zhou, Z., Tu, J., Xiong, X. et al. (2017). LipidCCS: prediction of collision cross-section values for lipids with high precision to support ion mobility–mass spectrometry-based lipidomics. *Anal. Chem.* 89 (17): 9559–9566. https://doi.org/10.1021/acs.analchem.7b02625.

26 Soper-Hopper, M.T., Petrov, A.S., Howard, J.N. et al. (2017). Collision cross section predictions using 2-dimensional molecular descriptors. *Chem. Commun.* 53 (54): 7624–7627. https://doi.org/10.1039/C7CC04257D.

27 Fenn, L.S. and McLean, J.A. (2008). Biomolecular structural separations by ion mobility–mass spectrometry. *Anal. Bioanal. Chem.* 391 (3): 905–909. https://doi.org/10.1007/s00216-008-1951-x.

28 Woods, A.S., Ugarov, M., Egan, T. et al. (2004). Lipid/peptide/nucleotide separation with MALDI-ion mobility-TOF MS. *Anal. Chem.* 76 (8): 2187–2195. https://doi.org/10.1021/ac035376k.

29 May, J.C., Goodwin, C.R., Lareau, N.M. et al. (2014). Conformational ordering of biomolecules in the gas phase: nitrogen collision cross sections measured on a prototype high resolution drift tube ion mobility-mass spectrometer. *Anal. Chem.* 86 (4): 2107–2116. https://doi.org/10.1021/ac4038448.

30 Trimpin, S., Tan, B., Bohrer, B.C. et al. (2009). Profiling of phospholipids and related lipid structures using multidimensional ion mobility spectrometry-mass spectrometry. *Int. J. Mass Spectrom.* 287 (1): 58–69. https://doi.org/10.1016/j.ijms.2008.12.020.

31 Mason, E.A. and Schamp, H.W. (1958). Mobility of gaseous lons in weak electric fields. *Ann. Phys.* 4 (3): 233–270. https://doi.org/10.1016/0003-4916(58)90049-6.

32 Revercomb, H.E. and Mason, E.A. (1975). Theory of plasma chromatography/gaseous electrophoresis. Review. *Anal. Chem.* 47 (7): 970–983. https://doi.org/10.1021/ac60357a043.

33 Odenkirk, M.T. and Baker, E.S. (2020). Utilizing drift tube ion mobility spectrometry for the evaluation of metabolites and xenobiotics. *Methods Mol. Biol.* 2084: 35–54. https://doi.org/10.1007/978-1-0716-0030-6_2.

34 Mairinger, T., Causon, T.J., and Hann, S. (2018). The potential of ion mobility-mass spectrometry for non-targeted metabolomics. *Curr. Opin. Chem. Biol.* 42: 9–15. https://doi.org/10.1016/j.cbpa.2017.10.015.

35 Gabelica, V. and Marklund, E. (2018). Fundamentals of ion mobility spectrometry. *Curr. Opin. Chem. Biol.* 42: 51–59. https://doi.org/10.1016/j.cbpa.2017.10.022.

36 Marchand, A., Livet, S., Rosu, F., and Gabelica, V. (2017). Drift tube ion mobility: how to reconstruct collision cross section distributions from arrival time distributions? *Anal. Chem.* 89 (23): 12674–12681. https://doi.org/10.1021/acs.analchem.7b01736.

37 Stow, S.M., Causon, T.J., Zheng, X. et al. (2017). An interlaboratory evaluation of drift tube ion mobility–mass spectrometry collision cross section measurements. *Anal. Chem.* 89 (17): 9048–9055. https://doi.org/10.1021/acs.analchem.7b01729.

38 Ujma, J., Giles, K., Morris, M., and Barran, P.E. (2016). New high resolution ion mobility mass spectrometer capable of measurements of collision cross sections from 150 to 520 K. *Anal. Chem.* 88 (19): 9469–9478. https://doi.org/10.1021/acs.analchem.6b01812.

39 Dodds, J.N., May, J.C., and McLean, J.A. (2017). Correlating resolving power, resolution, and collision cross section: unifying cross-platform assessment of separation efficiency in ion mobility spectrometry. *Anal. Chem.* 89 (22): 12176–12184. https://doi.org/10.1021/acs.analchem.7b02827.

40 Morrison, K.A., Siems, W.F., and Clowers, B.H. (2016). Augmenting ion trap mass spectrometers using a frequency modulated drift tube ion mobility spectrometer. *Anal. Chem.* 88 (6): 3121–3129. https://doi.org/10.1021/acs.analchem.5b04223.

41 Belov, M.E., Buschbach, M.A., Prior, D.C. et al. (2007). Multiplexed ion mobility spectrometry-orthogonal time-of-flight mass spectrometry. *Anal. Chem.* 79 (6): 2451–2462. https://doi.org/10.1021/ac0617316.

42 Giles, K., Pringle, S.D., Worthington, K.R. et al. (2004). Applications of a travelling wave-based radio-frequency-only stacked ring ion guide. *Rapid Commun. Mass Spectrom.* 18 (20): 2401–2414. https://doi.org/10.1002/rcm.1641 (accessed 19 July 2022).

43 Morsa, D., Gabelica, V., and De Pauw, E. (2011). Effective temperature of ions in traveling wave ion mobility spectrometry. *Anal. Chem.* 83 (14): 5775–5782. https://doi.org/10.1021/ac201509p.

44 Giles, K., Williams, J.P., and Campuzano, I. (2011). Enhancements in travelling wave ion mobility resolution. *Rapid Commun. Mass Spectrom.* 25 (11): 1559–1566. https://doi.org/10.1002/rcm.5013 (accessed 19 July 2022).

45 Shvartsburg, A.A. and Smith, R.D. (2008). Fundamentals of traveling wave ion mobility spectrometry. *Anal. Chem.* 80 (24): 9689–9699. https://doi.org/10.1021/ac8016295.

46 Forsythe, J.G., Petrov, A.S., Walker, C.A. et al. (2015). Collision cross section calibrants for negative ion mode traveling wave ion mobility-mass spectrometry. *Analyst* 140 (20): 6853–6861. https://doi.org/10.1039/C5AN00946D.

47 Bush, M.F., Campuzano, I.D.G., and Robinson, C.V. (2012). Ion mobility mass spectrometry of peptide ions: effects of drift gas and calibration strategies. *Anal. Chem.* 84 (16): 7124–7130. https://doi.org/10.1021/ac3014498.

48 Gelb, A.S., Jarratt, R.E., Huang, Y., and Dodds, E.D. (2014). A study of calibrant selection in measurement of carbohydrate and peptide ion-neutral collision cross sections by traveling wave ion mobility spectrometry. *Anal. Chem.* 86 (22): 11396–11402. https://doi.org/10.1021/ac503379e.

49 Giles, K., Ujma, J., Wildgoose, J. et al. (2019). A cyclic ion mobility-mass spectrometry system. *Anal. Chem.* 91 (13): 8564–8573. https://doi.org/10.1021/acs.analchem.9b01838.

50 Deng, L., Ibrahim, Y.M., Baker, E.S. et al. (2016). Ion mobility separations of isomers based upon long path length structures for lossless ion manipulations combined with mass spectrometry. *ChemistrySelect* 1 (10): 2396–2399. https://doi.org/10.1002/slct.201600460.

51 Deng, L., Webb, I.K., Garimella, S.V.B. et al. (2017). Serpentine ultralong path with extended routing (SUPER) high resolution traveling wave ion mobility-MS using structures for lossless ion manipulations. *Anal. Chem.* 89 (8): 4628–4634. https://doi.org/10.1021/acs.analchem.7b00185.

52 May, J.C., Leaptrot, K.L., Rose, B.S. et al. (2021). Resolving power and collision cross section measurement accuracy of a prototype high-resolution ion mobility platform incorporating structures for lossless ion manipulation. *J. Am. Soc. Mass Spectrom.* 32 (4): 1126–1137. https://doi.org/10.1021/jasms.1c00056.

53 Vasilopoulou, C.G., Sulek, K., Brunner, A.-D. et al. (2020). Trapped ion mobility spectrometry and PASEF enable in-depth lipidomics from minimal sample amounts. *Nat. Commun.* 11 (1): 331. https://doi.org/10.1038/s41467-019-14044-x.

54 Michelmann, K., Silveira, J.A., Ridgeway, M.E., and Park, M.A. (2015). Fundamentals of trapped ion mobility spectrometry. *J. Am. Soc. Mass Spectrom.* 26 (1): 14–24. https://doi.org/10.1007/s13361-014-0999-4.

55 Hernandez, D.R., DeBord, J.D., Ridgeway, M.E. et al. (2014). Ion dynamics in a trapped ion mobility spectrometer. *Analyst* 139 (8): 1913–1921. https://doi.org/10.1039/C3AN02174B.

56 Delvaux, A., Rathahao-Paris, E., and Alves, S. (2021). Different ion mobility-mass spectrometry coupling techniques to promote metabolomics. *Mass Spectrom. Rev.* https://doi.org/10.1002/mas.21685.

57 Jeanne Dit Fouque, K., Ramirez, C.E., Lewis, R.L. et al. (2019). Effective liquid chromatography–trapped ion mobility spectrometry–mass spectrometry separation of isomeric lipid species. *Anal. Chem.* 91 (8): 5021–5027. https://doi.org/10.1021/acs.analchem.8b04979.

58 Guevremont, R. (2004). High-field asymmetric waveform ion mobility spectrometry: a new tool for mass spectrometry. *J. Chromatogr. A* 1058 (1): 3–19. https://doi.org/10.1016/j.chroma.2004.08.119.

59 Purves, R.W. and Guevremont, R. (1999). Electrospray ionization high-field asymmetric waveform ion mobility spectrometry—mass spectrometry. *Anal. Chem.* 71 (13): 2346–2357. https://doi.org/10.1021/ac981380y.

60 Guevremont, R. and Purves, R.W. (1999). Atmospheric pressure ion focusing in a high-field asymmetric waveform ion mobility spectrometer. *Rev. Sci. Instrum.* 70 (2): 1370–1383. https://doi.org/10.1063/1.1149599 (accessed 19 July 2022).

61 Kolakowski, B.M. and Mester, Z. (2007). Review of applications of high-field asymmetric waveform ion mobility spectrometry (FAIMS) and differential mobility spectrometry (DMS). *Analyst* 132 (9): 842–864. https://doi.org/10.1039/b706039d.

62 Zheng, X., Smith, R.D., and Baker, E.S. (2018). Recent advances in lipid separations and structural elucidation using mass spectrometry combined with ion mobility spectrometry, ion-molecule reactions and fragmentation approaches. *Curr. Opin. Chem. Biol.* 42: 111–118. https://doi.org/10.1016/j.cbpa.2017.11.009.

63 Deng, L., Ibrahim, Y.M., Hamid, A.M. et al. (2016). Ultra-high resolution ion mobility separations utilizing traveling waves in a 13 m serpentine path length structures for lossless ion manipulations module. *Anal. Chem.* 88 (18): 8957–8964. https://doi.org/10.1021/acs.analchem.6b01915.

64 Eldrid, C. and Thalassinos, K. (2020). Developments in tandem ion mobility mass spectrometry. *Biochem. Soc. Trans.* 48 (6): 2457–2466. https://doi.org/10.1042/BST20190788.

65 May, J.C., Knochenmuss, R., Fjeldsted, J.C., and McLean, J.A. (2020). Resolution of isomeric mixtures in ion mobility using a combined demultiplexing and peak deconvolution technique. *Anal. Chem.* 92 (14): 9482–9492. https://doi.org/10.1021/acs.analchem.9b05718.

66 Wojcik, R., Nagy, G., Attah, I.K. et al. (2019). SLIM ultrahigh resolution ion mobility spectrometry separations of isotopologues and isotopomers reveal mobility shifts due to mass distribution changes. *Anal. Chem.* 91 (18): 11952–11962. https://doi.org/10.1021/acs.analchem.9b02808.

67 Waraksa, E., Perycz, U., Namieśnik, J. et al. (2016). Dopants and gas modifiers in ion mobility spectrometry. *TrAC, Trends Anal. Chem.* 82: 237–249. https://doi.org/10.1016/j.trac.2016.06.009.

68 Dwivedi, P., Wu, C., Matz, L.M. et al. (2006). Gas-phase chiral separations by ion mobility spectrometry. *Anal. Chem.* 78 (24): 8200–8206. https://doi.org/10.1021/ac0608772.

69 Webb, I.K., Garimella, S.V., Tolmachev, A.V. et al. (2014). Experimental evaluation and optimization of structures for lossless ion manipulations for ion mobility spectrometry with time-of-flight mass spectrometry. *Anal. Chem.* 86 (18): 9169–9176. https://doi.org/10.1021/ac502055e.

70 Webb, I.K., Garimella, S.V., Tolmachev, A.V. et al. (2014). Mobility-resolved ion selection in uniform drift field ion mobility spectrometry/mass spectrometry: dynamic switching in structures for lossless ion manipulations. *Anal. Chem.* 86 (19): 9632–9637. https://doi.org/10.1021/ac502139e.

71 Ibrahim, Y.M., Hamid, A.M., Deng, L. et al. (2017). New frontiers for mass spectrometry based upon structures for lossless ion manipulations. *Analyst* 142 (7): 1010–1021. https://doi.org/10.1039/c7an00031f.

72 Li, A., Conant, C.R., Zheng, X. et al. (2020). Assessing collision cross section calibration strategies for traveling wave-based ion mobility separations in structures for lossless ion manipulations. *Anal. Chem.* 92 (22): 14976–14982. https://doi.org/10.1021/acs.analchem.0c02829.

73 Guevremont, R., Ding, L., Ells, B. et al. (2001). Atmospheric pressure ion trapping in a tandem FAIMS-FAIMS coupled to a TOFMS: studies with electrospray generated gramicidin S ions. *J. Am. Soc. Mass Spectrom.* 12 (12): 1320–1330. https://doi.org/10.1016/S1044-0305(01)00321-X.

74 Koeniger, S.L., Merenbloom, S.I., Valentine, S.J. et al. (2006). An IMS-IMS analogue of MS-MS. *Anal. Chem.* 78 (12): 4161–4174. https://doi.org/10.1021/ac051060w.

75 Shvartsburg, A.A., Anderson, G.A., and Smith, R.D. (2013). Pushing the frontier of high-definition ion mobility spectrometry using FAIMS. *Mass Spectrom. (Tokyo)* 2 (Special Issue): S0011. https://doi.org/10.5702/massspectrometry.S0011.

76 Ibrahim, Y.M., Baker, E.S., Danielson, W.F. et al. (2015). Development of a new ion mobility (quadrupole) time-of-flight mass spectrometer. *Int. J. Mass Spectrom.* 377: 655–662. https://doi.org/10.1016/j.ijms.2014.07.034.

77 Clowers, B.H., Siems, W.F., Hill, H.H., and Massick, S.M. (2006). Hadamard transform ion mobility spectrometry. *Anal. Chem.* 78 (1): 44–51. https://doi .org/10.1021/ac050615k.

78 Belov, M.E., Clowers, B.H., Prior, D.C. et al. (2008). Dynamically multiplexed ion mobility time-of-flight mass spectrometry. *Anal. Chem.* 80 (15): 5873–5883. https://doi.org/10.1021/ac8003665.

79 Bilbao, A., Gibbons, B.C., Stow, S.M. et al. (2021). A preprocessing tool for enhanced ion mobility-mass spectrometry-based omics workflows. *J. Proteome Res.* https://doi.org/10.1021/acs.jproteome.1c00425.

80 Kirk, A.T., Bohnhorst, A., Raddatz, C.R. et al. (2019). Ultra-high-resolution ion mobility spectrometry-current instrumentation, limitations, and future developments. *Anal. Bioanal. Chem.* 411 (24): 6229–6246. https://doi.org/10.1007/ s00216-019-01807-0.

81 Morris, C.B., May, J.C., Leaptrot, K.L., and McLean, J.A. (2019). Evaluating separation selectivity and collision cross section measurement reproducibility in helium, nitrogen, argon, and carbon dioxide drift gases for drift tube ion mobility-mass spectrometry. *J. Am. Soc. Mass Spectrom.* 30 (6): 1059–1068. https://doi .org/10.1007/s13361-019-02151-4.

82 Gabelica, V., Shvartsburg, A.A., Afonso, C. et al. (2019). Recommendations for reporting ion mobility mass spectrometry measurements. *Mass Spectrom. Rev.* 38 (3): 291–320. https://doi.org/10.1002/mas.21585.

83 Jackson, S.N., Ugarov, M., Post, J.D. et al. (2008). A study of phospholipids by ion mobility TOFMS. *J. Am. Soc. Mass Spectrom.* 19 (11): 1655–1662. https://doi .org/10.1016/j.jasms.2008.07.005.

84 Maccarone, A.T., Duldig, J., Mitchell, T.W. et al. (2014). Characterization of acyl chain position in unsaturated phosphatidylcholines using differential mobility-mass spectrometry. *J. Lipid Res.* 55 (8): 1668–1677. https://doi.org/10.1194/jlr .M046995.

85 Guevremont, R., Purves, R., and Barnett, D. (2004). FAIMS apparatus and method using carrier gas of mixed composition. United States US6774360B2.

86 Purves, R.W., Ozog, A.R., Ambrose, S.J. et al. (2014). Using gas modifiers to significantly improve sensitivity and selectivity in a cylindrical FAIMS device. *J. Am. Soc. Mass Spectrom.* 25 (7): 1274–1284. https://doi.org/10.1007/ s13361-014-0878-z.

87 Schneider, B.B., Covey, T.R., and Nazarov, E.G. (2013). DMS-MS separations with different transport gas modifiers. *Int. J. Ion Mobility Spectrom.* 16: 207–216.

88 Shvartsburg, A.A., Isaac, G., Leveque, N. et al. (2011). Separation and classification of lipids using differential ion mobility spectrometry. *J. Am. Soc. Mass Spectrom.* 22 (7): 1146–1155. https://doi.org/10.1007/s13361-011-0114-z.

89 Bowman, A.P., Abzalimov, R.R., and Shvartsburg, A.A. (2017). Broad separation of isomeric lipids by high-resolution differential ion mobility spectrometry with tandem mass spectrometry. *J. Am. Soc. Mass Spectrom.* 28 (8): 1552–1561. https://doi.org/10.1007/s13361-017-1675-2.

90 May, J.C., Morris, C.B., and McLean, J.A. (2017). Ion mobility collision cross section compendium. *Anal. Chem.* 89 (2): 1032–1044. https://doi.org/10.1021/acs.analchem.6b04905.

91 McLean, J.A. (2009). The mass-mobility correlation redux: the conformational landscape of anhydrous biomolecules. *J. Am. Soc. Mass Spectrom.* 20 (10): 1775–1781. https://doi.org/10.1016/j.jasms.2009.06.016.

92 Leaptrot, K.L., May, J.C., Dodds, J.N., and Mclean, J.A. (2019). Ion mobility conformational lipid atlas for high confidence lipidomics. *Nat. Commun.* 10 (1): https://doi.org/10.1038/s41467-019-08897-5 (accessed 19 July 2022).

93 Tu, J., Zhou, Z., Li, T., and Zhu, Z. (2019). The emerging role of ion mobility-mass spectrometry in lipidomics to facilitate lipid separation and identification. *TrAC, Trends Anal. Chem.* 116: 332–339. https://doi.org/10.1016/j.trac.2019.03.017.

94 Djambazova, K.V., Klein, D.R., Migas, L.G. et al. (2020). Resolving the complexity of spatial lipidomics using MALDI TIMS imaging mass spectrometry. *Anal. Chem.* 92 (19): 13290–13297. https://doi.org/10.1021/acs.analchem.0c02520.

95 Wojcik, R., Webb, I.K., Deng, L. et al. (2017). Lipid and glycolipid isomer analyses using ultra-high resolution ion mobility spectrometry separations. *Int. J. Mol. Sci.* 18 (1): https://doi.org/10.3390/ijms18010183.

96 Zhou, Z., Luo, M., Chen, X. et al. (2020). Ion mobility collision cross-section atlas for known and unknown metabolite annotation in untargeted metabolomics. *Nat. Commun.* 11 (1): 4334. https://doi.org/10.1038/s41467-020-18171-8.

97 Plante, P.L., Francovic-Fontaine, É., May, J.C. et al. (2019). Predicting ion mobility collision cross-sections using a Deep Neural Network: DeepCCS. *Anal. Chem.* 91 (8): 5191–5199. https://doi.org/10.1021/acs.analchem.8b05821.

98 Ross, D.H., Cho, J.H., and Xu, L. (2020). Breaking down structural diversity for comprehensive prediction of ion-neutral collision cross sections. *Anal. Chem.* 92 (6): 4548–4557. https://doi.org/10.1021/acs.analchem.9b05772.

99 Colby, S.M., Thomas, D.G., Nuñez, J.R. et al. (2019). ISiCLE: a quantum chemistry pipeline for establishing in silico collision cross section libraries. *Anal. Chem.* 91 (7): 4346–4356. https://doi.org/10.1021/acs.analchem.8b04567.

100 Paglia, G., Angel, P., Williams, J.P. et al. (2015). Ion mobility-derived collision cross section as an additional measure for lipid fingerprinting and identification. *Anal. Chem.* 87 (2): 1137–1144. https://doi.org/10.1021/ac503715v.

101 Maclean, B.X., Pratt, B.S., Egertson, J.D. et al. (2018). Using skyline to analyze data-containing liquid chromatography, ion mobility spectrometry, and mass spectrometry dimensions. *J. Am. Soc. Mass Spectrom.* 29 (11): 2182–2188. https://doi.org/10.1007/s13361-018-2028-5 (accessed 19 July 2022).

102 Beveridge, R. and Calabrese, A.N. (2021). Structural proteomics methods to interrogate the conformations and dynamics of intrinsically disordered proteins. *Front. Chem.* s: 603639. https://doi.org/10.3389/fchem.2021.603639.

103 Marklund, E.G., Degiacomi, M.T., Robinson, C.V. et al. (2015). Collision cross sections for structural proteomics. *Structure* 23 (4): 791–799. https://doi.org/10.1016/j.str.2015.02.010.

104 Bush, M.F., Hall, Z., Giles, K. et al. (2010). Collision cross sections of proteins and their complexes: a calibration framework and database for gas-phase structural biology. *Anal. Chem.* 82 (22): 9557–9565. https://doi.org/10.1021/ac1022953.

105 Kim, H.I., Kim, H., Pang, E.S. et al. (2009). Structural characterization of unsaturated phosphatidylcholines using traveling wave ion mobility spectrometry. *Anal. Chem.* 81 (20): 8289–8297. https://doi.org/10.1021/ac900672a.

106 Han, X. and Gross, R.W. (2005). Shotgun lipidomics: electrospray ionization mass spectrometric analysis and quantitation of cellular lipidomes directly from crude extracts of biological samples. *Mass Spectrom. Rev.* 24 (3): 367–412. https://doi.org/10.1002/mas.20023.

107 Buchberger, A.R., DeLaney, K., Johnson, J., and Li, L. (2018). Mass spectrometry imaging: a review of emerging advancements and future insights. *Anal. Chem.* 90 (1): 240–265. https://doi.org/10.1021/acs.analchem.7b04733.

108 Sans, M., Feider, C.L., and Eberlin, L.S. (2018). Advances in mass spectrometry imaging coupled to ion mobility spectrometry for enhanced imaging of biological tissues. *Curr. Opin. Chem. Biol.* 42: 138–146. https://doi.org/10.1016/j.cbpa.2017.12.005.

109 Lintonen, T.P., Baker, P.R., Suoniemi, M. et al. (2014). Differential mobility spectrometry-driven shotgun lipidomics. *Anal. Chem.* 86 (19): 9662–9669. https://doi.org/10.1021/ac5021744.

110 Hancock, S.E., Poad, B.L.J., Willcox, M.D.P. et al. (2019). Analytical separations for lipids in complex, nonpolar lipidomes using differential mobility spectrometry. *J. Lipid Res.* 60 (11): 1968–1978. https://doi.org/10.1194/jlr.D094854.

111 Wormwood Moser, K.L., Van Aken, G., DeBord, D. et al. (2021). High-defined quantitative snapshots of the ganglioside lipidome using high resolution ion mobility SLIM assisted shotgun lipidomics. *Anal. Chim. Acta* 1146: 77–87. https://doi.org/10.1016/j.aca.2020.12.022.

112 Li, T., Yin, Y., Zhou, Z. et al. (2021). Ion mobility-based sterolomics reveals spatially and temporally distinctive sterol lipids in the mouse brain. *Nat. Commun.* 12 (1): 4343. https://doi.org/10.1038/s41467-021-24672-x.

113 Nys, G., Nix, C., Cobraiville, G. et al. (2020). Enhancing protein discoverability by data independent acquisition assisted by ion mobility mass spectrometry. *Talanta* 213: 120812. https://doi.org/10.1016/j.talanta.2020.120812.

114 Castro-Perez, J., Roddy, T.P., Nibbering, N.M. et al. (2011). Localization of fatty acyl and double bond positions in phosphatidylcholines using a dual stage CID fragmentation coupled with ion mobility mass spectrometry. *J. Am. Soc. Mass Spectrom.* 22 (9): 1552–1567. https://doi.org/10.1007/s13361-011-0172-2.

115 Paglia, G. and Astarita, G. (2017). Metabolomics and lipidomics using traveling-wave ion mobility mass spectrometry. *Nat. Protoc.* 12 (4): 797–813. https://doi.org/10.1038/nprot.2017.013.

116 Ma, X., Liu, J., Zhang, Z. et al. (2017). Drift tube ion mobility and four-dimensional molecular feature extraction enable data-independent tandem mass spectrometric 'omics' analysis without quadrupole selection. *Rapid Commun. Mass Spectrom.* 31 (1): 33–38. https://doi.org/10.1002/rcm.7767.

117 Becker, C., Fernandez-Lima, F.A., Gillig, K.J. et al. (2009). A novel approach to collision-induced dissociation (CID) for ion mobility-mass spectrometry experiments. *J. Am. Soc. Mass Spectrom.* 20 (6): 907–914. https://doi.org/10.1016/j.jasms.2008.11.026.

118 Baker, E.S., Tang, K., Danielson, W.F. et al. (2008). Simultaneous fragmentation of multiple ions using IMS drift time dependent collision energies. *J. Am. Soc. Mass Spectrom.* 19 (3): 411–419. https://doi.org/10.1016/j.jasms.2007.11.018.

119 Feuerstein, M.L., Kurulugama, R.T., Hann, S., and Causon, T. (2021). Novel acquisition strategies for metabolomics using drift tube ion mobility-quadrupole resolved all ions time-of-flight mass spectrometry (IM-QRAI-TOFMS). *Anal. Chim. Acta* 1163: 338508. https://doi.org/10.1016/j.aca.2021.338508.

120 Poad, B.L.J., Zheng, X., Mitchell, T.W. et al. (2018). Online ozonolysis combined with ion mobility-mass spectrometry provides a new platform for lipid isomer analyses. *Anal. Chem.* 90 (2): 1292–1300. https://doi.org/10.1021/acs.analchem.7b04091.

121 Xia, T., Yuan, M., Xu, Y. et al. (2021). Deep structural annotation of glycerolipids by the charge-tagging Paterno–Büchi reaction and supercritical fluid chromatography-ion mobility mass spectrometry. *Anal. Chem.* 93 (23): 8345–8353. https://doi.org/10.1021/acs.analchem.1c01379.

122 Cody, R.B. and Freiser, B.S. (1979). Electron impact excitation of ions from organics: an alternative to collision induced dissociation. *Anal. Chem.* 51 (4): 96–101.

123 Baba, T., Campbell, J.L., Le Blanc, J.C.Y. et al. (2018). Quantitative structural multiclass lipidomics using differential mobility: electron impact excitation of ions from organics (EIEIO) mass spectrometry. *J. Lipid Res.* 59 (5): 910–919. https://doi.org/10.1194/jlr.D083261.

7

Structural Characterization of Lipids Using Advanced Mass Spectrometry Approaches

Josef Cvačka, Vladimír Vrkoslav, and Štěpán Strnad

Institute of Organic Chemistry and Biochemistry of the Czech Academy of Sciences, Mass Spectrometry Group, Flemingovo náměstí 542/2, Prague, CZ-166 00, Czech Republic

7.1 Introduction

Mass spectrometry determines the structure of lipids by measuring the masses of ions and their fragments [1]. Various ions can be formed in the ion sources. These ions can be positive or negative, singly or sometimes multiply charged, odd- or even-electron species. Lipids that do not provide structurally informative fragments can be chemically modified [2]. The nature of the lipid ions depends on the ion source type, its settings, and the solvents and additives used. In atmospheric-pressure ion sources, protonated, or deprotonated molecules are often formed. As fragmentation of these ions may not always provide sufficient information, other ion types, including alkali, alkali earth, or transition metal adducts, are employed to access alternative fragmentation channels. It can sometimes be advantageous to form and fragment ions having an odd number of electrons. Such ions are typically formed in electron ionization (EI) sources operated at low pressure. Odd electron ions can be, however, formed from some lipids in atmospheric-pressure ions sources as well by using specific conditions in atmospheric-pressure chemical ionization (APCI) or atmospheric-pressure photoionization (APPI) [3]. Certain lipid derivatives make it possible to obtain radical ions by fragmenting precursor ions with an even number of electrons. An example is electrospray ionization of iodine-containing derivatives and their subsequent activation by UV photons [4].

Lipid ions can be activated in several ways, using interactions with neutral gaseous molecules, solid surfaces, photons, or electrons [5]. Chemical reactions can also be considered as a way to activate ions [6]. Collision-induced dissociation (CID), also referred to as collisionally activated dissociation (CAD), induces the fragmentation of ions by accelerating them and colliding them with neutral atoms or molecules in the gas phase. Low-energy CID is the most frequently used fragmentation technique, implemented in virtually all tandem mass spectrometers. High-energy CID is very

Mass Spectrometry for Lipidomics: Methods and Applications, First Edition.
Edited by Michal Holčapek and Kim Ekroos.
© 2023 WILEY-VCH GmbH. Published 2023 by WILEY-VCH GmbH.

useful for lipid structural analysis because it opens fragmentation channels that are not accessible in low-energy CID, for instance, charge-remote fragmentation (CRF). Unfortunately, CID with the ion kinetic energies in the kilovolt range is limited to less common mass spectrometers such as magnetic sector and tandem time-of-flight instruments. Collisions between precursor ions and a solid target surface take place in surface-induced dissociation (SID). In theory, the use of a massive surface target leads to higher energy deposition on the activated ions. Therefore, SID is particularly useful for characterizing large systems like protein complexes, including those binding lipids [7, 8]. Although SID was pioneered more than 40 years ago, commercial instruments with SID capabilities appeared only recently, and applications of SID to lipids have yet to be explored. Interactions with photons are used in photodissociation techniques [9]. In a photodissociation experiment, an ion is excited above the dissociation threshold by absorption of a single photon or sequential absorption of several photons of equal or different energy. While high-energy photons may induce single-photon fragmentation, low-energy photons activate an ion gradually, similar to the slow heating process achieved by many collisions in low-energy CID. Low-energy photons find application in infrared multiple photon dissociation (IRMPD) that provides fragmentation of the most labile bonds. Both low-energy CID and IRMPD afford relatively simple spectra that characterize building blocks and the main structural features of lipids. They typically do not provide detailed information on the acyl chains structure. In contrast, ultraviolet photodissociation (UVPD) promotes specific fragmentations, including carbon–carbon bond cleavages along the acyl chains. The energy of ultraviolet photons is high enough to excite electronic states of ions, which results in higher-energy dissociation pathways. Since UV photons of different energy may excite ions to different electronic states, UVPD spectra vary depending on the laser wavelength [10]. Ion fragmentation induced by electrons is used in several methods, including electron capture dissociation (ECD), electron transfer dissociation (ETD), electron-induced dissociation (EID), and electron detachment dissociation (EDD). They are collectively termed electron-ion reaction-based dissociation (ExD) methods [11]. ECD and ETD are typically used for peptides and proteins. Their multiply charged cations interact with thermal (<1 eV) electrons (ECD) or reactive radical anions (ETD) to form charge-reduced, odd-electron ions which readily fragment. The use of ECD/ETD for lipids is limited because these molecules do not tend to provide multiply charged ions. Nevertheless, doubly charged lipid ions can be formed by adding divalent metal ions [12] or two monovalent ions [13]. In EDD, irradiating of multiply charged anions by electrons (>10 eV) causes the loss of an electron and the formation of charge-reduced excited ions that break down into fragments. EDD finds application in the structural analysis of glycolipids [14]. In contrast to ECD/ETD and EDD, EID is used to induce fragmentation in singly charged ions, typically formed from lipids. Multiple interactions with high-energy (>10 eV) electrons lead to electronic and vibrational excitations. EID provides information-rich spectra with extensive cleavages across the acyl chains.

The use of mass spectrometry for lipids dates back to the origins of organic mass spectrometry. Many methods for structural analysis of lipids have been developed and applied to countless samples. In recent years, we have witnessed the rapid development of new methods that make it possible to characterize lipid structures faster, in more detail, and from more complex mixtures. This great progress is made possible, among other things, by the availability of new mass spectrometers with improved parameters that are capable of novel ways of ion analysis and fragmentation. The basic characterization of lipids from their spectra, i.e. determining the lipid class, acyl chain lengths, and degree of unsaturation is usually straightforward. However, more detailed structural characterization, such as determining the position of unsaturated bonds, stereoisomerism of double bonds, the position of functional groups in acyl chains, etc. is considerably more challenging.

This chapter deals with applications of advanced mass spectrometry for characterizing acyl chains in lipids. It covers atmospheric-pressure ionization of liquid samples, i.e. the methods most used in current lipidomics workflows. The chapter is divided according to the typical structural elements we encounter in lipid molecules.

7.2 Structure and Position of Aliphatic Chains in Lipids

7.2.1 Double and Triple Bonds

Lipids can form double- or triple-bond positional isomers. The position and stereoisomerism of unsaturated bonds play critical roles in the biophysical and biochemical properties of lipids and can significantly influence the development of many pathologies [15].

The localization of double bonds in unsaturated aliphatic chains of lipids is a classical analytical problem that can be addressed by mass spectrometry. The first methods developed for localizing double bonds were based on EI. Fragments indicating the double-bond position can be obtained from lipids derivatized at either the double-bond site [16] or a distant functional group [17]. In the first case, the newly introduced groups weaken the carbon–carbon bond at the original double-bond site, while the second approach relies on gas-phase decompositions that occur physically remote from the charge site. The derivatization strategies utilizing charge-proximal and charge-remote fragmentations were later developed for soft ionizations; some of these methods will be discussed in the following sections. Distinguishing double-bond stereoisomers (cis/trans isomers) is comparatively easy using chromatography, but it might be difficult from mass spectra because it usually relies on relatively small differences in fragment ion abundances. Evidence for double-bond geometry can be found in high-energy CID [18], EID [19], or ozone-induced dissociation (OzID) [20] spectra.

Only a few methods for determining the position of triple bonds in lipids have been developed to date. EI spectra of 4,4-dimethyloxazoline (DMOX) derivatives of fatty acids with triple bonds show CRF ions separated by 10 Da [21]. Fatty acids with triple bonds were also investigated by acetonitrile covalent adduct chemical ionization (CI) [22]. Probably the only atmospheric-pressure ionization method for pinpointing triple-bond positions utilizes gas-phase chemistry of acetonitrile in APCI [23].

7.2.1.1 Charge-Switch Derivatization of Fatty Acids

Fatty acid identification and structural analysis have traditionally been performed by (GC)/EI-MS [24]. The most informative spectra are obtained for derivatives with a readily chargeable functional group where a positive charge is fixed after ionization, e.g. pyrrolidides [25, 26], picolinyl (3-hydroxymethylpyridinyl) esters [17], or DMOXs [17, 27]. CRF pathways in straight, unsubstituted alkyl chains yield groups of ions separated by 14 mass units. The presence of a functional group causes changes in the peak pattern, which is helpful for the localization of double bonds [28], alkyl (most frequently methyl) branching [28], hydroxyl [29], epoxy [30], cyclopropane [31], and other groups within the acyl chain. In addition to positively charged ions, deprotonated fatty acids can be created by fast atom bombardment (FAB) and fragmented by high-energy CID to obtain informative CRF ions [32].

The advent of atmospheric-pressure ionization techniques, especially electrospray, has made it possible to analyze fatty acids by HPLC/MS or direct infusion of a liquid sample into a mass spectrometer. Analysis of underivatized fatty acids by electrospray ionization (ESI-MS) is not very useful because the detection sensitivity is low, and low-energy CID spectra are uninformative regarding the structure of the aliphatic chains. A dramatic increase in the signal is achieved after derivatizations that introduce a permanent positive charge [33–36]. Since the derivatives with a permanent positive charge originate from molecules that are easily deprotonated to negatively charged ions, the reaction is referred to as charge-switch derivatization. Among the derivatives, *N*-(4-aminomethylphenyl)pyridinium ($AMPP^+$) amides proved particularly helpful in the structural analysis of fatty acids [37] (Figure 7.1). The reagent was designed to minimize fragmentations of the derivatives close to the permanent charge site, thus providing CRF ions at appreciable intensities. Importantly, $AMPP^+$ is commercially available.

The CID spectra of $AMPP^+$-derivatized saturated fatty acids [37] show a periodic pattern of fragments separated by 14 mass units. These ions are products of carbon–carbon bond cleavages, likely formed by the 1,4-H_2 elimination mechanism. The presence of double bond(s) disrupts the pattern by lowering some ions' intensities and creating new fragments that unambiguously identify the positions of double bonds. All $AMPP^+$-derivatized fatty acids provide the same fragments by the amide and benzyl bond cleavages, which can be utilized for precursor ion scan (PIS) profiling of a wide range of fatty acids (Figure 7.2).

Besides double bonds, $AMPP^+$ derivatives help localize other features on acyl chains like methyl branching sites [38, 39] or hydroxy groups [40, 41]. To increase the abundance of CRF ions providing information on structural features in the aliphatic chains, new derivatives capable of generating odd-electron ions were

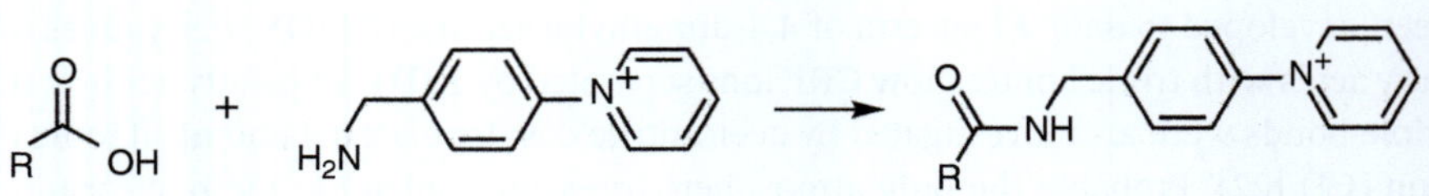

Figure 7.1 Reaction scheme for derivatization of fatty acid with *N*-(4-aminomethylphenyl) pyridinium ($AMPP^+$).

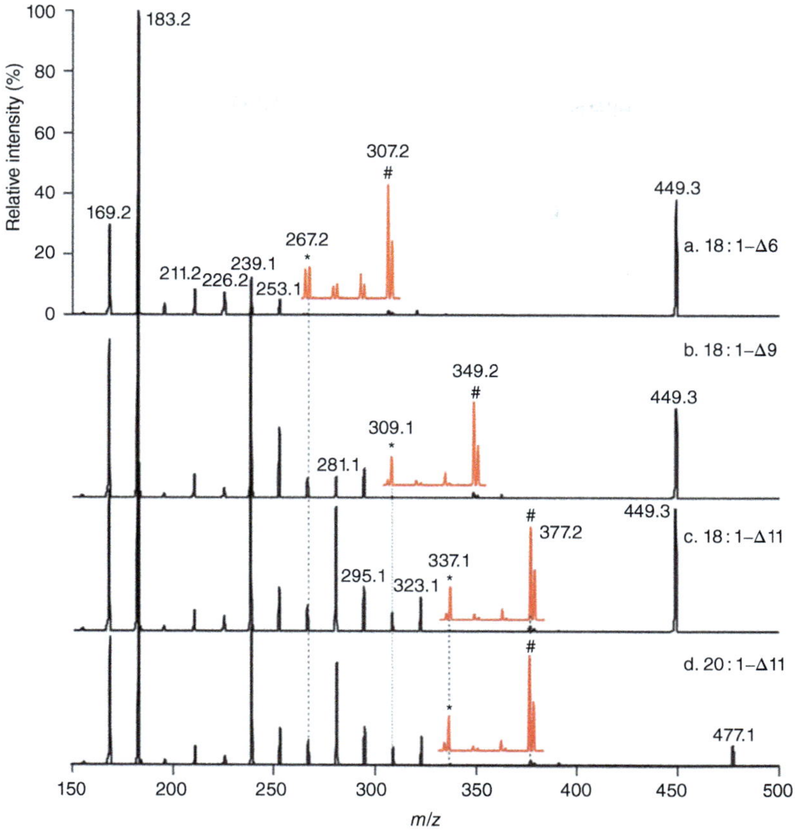

Figure 7.2 Tandem mass spectra of AMPP$^+$-derivatized monounsaturated FAs having different double-bond positions. Source: Reprinted with permission from Yang et al. [37]. Copyright 2013 American Chemical Society.

developed [42]. The radical ions are produced by photodissociation of electrospray-generated, even electron precursors containing photocleavable iodine. The derivatives, 1-(3-(aminomethyl)-4-iodophenyl)pyridin-1-ium (4-I-AMPP$^+$) or 1-(4-(aminomethyl)-3-iodophenyl)pyridin-1-ium (3-I-AMPP$^+$), are conjugated to fatty acids using a similar protocol developed for AMPP$^+$ [36].

Irradiation of the mass-selected precursor ions with a UV (266 nm) laser yields $[M-I]^{\bullet+}$ radical cation and secondary fragment ions that correspond to acyl chain cleavages and to the elimination of the AMPP$^+$ moiety (Figure 7.3).

7.2.1.2 Ozone-Induced Dissociation

The reaction of the double bond with ozone was described in 1847 by Christian F. Schönbein [43], and its mechanism was proposed a 100 years later by Rudolf Criegee [44]. The reactants first form an unstable molozonide (1,2,3-trioxolane), which reverts to its corresponding carbonyl oxide (Criegee intermediate) and

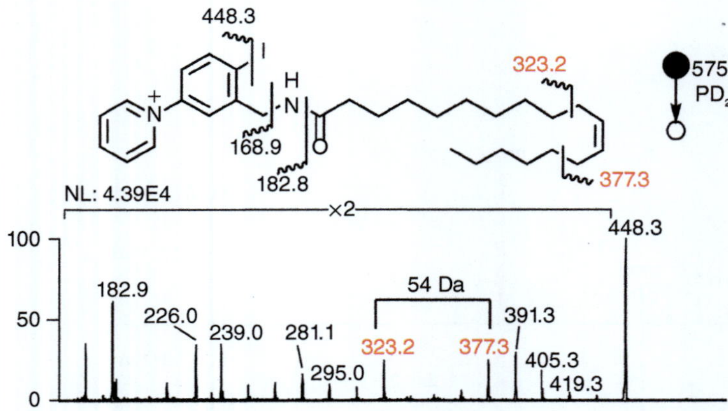

Figure 7.3 Photodissociation mass spectrum of 4-I-AMPP+ derivative of cis-vaccenic acid. Source: Reprinted with permission from Narreddula et al. [42]. Copyright 2019 American Chemical Society.

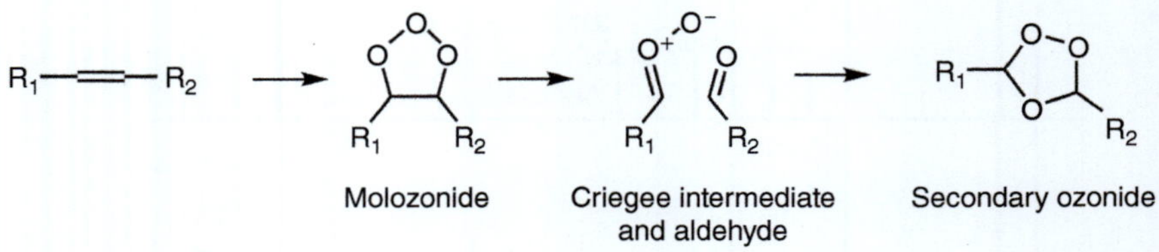

Figure 7.4 Reaction scheme for derivatization of the double bond with ozone.

aldehyde. The oxide and aldehyde react again to produce a secondary ozonide with a 1,2,4-trioxolane structure (Figure 7.4).

The decomposition of ozonides leads to aldehydes which can be used to determine the position of a double bond. In the 1960s, a one-step method was developed. It was based on the thermal decomposition of ozonide in a GC injector, followed by a separation of breakdown products [45]. The first mass spectrometric analysis of intact ozonides was conducted with CI [46]. Later, electrospray ionization tandem mass spectrometry of phosphatidylcholine ozonides was shown to provide fragments indicative of the double-bond position [47, 48]. In the following years, ozonization developed into a widely used approach for determining the positions of double bonds. The reaction of unsaturated lipids with ozone can take place at various stages of mass spectrometric analysis, as indicated in Figure 7.5.

The major contribution to the analytical use of ozonolysis was made by the group of Blanksby [20, 51, 52, 54–73]. They proposed reacting the analytes with ozone directly in a mass spectrometer, initially in an electrospray ion source (referred to as ozone electrospray ionization mass spectrometry, OzESI-MS) and later in various mass analyzers (OzID). The first ion source ozonizations were carried out with oxygen nebulizing gas, and an electrospray needle tip was kept at a high negative potential, creating ozone-producing plasma [54]. Later, an external generator was

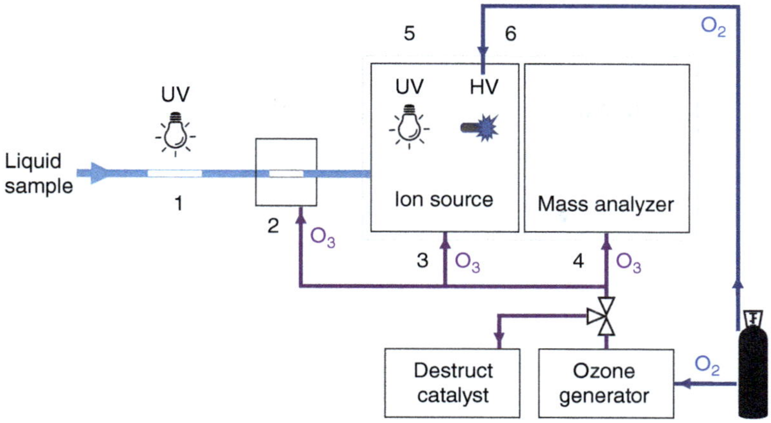

Figure 7.5 Schematic representation of various possibilities of ozonolysis in an LC/MS instrument. (1) ozonolysis in a liquid phase after irradiating the sample in a fused silica flow cell with UV light [49]; (2) ozonolysis in a liquid phase by ozone penetrating through semi-permeable Teflon tubing (O_3-MS) [50]; (3) in-source ozonolysis during electrospray ionization (OzESI) [51]; (4) ozone-induced dissociation (OzID) in a mass analyzer [52]; (5) in-source ozonolysis using ozone generated by irradiation of oxygen with UV light [53]; (6) in-source ozonolysis using ozone generated from oxygen by a corona discharge [54].

employed to deliver ozone into the ion source, which improved sensitivity and made it possible to use both ionization polarities [51]. OzESI-MS yields fragments of two types for each double bond: an aldehyde and a Criegee intermediate, which adds methanol from the solvent. To overcome the method's limitations for complex mixtures, ozonization of mass-selected ions (referred to as OzID) was developed. During OzID, lipid ions are exposed to ozone within a mass analyzer [20, 52, 55–57, 59–65, 67–76]. The first implementation of OzID was realized on a Thermo ion trap mass spectrometer modified to introduce ozone through helium (buffer gas) supply line [52]. Two diagnostics product ions were formed for each double bond, allowing for unambiguous assignment of double-bond position(s), see Figures 7.6 and 7.7.

The performance of OzID was significantly improved using a hybrid triple quadrupole linear ion trap mass spectrometer from AB SCIEX, where the ion selection, reaction with ozone, and product detection are physically separated from each other [20]. Improved detection sensitivity and speed were achieved due to higher ozone concentrations in the buffer gas. Interpretable OzID spectra were acquired on the sub-second timescale, making the method suitable for high-throughput lipidomic workflows, including the LC/MS-based ones [61, 62]. OzID proved to be useful for investigating double-bond geometry and the position of the unsaturated acyl chain on the glycerol backbone [20]. The experiments indicated that the reactivity of cis and trans double bonds with ozone are markedly different, which manifests itself in different intensity ratios of OzID product ions in the spectra (Figure 7.8). For a range of lipid classes, the reactivity of trans isomer is higher [68, 73, 74].

The reaction rate of ozonolysis also depends on the nature of adducted alkali metal and the arrangement of double bonds within aliphatic chains of lipids [59].

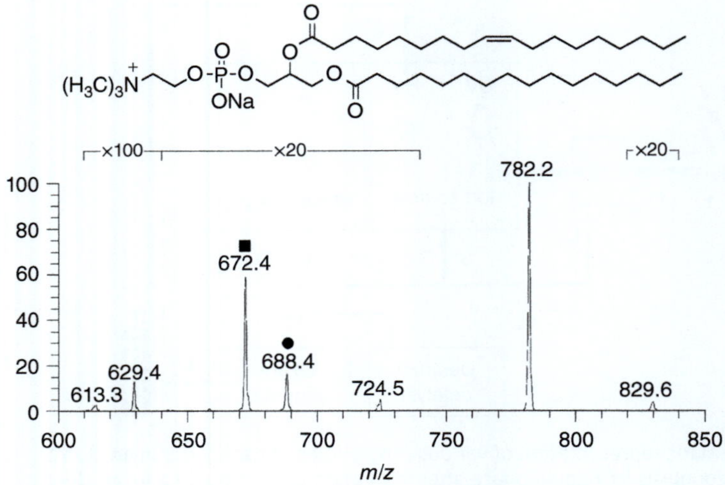

Figure 7.6 OzID mass spectrum of phosphatidylcholine PC (16:0/9*Z*-18:1) sodium adduct. Source: Reprinted with permission from Thomas et al. [52]. Copyright 2008 American Chemical Society.

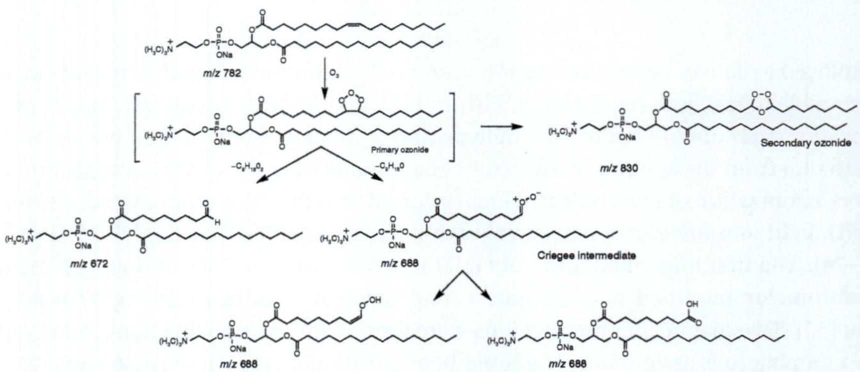

Figure 7.7 Proposed mechanism for the reaction of [PC (16:0/9*Z*-18:1)+Na]$^+$ with ozone during OzID. Source: Reprinted with permission from Thomas et al. [52]. Copyright 2008 American Chemical Society.

In the case of octadecadienoic fatty acid methyl esters (FAMEs) with conjugated double bonds (conjugated linoleic acids, CLAs), the reaction is so fast that the trapping step is no longer needed, and a beam-type instrument such as a triple quadrupole can be used for OzID [59].

OzID can be combined with CID to achieve even more detailed structural information. The CID/OzID experiments on a single-stage linear ion trap or a quadrupole-linear ion trap (QTRAP) are useful for the unambiguous assignment of double-bond position (s) and the *sn*-position of fatty acyl chains in glycerophospholipids [60]. OzID can be realized in traveling-wave-based quadrupole time-of-flight mass spectrometers. Two research groups presented their implementations at the

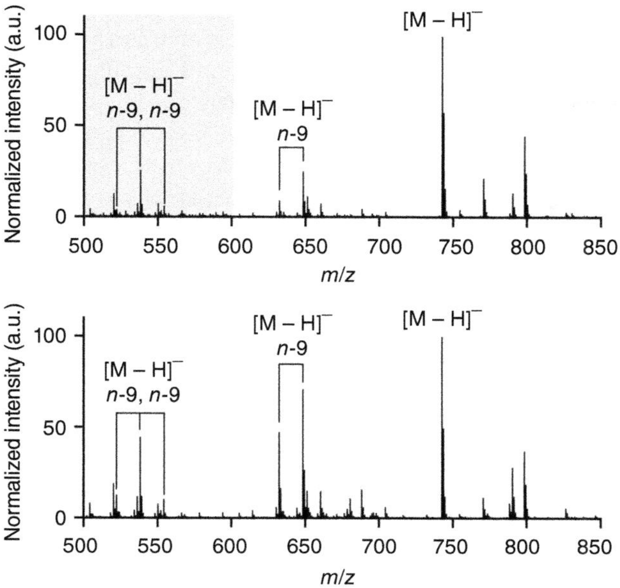

Figure 7.8 OzID spectra of phosphatidylethanolamine (PE) 18:1 (*n*-9, cis)/18:1 (*n*-9, cis) (upper spectrum) and PE 18:1 (*n*-9, trans)/18:1 (*n*-9, trans) (lower spectrum) showing higher intensities of OzID product ions for the trans isomer. Source: Reprinted with permission from Poad et al. [68]. Copyright 2018 American Chemical Society.

same time, using different generations of Synapt mass spectrometers (Waters) [64, 74]. In one arrangement, ozone was introduced into the trap and transfer cells using a collision gas line [74], while in the other approach, ozone was directed to the high-pressure ion-mobility separation cell [64]. In both configurations, modification of the stacked ring ion guides settings was required to achieve optimum performance. High ozone concentrations ensured abundant OzID product ions and short analysis times, which outperformed the previous OzID implementations. The Synapt implementation is compatible with ultrahigh-performance liquid chromatography as demonstrated when separating isomeric phosphatidylcholines [64]. OzID implemented on a high-resolution instrument can help to increase the number of identified lipids in shotgun lipidomics, as demonstrated with plasma samples [71]. The experiments were carried out with an Orbitrap hybrid mass spectrometer (Thermo) modified to introduce ozone via an higher-energy collisional dissociation (HCD) gas supply line to an octopole collision cell. The instrument's high resolution made it possible to distinguish between nearly isobaric lipids like plasmalogens and plasmanyl ether lipids. OzID combined with ion mobility offers another attractive method for analyzing lipid isomers in biological samples. The discrimination of double-bond stereoisomers in LC-OzID-ion mobility spectrometry (IMS)-MS was demonstrated using an Agilent IMS quadrupole time of flight (QTOF) mass spectrometer [68]. The instrument was modified to introduce ozone into the high-pressure trapping ion funnel region preceding the IMS cell. The fast reaction of trapped ions with ozone yielded OzID product ions allowing for the identification of double-bond positions. Geometric isomers exhibit different arrival times and different OzID product ion ratios, making it possible to discriminate cis/trans double bonds. The workflow does not include any mass selection step, which reduces the duty cycle and makes it consistent with high throughput lipidomics [68]. The effect of metals on the ion mobility separation and OzID was investigated for phosphatidylcholines and triacylglycerols using high-resolution differential field asymmetric waveform ion mobility spectrometry (FAIMS) coupled to an ion trap instrument [73]. Although cationization with Ag^+ and Cu^+ improved the ion mobility separation, it diminished OzID yield, likely due to strong interactions of metals with double bonds. As discussed in Section 7.2.1.1, $AMPP^+$ derivatives improve fatty acid detection due to the fixed positive charge. Easy ion formation is useful for sensitive OzID, which provides straightforward identification of the site(s) of unsaturation [72]. OzID of $AMPP^+$ derivatives is particularly useful for direct infusion (shotgun) workflows. The method is initiated by a CID precursor ion scan for the AMPP headgroup fragment, which triggers OzID analysis. The workflow has been applied for structural analysis of the fatty acids in vernix caseosa [72]. OzID was shown to provide information on double bonds in a range of lipids, including phospholipids [20, 52, 55, 60–65, 68, 71, 73, 74], sphingolipids [52, 67, 68, 75, 77], acylglycerols [20, 52, 68, 71, 73], fatty acid methyl esters [59, 74], (*O*-acyl) hydroxy fatty acids [66], $AMPP^+$ derivatives of fatty acids [72], cholesteryl esters [68, 70, 71], and plant metabolites [69, 76].

OzID is an excellent tool for studying the structure of unsaturated lipids, but it does require instrument modifications. If such instrumentation is not available, ozonolysis can be achieved by simply using an in-line reactor in front of a mass spectrometer [50]. The liquid sample flows through a length of Teflon tubing inserted into a bottle containing ozone. Unsaturated lipids react with the ozone that penetrates the tubing wall, and the aldehyde ozonolysis products are subsequently ionized in an ion source (O_3-MS). This approach was coupled to LC and used to identify FAMEs [50], including CLA isomers [78] and phospholipids [79, 80]. Another way to perform ozonolysis in solution is based on the irradiation of a fused silica capillary with a low-pressure mercury UV lamp [49]. Oxygen dissolved in the mobile phase is converted to ozone and reacts with unsaturated lipids. The device coupled to ion mobility mass spectrometry allows for the determination of the double-bond position in multiple lipid species. In another online device, the microreactor consists of a semi-preparative Teflon tubing wrapped around a UV lamp [53]. Ambient ozone generated by the lamp diffuses into the reactor and initiates the ozonolysis reaction. The UV lamp can also be placed close to the emitter in the nanoESI ion source [53].

7.2.1.3 Paternò–Büchi Reaction

The Paternò–Büchi (PB) reaction, known since 1909 [81], is a photochemical reaction between a carbonyl compound and an alkene that yields oxetane products (Figure 7.9). It is used in organic chemistry as a typical [2+2] cycloaddition.

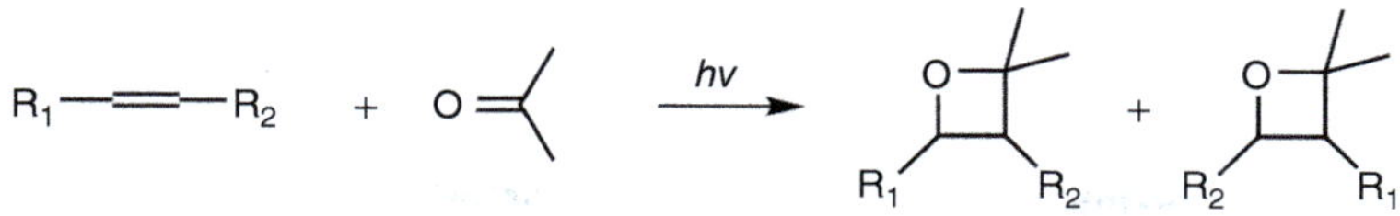

Figure 7.9 Reaction scheme of Paternò–Büchi derivatization of the double bond with acetone.

The usefulness of the PB reaction for localizing double bonds in lipids was demonstrated by Ma and Xia in 2014 [82]. They irradiated a nanoelectrospray plume with lipids and acetone using a low-pressure mercury UV lamp (254 nm). The oxetane products formed from the lipids were fragmented by CID, yielding retro-PB product ions specific to the double-bond location (Figure 7.10).

The PB-MS/MS method has several advantages: simple experimental setup, fast derivatization, applicability to multiple lipid classes, and reagents compatible with ESI ionization and LC [83, 84]. Since its introduction, the method has been used to characterize a wide range of unsaturated lipids, including phospholipids [85–93], sphingolipids [94], glycerolipids [95–97], fatty acids [98–102], and steroids [103–105] in different matrices.

Acetone used in the original paper [82] is still the most widely used PB reagent. It offers compatibility with ESI ionization, good solubility for lipids with a wide range of polarities, and miscibility with water and organic solvents [82, 83, 106]. The disadvantage is its proneness to side reactions, which reduce the reaction yield and detection sensitivity. The side reactions include lipid oxidation and the addition of acetyl radicals to lipids (Norrish reactions) [82]. PB reagents for light sources operating at longer wavelengths, including benzophenone [89, 102], benzaldehyde [107], acetylpyridines (APs) [93], 2-benzoylpyridine [108], and anthraquinone [109], have been proposed to overcome the limitation. Activating the carbonyl group with lower-energy photons diminishes side reactions [110], and the light sources of longer wavelengths minimize health risks [101, 109]. The introduction of electron-withdrawing groups can improve the yield of the PB reaction. For instance, 2,4,6-trifluoroacetophenone offers a good reaction yield for different types of double bonds and a significant reduction of chemical interferences [111]. The first work on

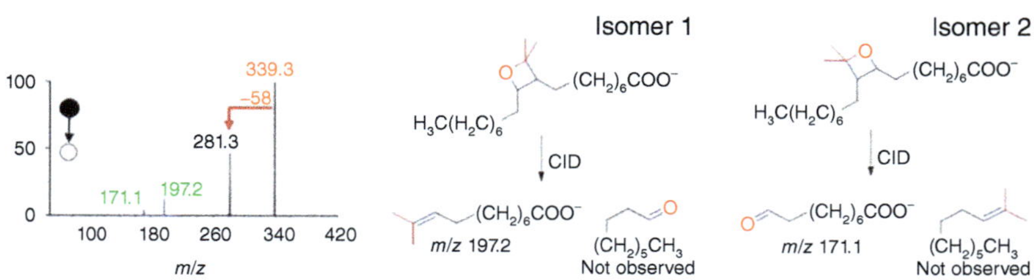

Figure 7.10 ESI CID MS^2 spectrum and fragmentation scheme of PB reaction products of oleic acid. Source: Ma and Xia [82]. Copyright 2014 Wiley-VCH GmbH. Reproduced with permission.

the formation of oxetanes under visible light used benzophenone and a fluorescent lamp (>400 nm) or an optical parametric oscillator (OPO) laser (520 nm) [112]. The [2+2] cycloaddition reaction leads to the formation of oxetanes by a different mechanism than the Paternò–Büchi reaction. The visible light activates a proton-bound complex formed from the reagent and unsaturated lipid rather than the carbonyl group itself, as in the PB reaction initiated by UV light.

PB derivatizations performed online or offline are used in various lipidomic workflows, namely in shotgun approaches [82, 85, 102, 106] and LC/MS [90, 92, 113, 114]. In a shotgun approach, a nanoESI tip is irradiated by a UV or VIS lamp, and the derivatized lipids are directly characterized by MS^2 [82]. Since detecting low abundant species can be challenging in shotgun workflows, chromatography-based approaches offer a solution. LC separation can be coupled to a flow microreactor, where the derivatization reaction takes place [92]. PB-MS^2 is also applicable for single-cell analysis [97]. The derivatization reaction is achieved in a micropipette needle that acts as a single-cell sampling probe, cell lysis container, PB microreactor, and nanoESI emitter [97]. The PB reaction can also be performed on platforms involving ion mobility to improve the separation and identification of lipids further [96, 115]. Xie and Xia developed a method for the quantitative analysis of conjugated fatty acids. It combines PB derivatization with trapped ion mobility spectrometry (TIMS) before MS^2 to determine the CLAs geometry and double-bond position [115].

7.2.1.4 Epoxidation of Double Bonds

Epoxidation-based methods were originally developed for GC/MS [16]. They were later adapted for the liquid phase, extending their applicability to non-volatile lipids like glycerophospholipids. The reaction can be performed by selective chemical derivatization before MS analysis [116–119], using plasma [120–122], or electrochemical reactions [123, 124]. *Meta*-chloroperoxybenzoic acid (*m*-CPBA) is frequently used for gentle epoxidation of double bonds [116, 117]. The reaction is fast, quantitative, and yields minimum overoxidized byproducts. The epoxide group can be cleaved by CID to generate characteristic pair of fragments, an alkene and an aldehyde differing by 15.9949 Da (Figure 7.11). In addition to diagnostic product ions, fragments corresponding to head group loss or acyl chain loss are observed.

The epoxidation products can be detected in positive- or negative-ion modes of ESI, depending upon the lipid structure. The *m*-CPBA epoxidation has been demonstrated for fatty acids, phospholipids, and lysophospholipids [116]. Double bond(s) in glycerophospholipids can be localized in negative-ion mode using an MS^3 workflow [117]. MS^2 yields negatively charged acyl chain ions which, in the subsequent MS^3 step, provide fragments indicating the position of double bonds. The reaction conditions

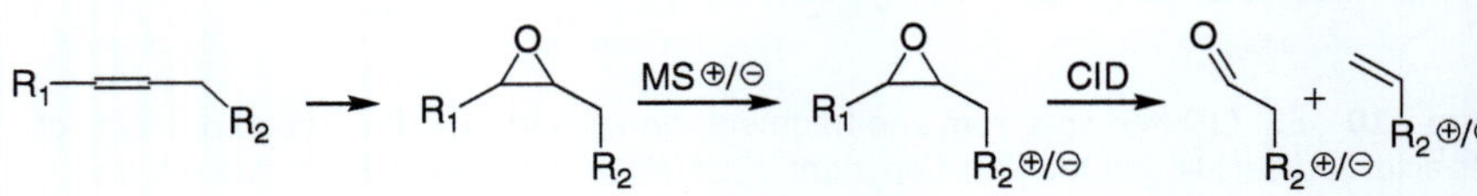

Figure 7.11 Scheme of epoxidation and fragmentation of epoxidized lipid ions in CID.

need to be optimized to prevent epoxidation of two or more double bonds in polyunsaturated fatty acid chains because spectra of such multiply epoxidized species are difficult to interpret. MS^2 analysis of the singly tagged products is preferred for determining the positions of all the double bonds in polyunsaturated chains. Zhang et al. [118] introduced peracetic acid (PPA) as an alternative derivatization reagent for epoxidation of double bonds. Compared to *m*-CPBA, PPA offers easier sample clean-up. Epoxidation is believed to occur in ESI in the presence of chloroauric acid that oxidizes double bonds in lipids and produces diagnostic aldehyde ions [119].

Plasma or electrochemical methods often lead to incomplete epoxidation. However, their simplicity, speed, and the possibility of using online implementation make them attractive for determining double bonds in lipids. Zhao et al. reported epoxidation of unsaturated fatty acids by low-temperature plasma [120], and the method was later applied to major phospholipid classes [122]. Takashima et al. introduced solvent plasmatization in ESI compatible with chromatographic workflows [121]. The ESI needle was kept at a negative voltage high enough to create corona discharge. In addition to epoxidation, peroxidized forms of lipids were generated. CID of peroxidized lipids was useful for localizing double bonds in polyunsaturated fatty acids. An electrochemical epoxidation of unsaturated lipids in a nanoESI emitter with a large orifice source was presented by Tang et al. [123]. The epoxidation can be controlled by tuning the applied voltage while maintaining the electrospray process. The electro-epoxidized products are then fragmented to generate ions indicating the double-bond position(s). Chintalapudi and Badu-Tawiah [124] developed a nanoESI platform with non-inert metal electrodes to epoxidize unsaturated fatty acids. A negative voltage applied to the electrode resulted in the epoxidation of double bonds of free fatty acids in a plasma sample.

7.2.1.5 Acetonitrile-Related Adducts in APCI

Electrospray is the major ionization method in lipid analysis. It offers high sensitivity and wide applicability in chromatography-based and shotgun workflows. Other ionizations, such as APCI, are used much less frequently. APCI is suitable for less polar and nonpolar lipids, which might be difficult to ionize by ESI. Gas-phase reactions taking place during APCI are primarily used to ionize lipid molecules. In addition, ion–molecule reactions can be utilized for gas-phase derivatizations. In an APCI source, acetonitrile yields reactive species that add to double and triple bonds. The reaction products provide spectra suitable for localizing unsaturated bonds in lipid aliphatic chains.

Gas-phase chemistry of acetonitrile was initially utilized for structural analysis of unsaturated lipids in classical CI. Unsaturated compounds react with (1-methylenimino)-1-ethenylium ($H_2C{=}N^+{=}C{=}CH_2$) to form $[M+54]^+$ adducts, which provide fragments indicating the position of the double bond [125, 126]. The reaction is typically performed in ion trap spectrometers with internal ionization, where the reactive ions arise from an ion–molecule reaction between $C_2H_2N^+$ and neutral acetonitrile [127, 128]. Diagnostic fragments are observed either in MS spectra [127, 129–131], or MS^2 spectra after collisional activation of the $[M+54]^+$ adducts [22, 132–139]. The $[M+54]^+$ adducts can be generated at atmospheric

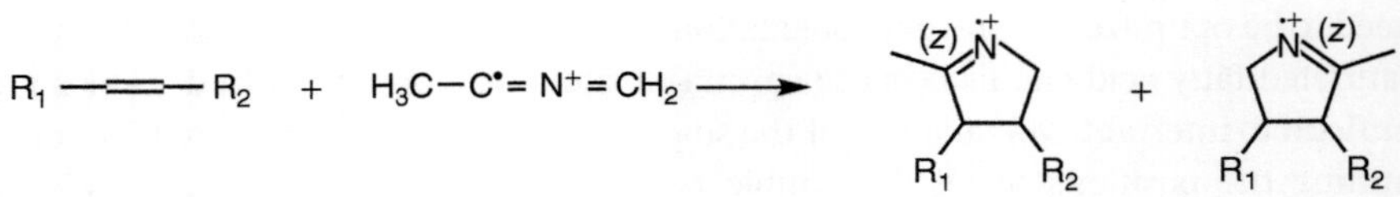

Figure 7.12 Scheme proposed for the reaction of the double bond with acetonitrile *N*-methylide in an APCI source.

pressure using APCI-MS with nebulizing helium gas. Fragmentation of such adducts formed from triacylglycerols provides fragments suitable for localizing double bonds [140]. Our group showed that somewhat different acetonitrile-related ions are generated in APCI operated under common conditions with nebulizing nitrogen gas. Instead of even-electron $C_3H_4N^+$, a radical-cation $C_3H_5N^{+\bullet}$ is formed and reacts with unsaturated lipids. Upon collisional activation, the $[M+55]^{+\bullet}$ adducts provide spectra with abundant diagnostic fragments indicating the position of the original double bonds. Experiments and theoretical calculations suggest [141] that the adducts are 2-methyl-1-pyrroline derivatives formed by a (3+2) cycloaddition reaction with acetonitrile *N*-methylide ($H_3C{-}C^\bullet{=}N^+{=}CH_2$), see Figure 7.12.

Upon CID, the derivatives are cleaved by the ring-opening followed by the elimination of an alkyl radical. Two diagnostic fragments, representing cleavages on each side of the original double bond, are formed (Figure 7.13). They are denoted α if they contain a lipid functional group or omega if they carry the terminal-carbon end.

The advantage of this approach lies in its simplicity. The only requirement is the presence of acetonitrile in the ion source, which can be easily ensured using acetonitrile-containing mobile phases. The method has been applied to the structure elucidation of various unsaturated lipids, including FAMEs [143–145], hydroxy-FAMEs [146], wax esters [142], diol diesters [147], and triacylglycerols [148]. Besides double bonds, this approach is also applicable to triple bonds [23].

Acetonitrile-related adducts are formed from lipids with various arrangements of double and triple bonds in an aliphatic chain. When the unsaturated bonds are far apart, each provides intense diagnostic fragments, independent of the other bond.

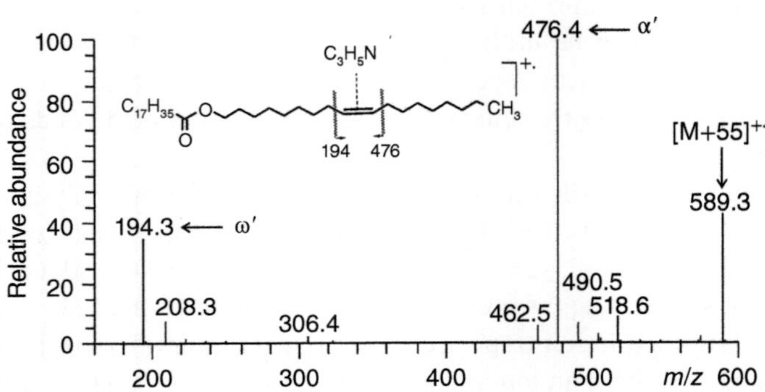

Figure 7.13 APCI ion trap CID MS^2 spectrum of the $[M+55]^{+\bullet}$ adduct of oleyl stearate (WE 18:1 (*n*-9)-18:0). Source: Reprinted with permission from Vrkoslav et al. [142]. Copyright 2011 American Chemical Society.

However, when two or more unsaturated bonds are close, the fragments corresponding to the cleavages in front of the first and behind the last double or triple bond tend to be more abundant. These abundant fragments are useful for deducing the arrangement of the double and triple bonds within polyunsaturated chains. The calculation is based on the fact that the weight of the polyunsaturated part of a chain differs for various arrangements of unsaturated bonds. For instance, the region spanning the first to the last double bond in methylene-interrupted double-bond motif consists of C_5H_6, while it is C_4H_4 in conjugated double bonds. Therefore, the arrangement of unsaturated bonds can be obtained by comparing the value of an multiple bond region (MBR) parameter calculated from the masses of the most abundant fragments and the precursor with a list of theoretical values [23]. The fragments indicating individual double bonds in the polyunsaturated region are usually detected as well, and they are useful for confirming the location of all unsaturated bonds. Double and triple bonds can be distinguished using satellite ions, which are formed by fragmentations at more distant carbon–carbon bonds. Double-bond satellite ions are substantially less abundant than diagnostic ions, from which their masses differ by 14 Da. On the contrary, triple-bond diagnostic peaks are typically abundant and differ by +15 Da from diagnostic fragments, making them easy to find in spectra [23] (Figure 7.14).

Unsaturated bonds may be present in two or more chains in more complex lipids. Fragmentation of diagnostic ions carrying the functional moiety (α fragments) in an MS^3 step helps to determine where the unsaturated bond is in the molecule. For instance, double bond in monounsaturated wax esters can be present in acid or

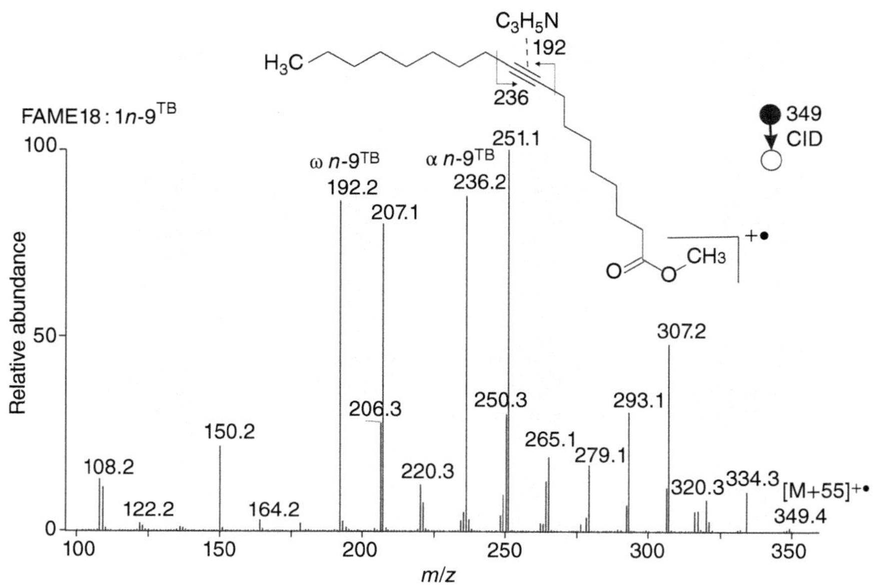

Figure 7.14 APCI ion trap CID MS^2 spectrum of the $[M+55]^{+\bullet}$ adduct of stearolic acid methyl ester (FAME 18:1*n*-9^{TB}). Source: Horká et al. [23].

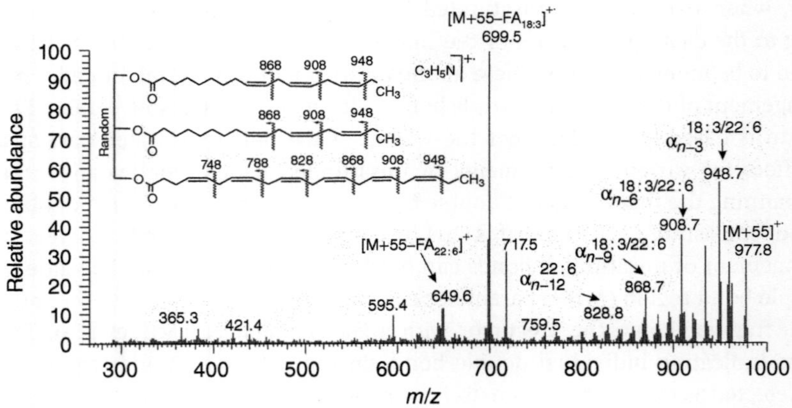

Figure 7.15 APCI ion trap CID MS^2 spectrum of the $[M+55]^{+\bullet}$ adduct of di-α-linolenin-docosahexaenoin (TG 18:3 (*n*-3)_18:3 (*n*-3)_22:6 (*n*-3)). Source: Háková et al. [148]. Copyright 2015 Springer. Reproduced with permission.

alcohol moiety. The α fragment in MS^3 eliminates fatty acid if the double bond is located in the alcohol moiety; it eliminates alcohol if the double bond is located in the acid moiety. Thus, the experiment shows whether the double bond exists in the alcohol or acid chain and localizes its position in the chain [142]. With the increasing number of aliphatic chains in the lipid molecules [147, 148], the spectra interpretation becomes more challenging. In the case of triacylglycerols [148], the spectra are unambiguously interpretable for molecular species with one unsaturated chain, two unsaturated chains of the same structure, or three identical unsaturated chains. Since each double bond manifests itself by diagnostic and satellite ions, mass spectra of triacylglycerols with two or three unsaturated chains of a different structure contain numerous signals, making the spectra rather complex. When the chains contain double bonds at the same position (counting from the methyl terminus), the corresponding fragments become more intense in the spectra (Figure 7.15).

MS^3 spectra of the α fragments formed from triacylglycerols provide more detailed insight into the structure, showing neutral loss signals of non-modified fatty acids. Since the masses of omega fragments are independent of the masses of investigated lipids, they can be utilized for visualizing the distribution of lipids bearing double bonds in particular positions. For instance, lipids with double bonds in the *n*-9, *n*-7, and *n*-5 positions provide omega fragments at *m/z* 194.2, *m/z* 166.2, and *m/z* 138.13, respectively. Extracted ion chromatograms for these ions show distribution of double-bond positional isomers, e.g. in a complex mixture of 1,2-diol diesters, a minor class of lipids associated with the skin of mammals (Figure 7.16).

When using an ion trap-based instrument for relatively large lipids like triacylglycerols or 1,2-diol diesters, the masses of omega fragments might be below the low mass range limit of the analyzer. Although omega fragments are not necessary for establishing the position of double bonds, they are useful for confirming the proposed structures. Therefore, tandem mass spectrometry in space is more convenient

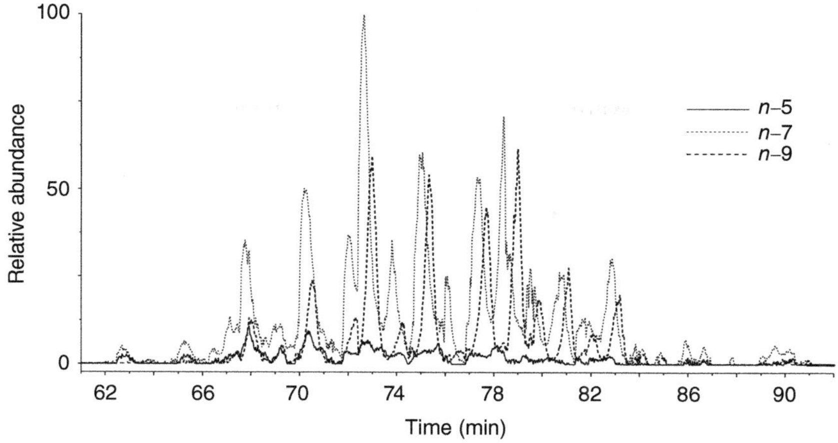

Figure 7.16 Chromatograms of 1,2-diol diesters from vernix caseosa extracted for molecular species with double bonds in the *n*-5 (solid line), *n*-7 (dotted line), and *n*-9 (dashed line) positions. Source: Šubčíková et al. [147]. Copyright 2014 Elsevier B.V. Reproduced with permission.

for fragmenting acetonitrile-related adducts. The gas-phase reaction in APCI inserts a charged moiety into a neutral lipid molecule. This approach differs in principle from most of the other approaches that modify charged lipid ions with neutral functional groups (e.g. OzID, Paternò–Büchi reaction). Acetonitrile-related adducts are an excellent tool for localizing double and triple bonds in neutral lipids and complement the portfolio of methods based on electrospray ionization.

7.2.1.6 Photodissociation of Unsaturated Lipids

The first photodissociation studies of polyatomic ions date back to the 1970s [149, 150]. Over the past years, UVPD has become an important activation method in the structural analysis of lipids and other biological molecules [151]. UVPD spectra of lipids show distinctive fragmentation patterns that facilitate *de novo* assignment of various structural features, including site(s) of unsaturation, methyl branching, hydroxylation, cyclopropanation, or localization of the acyl chains to *sn*-positions. UV light can either open dissociation channels through excited states or induce radical-directed dissociations (RDDs). The ability of UVPD to differentiate cis/trans double-bond stereoisomers is likely unfeasible due to photoisomerization of the double bond upon absorption of a UV photon [152].

UV light can open RDD channels by generating radical ions from even electron precursors. Methods based on this idea have been developed by the groups of Blanksby [4, 42, 153, 154] and Julian [155]. Lipids are derivatized either noncovalently [153, 155] or covalently [4, 42, 154, 155] with a reagent containing a photocleavable aryl-iodine bond, which serves as a radical initiator. After irradiating the mass-selected precursor with 266 nm photons, the iodine radical is cleaved off to form a radical cation and secondary fragments. Non-covalent gaseous complexes can be formed with 4-iodobenzoate or 4-iodoaniline (glycerophospholipids, sphingomyelins, and triacylglycerols) [153], or 4-iodobenzoyl 18-crown-6 (phosphatidylethanolamines, phosphatidylserines) [155]. Irradiating the complexes with a 266 nm laser eliminates iodine. Subsequent CID of the odd-electron fragments leads to radical-directed carbon–carbon bond cleavages along the acyl chain, manifested by a series of an alkyl radical or alkene losses. The spacing between adjacent peaks is 14 Da for single bonds, while the peak spacing of 12 Da indicates the double-bond site. Since the non-covalent attachment does not apply to fatty acids, a method based on the esterification of fatty acids with 4-iodobenzyl alcohol was developed [4]. Sodium adducts of 4-iodobenzyl esters eliminate atomic iodine after irradiation with a 266 nm laser. Subsequent CID of the $[M+Na-I]^{+\bullet}$ provides fragments bearing information on the double-bond positions. Significantly higher photofragmentation efficiency at 266 nm is achieved with *N*-(2-aminoethyl)-4-iodobenzamide (NIBA) derivatives of fatty acids [154]. They exhibit near-complete conversion of the $[M+Na]^+$ precursor ion to the $[M+Na-I]^{+\bullet}$ cation radical. Due to high photoproduct yield, the NIBA derivatives are suitable for liquid chromatography-based workflows. The derivatives for RDD can also be designed to maximize intensity of precursor ions. Thanks to their permanent charge, 1-(3-(aminomethyl)-4-iodophenyl)pyridin-1-ium (4-I-AMPP$^+$) derivatives [42] are efficiently ionized in electrospray (see Section 7.2.1.1). Photocleavable iodine serves as an initiator for radical directed cleavages of the carbon–carbon bonds along the acyl chain.

In the RDD methods described above, UV light generates radical ions that provide structure-related fragments after migration of the radical site. UVPD that directly induces fragmentations from the excited states is also highly relevant to the structural analysis of lipids. The groups of Brodbelt and Reid investigated the use of UVPD at 193 nm for lipid analysis. As first described for phosphatidylcholines [156], UVPD at 193 nm produces unique ions suitable for localizing double bonds within the acyl chains. Absorption of UV photons into the double bond yields photoexcited species that undergo a 1,2-elimination reaction [152] (Figure 7.17). Both carbon–carbon bonds adjacent to the double bond are cleaved, and two product ions differing by 24.0000 Da (mass of two carbon atoms) are formed (Figure 7.18).

This fragmentation pathway is independent of the charge site or charge type. As regards positively charged ions, protonated [152, 156], lithiated [152, 157, 158],

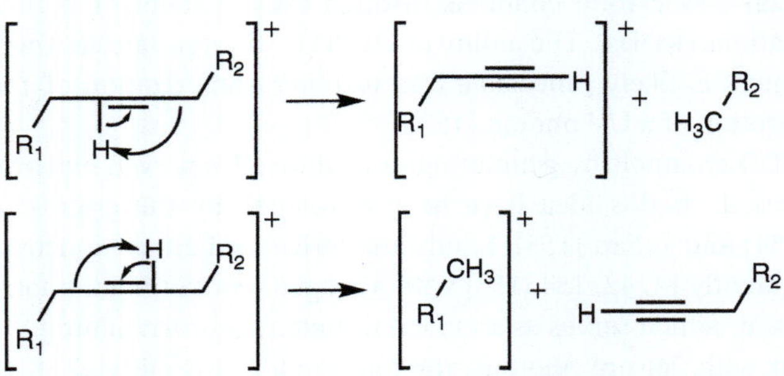

Figure 7.17 1,2-Elimination after absorption of UV photon resulting in two products differing by 24 Da.

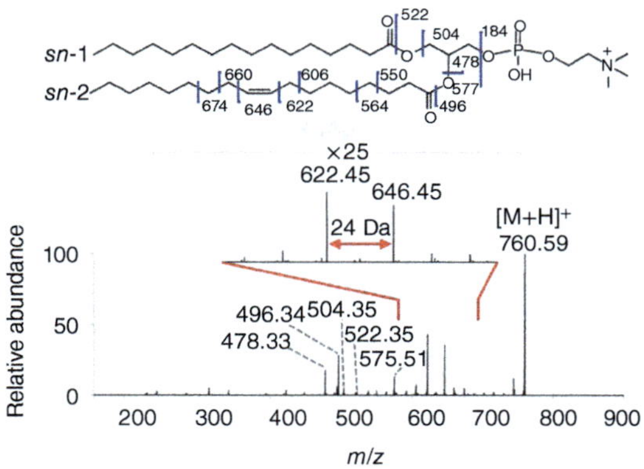

Figure 7.18 193 nm UVPD-MS^2 of protonated phosphatidylcholine PC 16:0/18:1 (9Z). Source: Adapted with permission from Klein and Brodbelt [156]. Copyright 2017 American Chemical Society.

sodiated [156–158], or potassiated [157, 158] lipid molecules can be used for UVPD experiments. Fragmentation of alkali metal adducts provides more abundant diagnostic product ions, likely due to the smaller mobility of the metal ion compared to a proton [152]. Lithium adducts of sphingolipids thus promote CRF more efficiently than protonated molecules [152]. A sodium adduct is more appropriate than lithium for UVPD of phosphatidylcholines [158]. Di-lithiated fatty acids afford more abundant diagnostic ions when compared to di-sodiated and di-potassiated adducts [157]. The double-bond diagnostic fragments spaced 24.0000 Da apart are also formed from negatively charged precursors [159, 160]. 193 nm UVPD of both singly and doubly deprotonated cardiolipins yields product ions indicating a double-bond position [159]. The high structural complexity of these lipids requires a two-step CID/UVPD approach to locate double bonds on all acyl chains. Phospholipids from several subclasses, including phosphatidic acids, phosphatidylethanolamines, phosphatidylserines, or phosphatidylinositols, form anions easily, and negatively charged ions can also be prepared from phosphatidylcholines after formate adduction. Using 193 nm UVPD, all of these anions provide the pair of diagnostic fragment ions [160, 161]. UVPD can localize multiple double bonds within polyunsaturated acyl chains because diagnostic ion pairs are formed from all unsaturation sites in the chains [157]. The relative abundance of diagnostic ions can be used to determine the relative concentration of double-bond positional isomers in mixtures, as demonstrated with fatty acid isomers in colorectal cancer cells in a direct-infusion experiment [157]. Despite limitations in sensitivity, UVPD is compatible with liquid chromatographic workflows [160–162]. Recently, quantitation of phospholipids incorporating isomeric polyunsaturated fatty acids was achieved by RPLC-UVPD; the isomer ratios were compared across normal and tumor breast tissue [162].

Commercially available UVPD mass spectrometers operate at 213 nm. Since this wavelength also overlaps with absorbance bands of unsaturated lipids, UVPD at 213 nm can be used for the structural analysis of lipids, similar to instruments with 193 nm UVPD. A combined MS^3 approach with HCD and 213 nm UVPD allows for the complete structural assignment of fatty acid esters of hydroxy fatty acids (FAHFAs) [163]. HCD of lithiated or di-lithiated FAHFAs provides fatty acid fragments containing endogenous double bonds and double bonds inserted after the neutral loss of fatty acid from FAHFA. Both types of double bonds can be localized using fragments differing by 24.0000 Da. Since the new double bonds are created in the place where the ester bond was attached, the method can localize the esterification position. The energy of 266 nm photons is not high enough to be absorbed directly by double bonds in lipids. Double-bond selective fragment ions can be achieved after derivatization with a suitable chromophore, e.g. using PB reaction with acetophenone [89].

7.2.1.7 Electron-Induced Dissociation of Unsaturated Lipids

Unimolecular dissociations of organic ions after their interaction with electrons have a rich history dating back to the late 1970s. The first electron-induced fragmentations were performed in an ion cyclotron resonance cell using a technique known as electron impact excitation of ions from organics (EIEIOs) [164]. The interest in electron-induced fragmentations of singly charged ions has increased recently, due to the launch of a new commercial QTOF mass spectrometer for EID [165]. Its fragmentation cell is a branched radio frequency ion trap that allows electrons and ions to be controlled independently [166].

Mass-selected protonated phospholipids provide EID spectra that allow their near-complete structural characterization [167]. The precursors provide headgroup-specific fragments, regioisomer-specific acyl chains loss peaks, and carbon–carbon bond cleavages within aliphatic chains. The chain fragments are even and odd electron fragments that form a series of ions separated by 14 Da. A double bond within a chain manifests itself by a V-shaped intensity profile of the fragments (Figure 7.19). Since the spectrum complexity increases with the number of double bonds, a

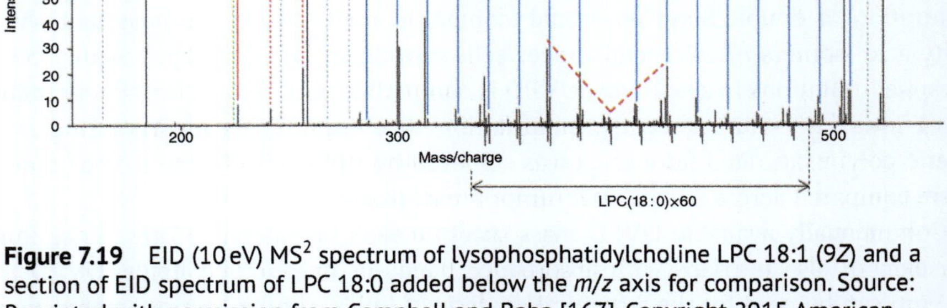

Figure 7.19 EID (10 eV) MS^2 spectrum of lysophosphatidylcholine LPC 18:1 (9*Z*) and a section of EID spectrum of LPC 18:0 added below the *m/z* axis for comparison. Source: Reprinted with permission from Campbell and Baba [167]. Copyright 2015 American Chemical Society.

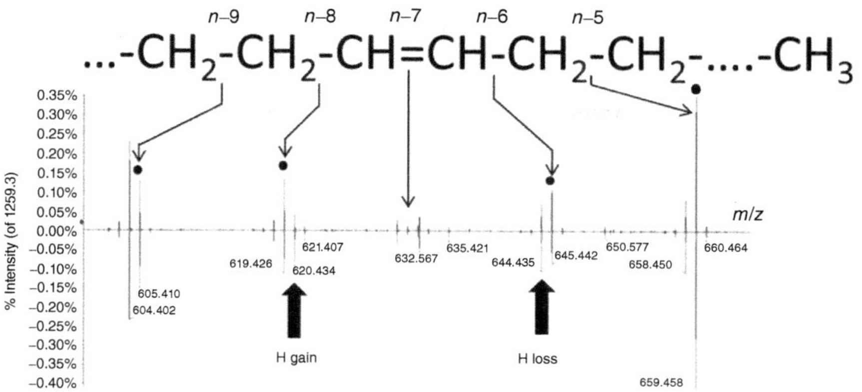

Figure 7.20 Sections of EID MS^2 spectra of protonated phosphatidylcholine PC 18:1 (*n*-9, cis)/18:1 (*n*-9, cis) (upper) and phosphatidylcholine PC 18:1 (*n*-9, trans)/18:1 (*n*-9, trans) (lower). Source: Reprinted with permission from Baba et al. [19]. Copyright 2017 American Chemical Society.

deconvolution of the product ion intensity using an automated program was suggested [167].

Experiments with high-energy electrons (>20 eV) on an ion cyclotron resonance (ICR) cell [168] provide more detailed insight into the fragmentation of phosphatidylcholines in EID. The carbon–carbon bond cleavages in saturated diacyl phosphatidylcholines result in alkane loss peaks. It still remains unclear whether an alkane or an alkene plus H_2 is lost during the CRF processes that occur remotely from the quaternary nitrogen charge site. In unsaturated phosphatidylcholines, odd-electron product ions consistent with homolytic chain cleavages are observed, along with the even electron products corresponding to the neutral loss of alkanes. These specific fragments help localize the double-bond position in phosphatidylcholines. In addition to localizing the position of the double bond, EID fragments also offer differentiation of stereoisomers [19]. Cis/trans geometry affects the intensities of fragments of the neighboring carbon–carbon bonds. The trans isomers show increased intensities of two even-electron ions differing by 24.0000 Da, i.e. a "hydrogen loss" peak at the (n–X–1) site and a "hydrogen gain" peak at the (n–X+1) site (Figure 7.20).

The localization of double bonds by EID was demonstrated for lipids from several classes, including phospholipids [167], sphingolipids [169], and triacylglycerols [170]. The initial efficiency of EID was relatively low, which required averaging the signal over a relatively long time. This averaging limited the use of EID in chromatographic workflows. Differential mobility spectrometry (DMS) with EID mass spectrometry offered an alternative separation of complex lipid samples [19, 169, 170]. A shotgun lipidomic platform combining DMS and EID was developed for the structural analysis of complex lipid extracts [171]. Recent technological development made it possible to achieve much stronger electron beam currents on a QTOF system [172]. Increased sensitivity makes it now possible to perform EID-based structural lipidomics on an LC time scale.

Charge transfer dissociation (CTD) is an interesting activation technique that offers spectra to some extent similar to EID [173]. It proceeds via exposure of gas-phase precursor cations to a keV beam of helium cations. Extensive cleavage along lipid acyl chains provides informative spectra with diagnostic fragments for the location of double bonds.

7.2.2 Methyl Branching of Aliphatic Chains

Branched-chain fatty acids (BCFAs) with one or more methyl branching groups in their chains can be found in many biological samples [174, 175]. The most common BCFAs are those with methyl groups located in the *n*-2 (iso) or *n*-3 (anteiso) position. Traditional methods for characterizing branching sites in lipids rely on derivatizations and GC/EI-MS [176], while newer procedures are based on (LC)/ESI-MS and RDD [4, 153, 177, 178] or charge-switch derivatizations [38, 39].

RDD provides intrachain fragments useful for the structural identification of methyl branching sites in fatty acyls. Even electron precursor ions formed by ESI are activated in CID or UVPD to create odd-electron fragments. Their decomposition proceeds via radical-directed pathways involving carbon–carbon bond cleavages. Several derivatives have been proposed to induce RDD of methyl branched lipid chains. One approach utilizes the amidation of fatty acids with *O*-benzylhydroxylamine [178]. In CID, lithium adducts of the derivatives eliminate benzyl radicals, forming nitroxide radical cations which decompose by RDD. In saturated acyl chains, a series of fragment ions due to consecutive C–C cleavages are formed at a constant mass spacing of 14 Da. The regular spacing is interrupted by a 28 Da gap for a methyl branching site. The method was used for LC/MS analysis of BCFAs in yak milk and human plasma samples [178]. The same group published an RDD method to characterize amino group-containing lipids such as phosphatidylethanolamines and lysophosphatidylethanolamines [177]. Lipids are derivatized with reagents containing TEMPO (2,2,6,6-tetramethylpiperidine-1-oxy) radical precursor group. Upon low-energy CID, the derivatives eliminate a TEMPO, leaving a benzyl or pyridine methyl radical that initiates RDD via hydrogen transfer from the chain to the radical site (Figure 7.21). The method was used for studying intrachain modifications in bacterial lipids.

The radical precursor can also be prepared by photodissociation of even electron ions containing aryl-iodine bonds (see Section 7.2.1.6). Irradiation of noncovalent [153] or covalent [4, 42] derivatives with 266 nm photons eliminates iodine radical, creating an odd electron ion that initiates RDD. Noncovalent complexes are formed during electrospray ionization, e.g. by complexation of phosphatidylcholines with 4-iodobenzoic acid [153]. Fatty acids can be covalently modified with 4-iodobenzoic acid by esterification [4]. Sodium adducts are cleaved by photodissociation to generate $[M+Na-I]^{\bullet +}$, which are further activated by CID. Methyl branching manifests itself by differences in peak spacing in the spectra. Derivatization with I-AMPP$^+$ provides increased sensitivity and offers a structural analysis of fatty acyl

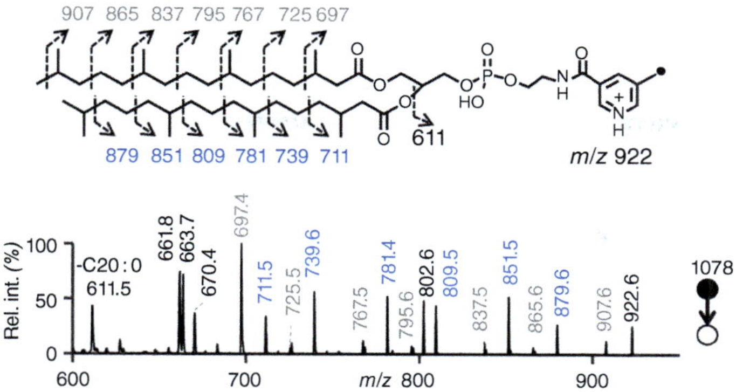

Figure 7.21 CID MS^2 spectrum of TPN-derivatized phosphatidylethanolamine PE 4Me-16:0/4Me-16:0. TPN stands for 3-(2,2,6,6-tetramethylpiperidin-1-yloxymethyl)-picolinic acid 2,5-dioxopyrrolidin-1-yl ester. Source: Adapted with permission from Lin et al. [177]. Copyright 2022 American Chemical Society.

chains by RDD [42]. Photodissociation mass spectra of 4-I-$AMPP^+$ derivatives of fatty acids show 28 Da spacing as characteristic markers for the presence of methyl branches. The I-$AMPP^+$ derivatization was integrated into an LC-MS^2 workflow and used for structural analysis of branched fatty acids in vernix caseosa [42].

The position of methyl branching sites can also be determined using CRF of collisionally activated even electron precursor ions. CRF of branched fatty acids was initially studied using FAB on magnetic sector instruments with high-energy CID [179, 180]. Low-energy CID available on current mass spectrometers also provides CRF ions for some derivatives with a fixed charge. For instance, $AMPP^+$ derivatives discussed in Section 7.2.1.1 made it possible to study methyl branching in bacterial lipids [38, 39].

7.2.3 Oxygen-Containing Functional Groups and Carbocyclic Structures

Besides methyl groups, various oxygen-containing functionalities and carbocyclic structures are present in bioactive lipids. Oxylipins are structurally diverse molecules with hydroxyl, epoxy, and other oxygen-containing groups that play important roles as signaling agents in inflammation and other biological processes [181, 182]. LC/MS is the method of choice for analyzing oxylipins in various biological matrices [183–185]. The analytical workflows usually combine ESI in negative-ion mode with MS^2 [186–189]. Limited sensitivity in the negative-ion mode can be overcome by derivatization, e.g. the introduction of perfluorobenzyl (PFB) moiety. The MS^2 spectra of negatively charged oxylipin ions are structure-specific and provide information about the position of oxygen-containing groups. In the case of the hydroxyl group, an α-hydroxy cleavage at the vinylic and/or allylic positions with a proton transfer usually takes place [190–192]. A wide range of derivatives was developed to analyze oxylipins in positive-ion mode [35, 36, 193–195], including charge-switch

AMPP$^+$ derivatives discussed in Section 7.2.1.1 [40, 41, 195]. The use of charge-switch AMPP$^+$ derivatization for analyzing oxylipins in plasma, serum, and cells in a non-targeted workflow was demonstrated recently [196]. CID of AMPP$^+$ derivates was also used to characterize polymethylated long-chain hydroxyphthioceranoic and phthioceranoic acids released from bacterial sulfolipids [40]. Photodissociation and RDD fragmentations lead to specific cleavages of carbon–carbon bonds adjacent to hydroxyl groups, making them useful for identifying the site of hydroxylation in hydroxy fatty acids (HFAs) [4, 161, 197]. LC-MS^2 that utilizes 266 nm photodissociation offers structural identification of 4-I-AMPP$^+$-derivatized eicosanoids from hydroxyeicosatetraenoic acid (HETE) and hydroxyeicosapentaenoic acid (HEPE) families [195] (Figure 7.22).

HFAs can be modified with 4-iodobenzoic acid by esterification. RDD spectrum, obtained by subsequent CID on the $[M+Na-I]^{\bullet+}$, leads to two product ions that characterize the hydroxylation site [4]. 193 nm UVPD was used by Brodbelt and coworkers for studying the hydroxylation of acyl chains of bacterial glycerophospholipids [161] and for the structural characterization of lipopolysaccharides [197].

An important functional group is an ester bond, which is formally created by the esterification of the hydroxy group in HFA by a carboxylic acid. The position of the ester bonds is often called the branching position [198]. Lipids modified in this way are estolides, termed FAHFAs. They are endogenous bioactive lipids with anti-diabetic and anti-inflammatory properties. The structural characterization of FAHFAs is mostly achieved by CID of negative ions generated by ESI. MS^2 spectra show a fatty acid fragment and a HFA fragment, accompanied by a dehydration product of the HFA fragment [199–206]. MS^3 of HFA fragment or MS^2 at higher energies yields fragments that are specific to the position of the hydroxyl group in HFA [200, 202–204]. FAHFAs containing α-HFAs show 46 Da neutral loss fragments

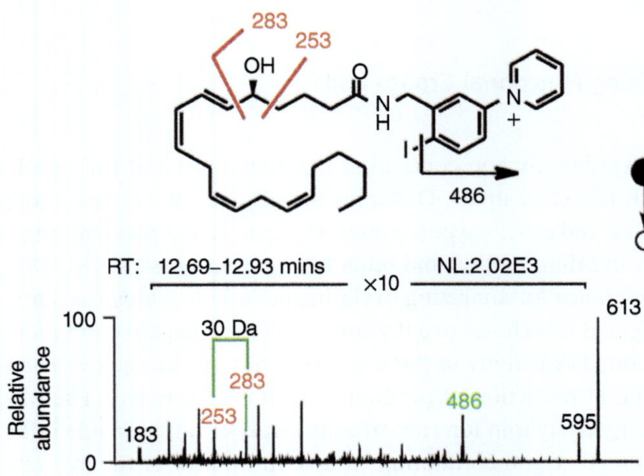

Figure 7.22 Photodissociation (266 nm) mass spectrum of the 4-I-AMPP$^+$ derivative of 5-hydroxyeicosatetraenoic acid (5-HETE). Source: Narreddula et al. [195]. Copyright 2020 John Wiley & Sons Ltd. Adapted with permission.

in MS^2 spectra [206] and MS^3 spectra [204]. Derivatization of the carboxylic group with $AMPP^+$ [66, 207], 4-I-$AMPP^+$ [66], or 2-dimethylaminoethylamine (DMED) [208, 209] increases the detection sensitivity, and spectra of the derivatives provide structure informative fragments. The complete characterization of FAHFA structure, including assignment of fatty acids and HFA constituents, unsaturation sites, and ester linkage regioisomerism, can be achieved by fragmentation of products formed from deprotonated FAHFA and trisphenanthroline magnesium complex in the gas phase [210]. These experiments are performed in a modified hybrid triple quadrupole/linear ion trap mass spectrometer with alternately pulsed nanoESI that permits the sequential injection of lipid anions and reagent dications.

Cyclopropane fatty acids (CFAs) are created by *in situ* methylenation of double bonds in unsaturated fatty acids. CFAs are often found in bacteria, e.g. *Escherichia coli* [211]. Characterization of cyclopropyl groups in lipids can be done via UVPD-MS [212], RDD [42, 177], or gas-phase charge inversion reactions [213]. Dual cross-ring carbon–carbon bond cleavages on both sides of the cyclopropane ring are observed in UVPD spectra. A pair of fragment ions spaced 14 Da apart localizes the cyclopropane moiety. 213 nm UVPD-MS was employed in a shotgun approach and in an LC-MS^2 workflow to characterize CFAs and mycolic acids in bacterial extracts [212]. RDD discussed in Sections 7.2.1.6 and 7.2.2 can also be useful for identifying cyclopropyl group positions [42, 177]. RDD of I-$AMPP^+$ derivatives resulted in chain cleavages on both sides of the cyclopropane moiety and yielded a distinctive 40 Da spacing pattern [42]. Lipids derivatized with reagents containing TEMPO showed cross-ring carbon–carbon cleavages on both sides of the cyclopropane [177], analogous to UVPD-MS. The position of cyclopropyl groups can also be determined using gas-phase charge inversion reactions. McLuckey group used charge inversion ion/ion reactions to characterize cyclopropyl position in cardiolipins from *E. coli* extracts [213]. Deprotonated cardiolipins formed by ESI were fragmented by CID. The product ions were subjected to gas-phase ion/ion charge inversion reactions with tris-phenanthroline magnesium dications. CID of the complex formed in this way promoted CRF of the aliphatic chain and yielded diagnostic fragments corresponding to cyclopropane cross-ring cleavages.

7.2.4 Stereospecific Position of Acyl Chain on Glycerol

Glycerol is not chiral, but different substitutions on two primary hydroxy groups make glycerolipids chiral molecules. A stereospecific numbering system defines the positions of substituents as *sn*-1, *sn*-2, and *sn*-3. Reliable analytical methods for the correct assignment of the position of the substituents are needed because the positioning of acyl groups to the various *sn* positions has important biological effects. Separation of enantiomers is impossible in achiral environments, thus limiting most methods to distinguishing the secondary position from the primary ones (*sn*-2 versus *sn*-1/3). Analytical workflows may include additional steps that allow the stereoisomers to be separated, for instance, stereoselective cleavage of fatty acyls by enzymes like phospholipase A2 [214] or separation by chromatography or ion mobility [215–218]. Determining the regiospecific position of acyl chains on glycerol is not usually straightforward. Stereoisomers may exhibit different fragment ion intensities, for instance, in the case of triacylglycerols analyzed by APCI-MS or ESI-MS^2. Since the elimination of neutral fatty acids from the *sn*-1 and *sn*-3 positions is equally favored and more likely than the loss from *sn*-2, the relative intensities of diacylglycerol fragment ions can be used to distinguish *sn*-2 from *sn*-1/3 substituents [219]. Phosphatidylcholine *sn*-isomers can be distinguished and quantified using intensities of fragment ions observed in UVPD and CID spectra of doubly charged metal adducts ($[PC+Fe]^{2+}$) [220]. Hsu and Turk investigated in detail the low-energy CID processes leading to regiospecific fragmentations of fatty acids in glycerophospholipids [221–223]. Tandem mass spectra of deprotonated molecules and various alkali metal adducts provided complete structural information, including the identification of the polar head group, fatty acyl substituents, and their *sn*-positions determined from the relative fragment ion abundances. Alkali metal ion (e.g. Li^+, Na^+) adducts produce abundant fragment ions from neutral headgroup loss. In phosphatidylcholines, the headgroup elimination proceeds via a five-membered ring intermediate, creating a fragment with a 1,3-dioxolane ring linked to the *sn*-2 fatty acyl chain by a newly created double bond (Figure 7.23a). An alternative pathway may lead to 1,3-dioxane fragments (Figure 7.23b) [222], but there is a growing body of evidence that the 1,3-dioxolane isomers are predominantly formed [224].

The use of the relative abundances of fragment ions for the assignment of fatty acids to *sn*-positions may not always be reliable because the ion intensities are affected by the structure of fatty acyl chains and headgroups. Even the instrument type and collision energy affect ion intensities. Therefore, the spectra are searched to find unique fragments for the unambiguous identification of regioisomers [60, 83, 158]. The 1,3-dioxolane fragments are suitable targets for further fragmentation. Brodbelt and coworkers presented an MS^3 method that employs HCD, followed by 193 nm UVPD for the *sn*-position assignment in glycerophospholipids [158].

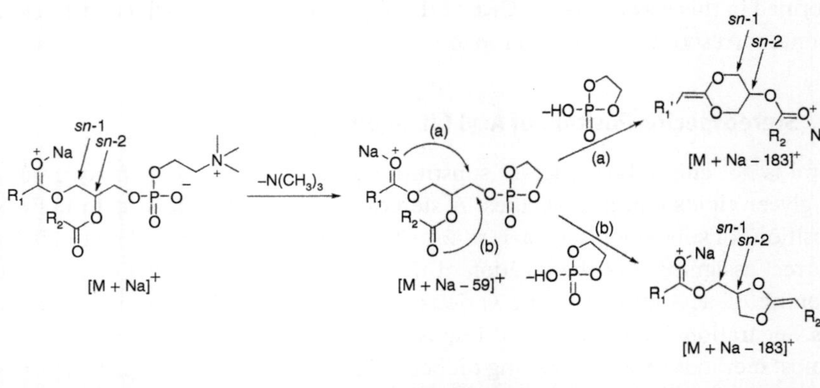

Figure 7.23 Headgroup loss from phosphatidylcholine metal adduct in low-energy CID. Source: Reprinted with permission from Williams et al. [158]. Copyright 2017 American Chemical Society.

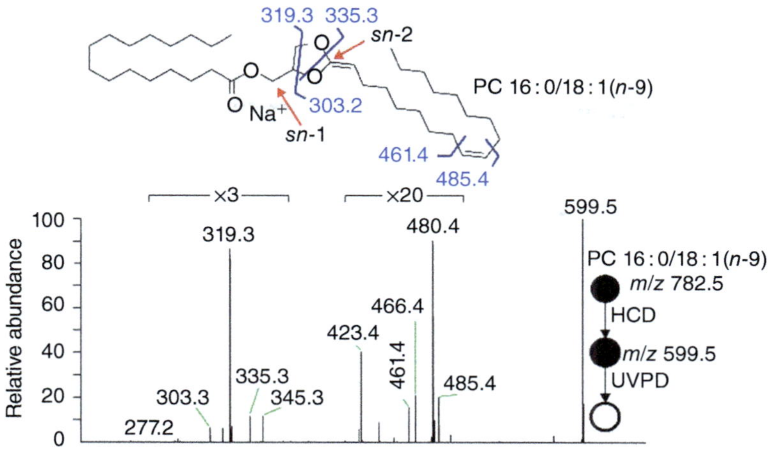

Figure 7.24 HCD/UVPD MS^3 spectrum of sodium adduct of phosphatidylcholine PC 16:0/18:1 (*n*-9). Source: Reprinted with permission from Williams et al. [158]. Copyright 2017 American Chemical Society.

A headgroup loss product ion created in HCD is activated by UV photons. Fatty acid in the *sn*-1 position provides an allyl ester fragment arising from photolytic cleavage across the dioxolane moiety. A minor peak due to a different photolytic cleavage describes fatty acid in the *sn*-2 position (Figure 7.24). The method was tested for various phospholipids and integrated with a data-dependent LC MS^3 workflow [158].

The double bond in the 1,3-dioxolane fragment can react with ozone, which is utilized in another MS^3 method to identify *sn*-isomers. Blanksby and coworkers demonstrated fragmentation of sodium-cationized phospholipids in CID followed by OzID in a linear ion-trap mass spectrometer [60]. In this method, the headgroup loss product ion generated in CID is subjected to ozonolysis. The major product ion is an aldehyde formed from the new double bond inserted in the previous HCD step; it allows for a clear differentiation of *sn*-positional isomers in glycerophospholipids [60]. CID of a 1,3-dioxolane fragment derived from lipids derivatized using PB reaction can also be used to assign fatty acids to *sn*-positions [83]. Ma and coworkers used 2-AP as a PB reagent for unsaturated glycerophospholipids. The advantage of 2-AP is its high affinity for sodium. Activation of a 2-AP-derivatized 1,3-dioxolane fragment obtained by headgroup loss in MS^2 provides fragments that characterize the *sn*-positions of fatty acids on the glycerol backbone and double-bond positions within the chains. The method is easy to implement into lipidomics workflows [83].

One CID step (MS^2) can be sufficient for regiospecific analysis of fatty acyls in phosphatidylcholines if bicarbonate anion adducts are used [225]. Its fragmentation is initiated by combined losses of an H_2CO_3 and *N,N*-dimethyl aminomethyl radical, and it proceeds by eliminating a fatty acid from the *sn*-2 position. The fragment ion

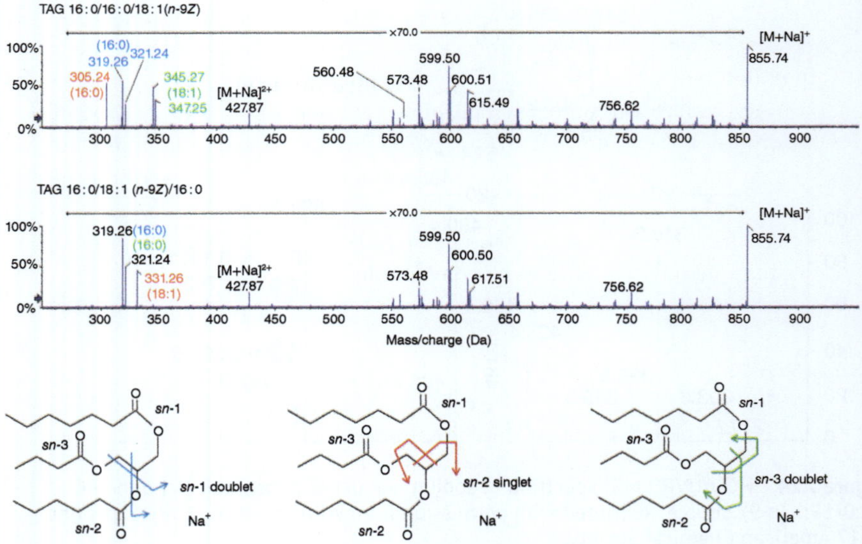

Figure 7.25 EID MS^2 spectra of sodium adducts of triacylglycerol regioisomers TG 16:0/16:0/18:1 (*n*-9*Z*), TG 16:0/18:1 (*n*-9*Z*)/16:0. Source: Baba et al. [170].

formed in this way and observed in the spectrum contains the an *sn*-1 fatty acyl, thus unambiguously identifying *sn*-positional isomers. This method can be easily implemented into an LC/MS workflow if ammonium bicarbonate is added to the mobile phase [225].

In EID, singly charged lipid ions generated by ESI are irradiated by an electron beam to produce diagnostic fragment ions (see Section 7.2.1.7). EID spectra provide an almost complete structural characterization of glycerolipids as demonstrated for phosphatidylcholines [167], sphingomyelins [169], and triacylglycerols [170]. Fragment ions formed at cleavage sites in the glycerol moiety characterize lipid regioisomers. For instance, the EID spectra of triacylglycerols show two distinct peak groups in the low mass range of spectra; singlets and doublet peaks separated by 2 Da. While the singlet peak identifies the acyl chain in the *sn*-2 position, the doublet peaks characterize the acyl chains in *sn*-1 and *sn*-3 (Figure 7.25).

7.3 Conclusions and Outlook

In recent years, we have witnessed an unprecedented development of new methods for the structural analysis of lipids. They are mostly based on the ingenious use of chemical derivatization reactions and new ways to activate ions. New methods make it possible to characterize the structure of lipids in more detail in increasingly complex samples and at low concentrations. The development of new methods is made possible by the technological advances in mass spectrometry and the availability of instruments with new technologies and improved parameters. Mass spectrometry-based methods will certainly continue to evolve. Simple integration into lipidomic workflows, easy and unambiguous interpretation of spectra, and compatibility with a chromatographic time scale are some of the requirements for successful methods. In addition to high-throughput analytical methods, there is a need to develop fast and reliable data processing tools to improve and accelerate data transformation into knowledge.

Advanced methods of lipid structural analysis will undoubtedly help us reveal new fascinating secrets of life at the molecular level.

References

1 Murphy, R.C. (2015). *Tandem Mass Spectrometry of Lipids: Molecular Analysis of Complex Lipids*. Cambridge: Royal Society of Chemistry.

2 Zaikin, V. and Halket, J.M. (2009). *A Handbook of Derivatives for Mass Spectrometry*. Chichester, West Sussex: IM Publications.

3 Strmeň, T., Vrkoslav, V., Bosáková, Z., and Cvačka, J. (2020). Atmospheric pressure chemical ionization mass spectrometry at low flow rates: importance of ion source housing. *Rapid Commun. Mass Spectrom.* 34 (10): e8722.

4 Pham, H.T., Trevitt, A.J., Mitchell, T.W., and Blanksby, S.J. (2013). Rapid differentiation of isomeric lipids by photodissociation mass spectrometry of fatty acid derivatives. *Rapid Commun. Mass Spectrom.* 27 (7): 805–815.

5 Sleno, L. and Volmer, D.A. (2004). Ion activation methods for tandem mass spectrometry. *J. Mass Spectrom.* 39 (10): 1091–1112.

6 McLuckey, S.A. and Mentinova, M. (2011). Ion/neutral, ion/electron, ion/photon, and ion/ion interactions in tandem mass spectrometry: do we need them all? Are they enough? *J. Am. Soc. Mass Spectrom.* 22 (1): 3–12.

7 Harvey, S.R., Liu, Y., Liu, W. et al. (2017). Surface induced dissociation as a tool to study membrane protein complexes. *Chem. Commun.* 53 (21): 3106–3109.

8 Heidemann, J., Kolbel, K., Konijnenberg, A. et al. (2020). Further insights from structural mass spectrometry into endocytosis adaptor protein assemblies. *Int. J. Mass Spectrom.* 447.

9 Brodbelt, J.S. (2014). Photodissociation mass spectrometry: new tools for characterization of biological molecules. *Chem. Soc. Rev.* 43 (8): 2757–2783.

10 Becher, S., Spengler, B., and Heiles, S. (2018). Effects of wavelength, fluence, and dose on fragmentation pathways and photoproduct ion yield in 213 nm and 266 nm ultraviolet photodissociation experiments. *Eur. J. Mass Spectrom.* 24 (1): 54–65.

11 Chen, X.F., Wang, Z., Wong, Y.L.E. et al. (2018). Electron-ion reaction-based dissociation: a powerful ion activation method for the elucidation of natural product structures. *Mass Spectrom. Rev.* 37 (6): 793–810.

12 James, P.F., Perugini, M.A., and O'Hair, R.A.J. (2008). Electron capture dissociation of complexes of diacylglycerophosphocholine and divalent metal

ions: competition between charge reduction and radical induced phospholipid fragmentation. *J. Am. Soc. Mass Spectrom.* 19 (7): 978–986.

13 Liang, X.L.R., Liu, J., Leblanc, Y. et al. (2007). Electron transfer dissociation of doubly sodiated glycerophosphocholine lipids. *J. Am. Soc. Mass Spectrom.* 18 (10): 1783–1788.

14 McFarland, M.A., Marshall, A.G., Hendrickson, C.L. et al. (2005). Structural characterization of the GM1 ganglioside by infrared multiphoton dissociation/ electron capture dissociation, and electron detachment dissociation electrospray ionization FT-ICR MS/MS. *J. Am. Soc. Mass Spectrom.* 16 (5): 752–762.

15 Natesan, V. and Kim, S.J. (2021). Lipid metabolism, disorders and therapeutic drugs – review. *Biomol. Ther.* 29 (6): 596–604.

16 Halket, J.M. and Zaikin, V.G. (2005). Review: derivatization in mass spectrometry – 5. Specific derivatization of monofunctional compounds. *Eur. J. Mass Spectrom.* 11 (1): 127–160.

17 Dobson, G. and Christie, W.W. (1996). Structural analysis of fatty acids by mass spectrometry of picolinyl esters and dimethyloxazoline derivatives. *TrAC, Trend Anal. Chem.* 15 (3): 130–137.

18 Jensen, N., Lam, K., Cody, R.B., and Tamura, J. (1990). Evidence for distinction of cis and trans isomers of monounsaturated fatty-acids by fast-atom bombardment tandem mass-spectrometric analysis. *Rapid Commun. Mass Spectrom.* 4 (7): 239–241.

19 Baba, T., Campbell, J.L., Le Blanc, J.C.Y., and Baker, P.R.S. (2017). Distinguishing cis and trans isomers in intact complex lipids using electron impact excitation of ions from organics mass spectrometry. *Anal. Chem.* 89 (14): 7307–7315.

20 Poad, B.L.J., Pham, H.T., Thomas, M.C. et al. (2010). Ozone-induced dissociation on a modified tandem linear ion-trap: observations of different reactivity for isomeric lipids. *J. Am. Soc. Mass Spectrom.* 21 (12): 1989–1999.

21 Zhang, J.Y., Yu, X.J., Wang, H.Y. et al. (1989). Location of triple bonds in the fatty-acids from the kernel oil of *Pyrularia edulis* by GC-MS of their 4,4-dimethyloxazoline derivatives. *J. Am. Oil Chem. Soc.* 66 (2): 256–259.

22 Lawrence, P. and Brenna, J.T. (2006). Acetonitrile covalent adduct chemical ionization mass spectrometry for double bond localization in non-methylene-interrupted polyene fatty acid methyl esters. *Anal. Chem.* 78 (4): 1312–1317.

23 Horká, P., Vrkoslav, V., Kindl, J. et al. (2021). Structural characterization of unusual fatty acid methyl esters with double and triple bonds using HPLC/ APCI-MS(2) with acetonitrile in-source derivatization. *Molecules* 26 (21).

24 Christie, W.W. (1998). Gas chromatography mass spectrometry methods for structural analysis of fatty acids. *Lipids* 33 (4): 343–353.

25 Andersson, B.A. and Holman, R.T. (1974). Pyrrolidides for mass-spectrometric determination of position of double-bond in monounsaturated fatty-acids. *Lipids* 9 (3): 185–190.

26 Andersson, B.A., Christie, W.W., and Holman, R.T. (1975). Mass-spectrometric determination of positions of double-bonds in polyunsaturated fatty-acid pyrrolidides. *Lipids* 10 (4): 215–219.

27 Spitzer, V. (1996). Structure analysis of fatty acids by gas chromatography low resolution electron impact mass spectrometry of their 4,4-dimethyloxazoline derivatives – a review. *Prog. Lipid Res.* 35 (4): 387–408.

28 Harvey, D.J. (1982). Picolinyl esters as derivatives for the structural determination of long-chain branched and unsaturated fatty-acids. *Biomed. Mass Spectrom.* 9 (1): 33–38.

29 Tulloch, A.P. (1985). Mass-spectra of pyrrolidides of oxo, hydroxy and trimethylsilyloxy octadecanoic acids. *Lipids* 20 (10): 652–663.

30 Balazy, M. and Nies, A.S. (1989). Characterization of epoxides of polyunsaturated fatty acids by mass spectrometry via 3-pyridinylmethyl esters. *Biomed. Environ. Mass Spectrom.* 18 (5): 328–336.

31 Harvey, D.J. (1984). Picolinyl derivatives for the characterization of cyclopropane fatty-acids by mass-spectrometry. *Biomed. Mass Spectrom.* 11 (4): 187–192.

32 Tomer, K.B., Crow, F.W., and Gross, M.L. (1983). Location of double-bond position in unsaturated fatty-acids by negative-ion MS/MS. *J. Am. Chem. Soc.* 105 (16): 5487–5488.

33 Barry, S.J., Carr, R.M., Lane, S.J. et al. (2003). Derivatisation for liquid chromatography/electrospray mass spectrometry: synthesis of pyridinium compounds and their amine and carboxylic acid derivatives. *Rapid Commun. Mass Spectrom.* 17 (6): 603–620.

34 Lamos, S.M., Shortreed, M.R., Frey, B.L. et al. (2007). Relative quantification of carboxylic acid metabolites by liquid chromatography-mass spectrometry using isotopic variants of cholamine. *Anal. Chem.* 79 (14): 5143–5149.

35 Bollinger, J.G., Thompson, W., Lai, Y. et al. (2010). Improved sensitivity mass spectrometric detection of eicosanoids by charge reversal derivatization. *Anal. Chem.* 82 (16): 6790–6796.

36 Bollinger, J.G., Rohan, G., Sadilek, M., and Gelb, M.H. (2013). LC/ESI-MS/MS detection of FAs by charge reversal derivatization with more than four orders of magnitude improvement in sensitivity. *J. Lipid Res.* 54 (12): 3523–3530.

37 Yang, K., Dilthey, B.G., and Gross, R.W. (2013). Identification and quantitation of fatty acid double bond positional isomers: a shotgun lipidomics approach using charge-switch derivatization. *Anal. Chem.* 85 (20): 9742–9750.

38 Tatituri, R.V.V., Wolf, B.J., Brenner, M.B. et al. (2015). Characterization of polar lipids of Listeria monocytogenes by HCD and low-energy CAD linear ion-trap mass spectrometry with electrospray ionization. *Anal. Bioanal. Chem.* 407 (9): 2519–2528.

39 Flentie, K.N., Stallings, C.L., Turk, J. et al. (2016). Characterization of phthiocerol and phthiodiolone dimycocerosate esters of *M. tuberculosis* by multiple-stage linear ion-trap MS. *J. Lipid Res.* 57 (1): 142–155.

40 Hsu, F.F. (2016). Characterization of hydroxyphthioceranoic and phthioceranoic acids by charge-switch derivatization and CID tandem mass spectrometry. *J. Am. Soc. Mass Spectrom.* 27 (4): 622–632.

41 Meckelmann, S.W., Hellhake, S., Steuck, M. et al. (2017). Comparison of derivatization/ionization techniques for liquid chromatography tandem mass spectrometry analysis of oxylipins. *Prostaglandins Other Lipid Mediat.* 130: 8–15.

42 Narreddula, V.R., Boase, N.R., Ailuri, R. et al. (2019). Introduction of a fixed-charge, photolabile derivative for enhanced structural elucidation of fatty acids. *Anal. Chem.* 91 (15): 9901–9909.

43 Schönbein, C.F. (1847). Ueber das Verhalten des Ozons zum oelbildenden Gas. *Bericht über die Verhandlungen der Naturforschenden Gesellschaft in Basel* 7: 7–9.

44 Criegee, R. (1975). Mechanism of ozonolysis. *Angew. Chem. Int. Ed.* 14 (11): 745–752.

45 Davison, V.L. and Dutton, H.J. (1966). Microreactor chromatography – quantitative determination of double bond positions by ozonization-pyrolysis. *Anal. Chem.* 38 (10): 1302.

46 Wu, M., Church, D.F., Mahier, T.J. et al. (1992). Separation and spectral data of the six isomeric ozonides from methyl oleate. *Lipids* 27 (2): 129–135.

47 Harrison, K.A. and Murphy, R.C. (1996). Direct mass spectrometric analysis of ozonides: application to unsaturated glycerophosphocholine lipids. *Anal. Chem.* 68 (18): 3224–3230.

48 Harrison, K.A., Davies, S.S., Marathe, G.K. et al. (2000). Analysis of oxidized glycerophosphocholine lipids using electrospray ionization mass spectrometry and microderivatization techniques. *J. Mass Spectrom.* 35 (2): 224–236.

49 Harris, R.A., May, J.C., Stinson, C.A. et al. (2018). Determining double bond position in lipids using online ozonolysis coupled to liquid chromatography and ion mobility-mass spectrometry. *Anal. Chem.* 90 (3): 1915–1924.

50 Sun, C.X., Zhao, Y.Y., and Curtis, J.M. (2013). The direct determination of double bond positions in lipid mixtures by liquid chromatography/in-line ozonolysis/mass spectrometry. *Anal. Chim. Acta* 762: 68–75.

51 Thomas, M.C., Mitchell, T.W., Harman, D.G. et al. (2007). Elucidation of double bond position in unsaturated lipids by ozone electrospray ionization mass spectrometry. *Anal. Chem.* 79 (13): 5013–5022.

52 Thomas, M.C., Mitchell, T.W., Harman, D.G. et al. (2008). Ozone-induced dissociation: elucidation of double bond position within mass-selected lipid ions. *Anal. Chem.* 80 (1): 303–311.

53 Stinson, C.A., Zhang, W.P., and Xia, Y. (2018). UV lamp as a facile ozone source for structural analysis of unsaturated lipids via electrospray ionization-mass spectrometry. *J. Am. Soc. Mass Spectrom.* 29 (3): 481–489.

54 Thomas, M.C., Mitchell, T.W., and Blanksby, S.J. (2006). Ozonolysis of phospholipid double bonds during electrospray ionization: a new tool for structure determination. *J. Am. Chem. Soc.* 128 (1): 58–59.

55 Deeley, J.M., Thomas, M.C., Truscott, R.J.W. et al. (2009). Identification of abundant alkyl ether glycerophospholipids in the human Lens by tandem mass spectrometry techniques. *Anal. Chem.* 81 (5): 1920–1930.

56 Thomas, M.C., Mitchell, T.W., and Blanksby, S.J. (2009). OnLine ozonolysis methods for the determination of double bond position in unsaturated lipids. *Methods Mol. Biol.* 579: 413–441.

57 Brown, S.H.J., Mitchell, T.W., and Blanksby, S.J. (2011). Analysis of unsaturated lipids by ozone-induced dissociation. *Biochim. Biophys Acta* 1811 (11): 807–817.

58 Ellis, S.R., Hughes, J.R., Mitchell, T.W. et al. (2012). Using ambient ozone for assignment of double bond position in unsaturated lipids. *Analyst* 137 (5): 1100–1110.

59 Pham, H.T., Maccarone, A.T., Campbell, J.L. et al. (2013). Ozone-induced dissociation of conjugated lipids reveals significant reaction rate enhancements and characteristic odd-Electron product ions. *J. Am. Soc. Mass Spectrom.* 24 (2): 286–296.

60 Pham, H.T., Maccarone, A.T., Thomas, M.C. et al. (2014). Structural characterization of glycerophospholipids by combinations of ozone- and collision-induced dissociation mass spectrometry: the next step towards "top-down" lipidomics. *Analyst* 139 (1): 204–214.

61 Kozlowski, R.L., Campbell, J.L., Mitchell, T.W., and Blanksby, S.J. (2015). Combining liquid chromatography with ozone-induced dissociation for the separation and identification of phosphatidylcholine double bond isomers. *Anal. Bioanal. Chem.* 407 (17): 5053–5064.

62 Kozlowski, R.L., Mitchell, T.W., and Blanksby, S.J. (2015). Separation and identification of phosphatidylcholine regioisomers by combining liquid chromatography with a fusion of collision- and ozone-induced dissociation. *Eur. J. Mass Spectrom.* 21 (3): 191–200.

63 Kozlowski, R.L., Mitchell, T.W., and Blanksby, S.J. (2015). A rapid ambient ionization-mass spectrometry approach to monitoring the relative abundance of isomeric glycerophospholipids. *Sci. Rep.* 5: 9243.

64 Poad, B.L.J., Green, M.R., Kirk, J.M. et al. (2017). High-pressure ozone-induced dissociation for lipid structure elucidation on fast chromatographic timescales. *Anal. Chem.* 89 (7): 4223–4229.

65 Batarseh, A.M., Abbott, S.K., Duchoslav, E. et al. (2018). Discrimination of isobaric and isomeric lipids in complex mixtures by combining ultra-high pressure liquid chromatography with collision and ozone-induced dissociation. *Int. J. Mass Spectrom.* 431: 27–36.

66 Hancock, S.E., Ailuri, R., Marshall, D.L. et al. (2018). Mass spectrometry-directed structure elucidation and total synthesis of ultra-long chain (*O*-acyl)-omega-hydroxy fatty acids. *J. Lipid Res.* 59 (8): 1510–1518.

67 Poad, B.L.J., Maccarone, A.T., Yu, H.B. et al. (2018). Differential-mobility spectrometry of 1-deoxysphingosine isomers: new insights into the gas phase structures of ionized lipids. *Anal. Chem.* 90 (8): 5343–5351.

68 Poad, B.L.J., Zheng, X.Y., Mitchell, T.W. et al. (2018). Online ozonolysis combined with ion mobility-mass spectrometry provides a new platform for lipid isomer analyses. *Anal. Chem.* 90 (2): 1292–1300.

69 Auranwiwat, C., Maccarone, A.T., Carroll, A.W. et al. (2019). Structure elucidation of cyclohexene (9*Z*)-octadec-9-enyl ethers isolated from the leaves of *Uvaria cherrevensis* (*Annonaceae*). *Tetrahedron* 75 (15): 2336–2342.

70 Hancock, S.E., Maccarone, A.T., Poad, B.L.J. et al. (2019). Reaction of ionised steryl esters with ozone in the gas phase. *Chem. Phys. Lipids* 221: 198–206.

71 Marshall, D.L., Criscuolo, A., Young, R.S.E. et al. (2019). Mapping unsaturation in human plasma lipids by data-independent ozone-induced dissociation. *J. Am. Soc. Mass Spectrom.* 30 (9): 1621–1630.

72 Poad, B.L.J., Marshall, D.L., Harazim, E. et al. (2019). Combining charge-switch derivatization with ozone-induced dissociation for fatty acid analysis. *J. Am. Soc. Mass Spectrom.* 30 (10): 2135–2143.

73 Berthias, F., Poad, B.L.J., Thurman, H.A. et al. (2021). Disentangling lipid isomers by high-resolution differential ion mobility spectrometry/ozone-induced dissociation of metalated species. *J. Am. Soc. Mass Spectrom.* 32 (12): 2827–2836.

74 Vu, N., Brown, J., Giles, K., and Zhang, Q.B. (2017). Ozone-induced dissociation on a traveling wave high-resolution mass spectrometer for determination of double-bond position in lipids. *Rapid Commun. Mass Spectrom.* 31 (17): 1415–1423.

75 Barrientos, R.C. and Zhang, Q.B. (2019). Fragmentation behavior and gas-phase structures of cationized glycosphingolipids in ozone-induced dissociation mass spectrometry. *J. Am. Soc. Mass Spectrom.* 30 (9): 1609–1620.

76 Knowles, S.L., Vu, N., Todd, D.A. et al. (2019). Orthogonal method for double-bond placement via ozone-induced dissociation mass spectrometry (OzID-MS). *J. Nat. Prod.* 82 (12): 3421–3431.

77 Barrientos, R.C., Vu, N., and Zhang, Q.B. (2017). Structural analysis of unsaturated glycosphingolipids using shotgun ozone-induced dissociation mass spectrometry. *J. Am. Soc. Mass Spectrom.* 28 (11): 2330–2343.

78 Sun, C.X., Black, B.A., Zhao, Y.Y. et al. (2013). Identification of conjugated linoleic acid (CLA) isomers by silver ion-liquid chromatography/in-line ozonolysis/mass spectrometry (Ag^+-LC/*O*-3-MS). *Anal. Chem.* 85 (15): 7345–7352.

79 Sun, C.X., Zhao, Y.Y., and Curtis, J.M. (2014). Elucidation of phosphatidylcholine isomers using two dimensional liquid chromatography coupled in-line with ozonolysis mass spectrometry. *J. Chromatogr. A* 1351: 37–45.

80 Sun, C.X., Zhao, Y.Y., and Curtis, J.M. (2015). Characterization of phospholipids by two-dimensional liquid chromatography coupled to in-line ozonolysis-mass spectrometry. *J. Agr. Food Chem.* 63 (5): 1442–1451.

81 Büchi, G., Inman, C.G., and Lipinsky, E.S. (1954). Light-catalyzed organic reactions. I. the reaction of carbonyl compounds with 2-methyl-2-butene in the presence of ultraviolet light. *J. Am. Chem. Soc.* 76 (17): 4327–4331.

82 Ma, X.X. and Xia, Y. (2014). Pinpointing double bonds in lipids by Paternò–Büchi reactions and mass spectrometry. *Angew. Chem. Int. Ed.* 53 (10): 2592–2596.

83 Ma, X.X., Zhang, W.P., Li, Z.S. et al. (2021). Enabling high structural specificity to lipidomics by coupling photochemical derivatization with tandem mass spectrometry. *Acc. Chem. Res.* 54 (20): 3873–3882.

84 Hu, Q.Y., Xia, Y., and Ma, X.X. (2021). Comprehensive structural characterization of lipids by coupling Paternò–Büchi reaction and tandem mass spectrometry. *Methods Mol. Biol.* 2306: 53–60.

85 Stinson, C.A. and Xia, Y. (2016). A method of coupling the Paternò–Büchi reaction with direct infusion ESI-MS/MS for locating the C=C bond in glycerophospholipids. *Analyst* 141 (12): 3696–3704.

86 Franklin, E.T., Shields, S.W.J., Manthorpe, J.M. et al. (2020). Coupling headgroup and alkene specific solution modifications with gas-phase ion/ion reactions for sensitive glycerophospholipid identification and characterization. *J. Am. Soc. Mass Spectrom.* 31 (4): 938–945.

87 Ren, H.L., Triebl, A., Muralidharan, S. et al. (2021). Mapping the distribution of double bond location isomers in lipids across mouse tissues. *Analyst* 146 (12): 3899–3907.

88 Liu, Z.Q. and Rochfort, S. (2022). Regio-distribution and double bond locations of unsaturated fatty acids in phospholipids of bovine milk. *Food Chem.* 373: 131515.

89 Waldchen, F., Becher, S., Esch, P. et al. (2017). Selective phosphatidylcholine double bond fragmentation and localisation using Paternò–Büchi reactions and ultraviolet photodissociation. *Analyst* 142 (24): 4744–4755.

90 Lin, Q.H., Zhang, D.H., and Xia, Y. (2020). Analysis of ether glycerophosphocholines at the level of C=C locations from human plasma. *Analyst* 145 (2): 513–522.

91 Xia, T., Ren, H.L., Zhang, W.P., and Xia, Y. (2020). Lipidome-wide characterization of phosphatidylinositols and phosphatidylglycerols on C=C location level. *Anal. Chim. Acta* 1128: 107–115.

92 Zhang, W.P., Zhang, D.H., Chen, Q.H. et al. (2019). Online photochemical derivatization enables comprehensive mass spectrometric analysis of unsaturated phospholipid isomers. *Nat. Commun.* 10: 79.

93 Cao, W.B., Cheng, S.M., Yang, J. et al. (2020). Large-scale lipid analysis with C=C location and *sn*-position isomer resolving power. *Nat. Commun.* 11 (1): 375.

94 Zhao, X., Wu, G., Zhang, W. et al. (2020). Resolving modifications on sphingoid base and *N*-acyl chain of sphingomyelin lipids in complex lipid extracts. *Anal. Chem.* 92 (21): 14775–14782.

95 Franklin, E.T. and Xia, Y. (2020). Structural elucidation of triacylglycerol using online acetone Paternò–Büchi reaction coupled with reversed-phase liquid chromatography mass spectrometry. *Analyst* 145 (20): 6532–6540.

96 Xia, T., Yuan, M., Xu, Y.W. et al. (2021). Deep structural annotation of glycerolipids by the charge-tagging Paternò–Büchi reaction and supercritical fluid chromatography-ion mobility mass spectrometry. *Anal. Chem.* 93 (23): 8345–8353.

97 Zhu, Y.L., Wang, W.H., and Yang, Z.B. (2020). Combining mass spectrometry with Paternò–Büchi reaction to determine double-bond positions in lipids at the single-cell level. *Anal. Chem.* 92 (16): 11380–11387.

98 Murphy, R.C., Okuno, T., Johnson, C.A., and Barkleyte, R.M. (2017). Determination of double bond positions in polyunsaturated fatty acids using the photochemical Paternò–Büchi reaction with acetone and tandem mass spectrometry. *Anal. Chem.* 89 (16): 8545–8553.

99 Chonglo, L., Tian, R., Shi, R.Y. et al. (2019). Coupling the Paternò–Büchi (PB) reaction with mass spectrometry to study unsaturated fatty acids in mouse model of multiple sclerosis. *Front. Chem.* 7: 807.

100 Xu, S.L., Wei, F., Xie, Y. et al. (2020). Localisation of C=C bond and absolute quantification of unsaturated fatty acids in vegetable oils based on photochemical derivatisation reaction coupled with mass spectrometry. *Int. J. Food Sci. Tech.* 55 (7): 2883–2892.

101 Han, Y.H., Chen, P.P., Li, Z.C. et al. (2022). Multi-wavelength visible-light induced [2+2] cycloaddition for identification of lipid isomers in biological samples. *J. Chromatogr. A.* 1662: 462742.

102 Xu, T.F., Pi, Z.F., Song, F.R. et al. (2018). Benzophenone used as the photochemical reagent for pinpointing C=C locations in unsaturated lipids through shotgun and liquid chromatography-mass spectrometry approaches. *Anal. Chim. Acta* 1028: 32–44.

103 Ren, J., Franklin, E.T., and Xia, Y. (2017). Uncovering structural diversity of unsaturated fatty acyls in cholesteryl esters via photochemical reaction and tandem mass spectrometry. *J. Am. Soc. Mass Spectrom.* 28 (7): 1432–1441.

104 Xie, X.B., Zhao, J., Lin, M. et al. (2020). Profiling of cholesteryl esters by coupling charge-tagging Paternò–Büchi reaction and liquid chromatography-mass spectrometry. *Anal. Chem.* 92 (12): 8487–8496.

105 Maddox, S.W., Olsen, S.S.H., Velosa, D.C. et al. (2020). Improved identification of isomeric steroids using the Paternò–Büchi reaction with ion mobility-mass spectrometry. *J. Am. Soc. Mass Spectrom.* 31 (10): 2086–2092.

106 Ma, X.X., Chong, L., Tian, R. et al. (2016). Identification and quantitation of lipid C=C location isomers: a shotgun lipidomics approach enabled by photochemical reaction. *Proc. Natl. Acad. Sci. U.S.A.* 113 (10): 2573–2578.

107 Bednarik, A., Bolsker, S., Soltwisch, J., and Dreisewerd, K. (2018). An on-tissue Paternò–Büchi reaction for localization of carbon–carbon double bonds in phospholipids and glycolipids by matrix-assisted laser-desorption-ionization mass-spectrometry imaging. *Angew. Chem. Int. Ed.* 57 (37): 12092–12096.

108 Wäldchen, F., Mohr, F., Wagner, A.H., and Heiles, S. (2020). Multifunctional reactive MALDI matrix enabling high-lateral resolution dual polarity MS imaging and lipid C=C position resolved MS2 imaging. *Anal. Chem.* 92 (20): 14130–14138.

109 Feng, G., Hao, Y., Wu, L., and Chen, S. (2020). A visible-light activated [2+2] cycloaddition reaction enables pinpointing carbon–carbon double bonds in lipids. *Chem. Sci. J.* 11 (27): 7244–7251.

110 Rykaczewski, K.A. and Schindler, C.S. (2020). Visible-light-Enabled Paternò–Büchi reaction via triplet energy transfer for the synthesis of oxetanes. *Org. Lett.* 22 (16): 6516–6519.

111 Zhao, J., Xie, X.B., Lin, Q.H. et al. (2020). Next-generation Paternò–Büchi reagents for lipid analysis by mass spectrometry. *Anal. Chem.* 92 (19): 13470–13477.

112 Li, H.-F., Cao, W., Ma, X. et al. (2020). Visible-light-driven [2+2] photocycloadditions between benzophenone and C=C bonds in unsaturated lipids. *J. Am. Chem. Soc.* 142 (7): 3499–3505.

113 Jeck, V., Korf, A., Vosse, C., and Hayen, H. (2019). Localization of double-bond positions in lipids by tandem mass spectrometry succeeding high-performance liquid chromatography with post-column derivatization. *Rapid Commun. Mass Spectrom.* 33: 86–94.

114 Zhang, W., Shang, B., Ouyang, Z., and Xia, Y. (2020). Enhanced phospholipid isomer analysis by online photochemical derivatization and RPLC-MS. *Anal. Chem.* 92 (9): 6719–6726.

115 Xie, X.B. and Xia, Y. (2019). Analysis of conjugated fatty acid isomers by the Paternò–Büchi reaction and trapped ion mobility mass spectrometry. *Anal. Chem.* 91 (11): 7173–7180.

116 Feng, Y., Chen, B., Yu, Q., and Li, L. (2019). Identification of double bond position isomers in unsaturated lipids by *m*-CPBA epoxidation and mass spectrometry fragmentation. *Anal. Chem.* 91 (3): 1791–1795.

117 Kuo, T.H., Chung, H.H., Chang, H.Y. et al. (2019). Deep lipidomics and molecular imaging of unsaturated lipid isomers: a universal strategy initiated by *m*CPBA epoxidation. *Anal. Chem.* 91 (18): 11905–11915.

118 Zhang, H., Xu, M., Shi, X. et al. (2021). Quantification and molecular imaging of fatty acid isomers from complex biological samples by mass spectrometry. *Chem. Sci.* 12 (23): 8115–8122.

119 Luo, K., Chen, H., and Zare, R.N. (2021). Location of carbon–carbon double bonds in unsaturated lipids using microdroplet mass spectrometry. *Analyst* 146 (8): 2550–2558.

120 Zhao, Y., Zhao, H., Zhao, X. et al. (2017). Identification and quantitation of C=C location isomers of unsaturated fatty acids by epoxidation reaction and tandem mass spectrometry. *Anal. Chem.* 89 (19): 10270–10278.

121 Takashima, S., Toyoshi, K., Yamamoto, T., and Shimozawa, N. (2020). Positional determination of the carbon–carbon double bonds in unsaturated fatty acids mediated by solvent plasmatization using LC-MS. *Sci. Rep.* 10 (1): 12988.

122 Cao, W., Ma, X., Li, Z. et al. (2018). Locating carbon–carbon double bonds in unsaturated phospholipids by epoxidation reaction and tandem mass spectrometry. *Anal. Chem.* 90 (17): 10286–10292.

123 Tang, S., Cheng, H., and Yan, X. (2020). On-demand electrochemical epoxidation in nano-electrospray ionization mass spectrometry to locate carbon–carbon double bonds. *Angew. Chem. Int. Ed.* 59 (1): 209–214.

124 Chintalapudi, K. and Badu-Tawiah, A.K. (2020). An integrated electrocatalytic nESI-MS platform for quantification of fatty acid isomers directly from untreated biofluids. *Chem. Sci. J.* 11 (36): 9891–9897.

125 Van Pelt, C.K., Carpenter, B.K., and Brenna, J.T. (1999). Studies of structure and mechanism in acetonitrile chemical ionization tandem mass spectrometry of polyunsaturated fatty acid methyl esters. *J. Am. Soc. Mass Spectrom.* 10 (12): 1253–1262.

126 Michaud, A.L., Lawrence, P., Adlof, R., and Brenna, J.T. (2005). On the formation of conjugated linoleic acid diagnostic ions with acetonitrile chemical ionization tandem mass spectrometry. *Rapid Commun. Mass Spectrom.* 19 (3): 363–368.

127 Moneti, G., Pieraccini, G., Favretto, D., and Traldi, P. (1998). Acetonitrile in chemical ionization of monounsaturated hydrocarbons: a C-13 and H-2 labeling study. *J. Mass Spectrom.* 33 (11): 1148–1149.

128 Oldham, N.J. (1999). Ion/molecule reactions provide new evidence for the structure and origin of. *Rapid Commun. Mass Spectrom.* 13 (16): 1694–1698.

129 Moneti, G., Pieraccini, G., Dani, F. et al. (1997). Ion-molecule reactions of ionic species from acetonitrile with unsaturated hydrocarbons for the identification of the double-bond position using an ion trap. *J. Mass Spectrom.* 32 (12): 1371–1373.

130 Moneti, G., Pieraccini, G., Favretto, D., and Traldi, P. (1999). Reactions of ionic species from acetonitrile with long-chain saturated and unsaturated alcohols. *J. Mass Spectrom.* 34 (12): 1354–1360.

131 Oldham, N.J. and Svatos, A. (1999). Determination of the double bond position in functionalized monoenes by chemical ionization ion-trap mass spectrometry using acetonitrile as a reagent gas. *Rapid Commun. Mass Spectrom.* 13 (5): 331–336.

132 Van Pelt, C.K. and Brenna, J.T. (1999). Acetonitrile chemical ionization tandem mass spectrometry to locate double bonds in polyunsaturated fatty acid methyl esters. *Anal. Chem.* 71 (10): 1981–1989.

133 Van Pelt, C.K., Huang, M.C., Tschanz, C.L., and Brenna, J.T. (1999). An octaene fatty acid, 4,7,10,13,16,19,22,25-octacosaoctaenoic acid (28:8*n*-3), found in marine oils. *J. Lipid Res.* 40 (8): 1501–1505.

134 Michaud, A.L., Diau, G.Y., Abril, R., and Brenna, J.T. (2002). Double bond localization in minor homoallylic fatty acid methyl esters using acetonitrile chemical ionization tandem mass spectrometry. *Anal. Biochem.* 307 (2): 348–360.

135 Michaud, A.L., Yurawecz, M.P., Delmonte, P. et al. (2003). Identification and characterization of conjugated fatty acid methyl esters of mixed double bond geometry by acetonitrile chemical ionization tandem mass spectrometry. *Anal. Chem.* 75 (18): 4925–4930.

136 Saba, A., Mazzini, F., Raffaelli, A. et al. (2005). Identification of 9(*E*),11(*E*)-18 : 2 fatty acid methyl ester at trace level in thermal stressed olive oils by GC coupled to acetonitrile CI-MS and CI-MS/MS, a possible marker for adulteration by addition of deodorized olive oil. *J. Agr. Food Chem.* 53 (12): 4867–4872.

137 Gomez-Cortes, P., Tyburczy, C., Brenna, J.T. et al. (2009). Characterization of cis-9 trans-11 trans-15 C18:3 in milk fat by GC and covalent adduct chemical ionization tandem MS. *J. Lipid Res.* 50 (12): 2412–2420.

138 Alves, S.P., Tyburczy, C., Lawrence, P. et al. (2011). Acetonitrile covalent adduct chemical ionization tandem mass spectrometry of non-methylene-interrupted pentaene fatty acid methyl esters. *Rapid Commun. Mass Spectrom.* 25 (14): 1933–1941.

139 Kroiss, J., Svatos, A., and Kaltenpoth, M. (2011). Rapid identification of insect cuticular hydrocarbons using gas chromatography-ion-trap mass spectrometry. *J. Chem. Ecol.* 37 (4): 420–427.

140 Xu, Y. and Brenna, J.T. (2007). Atmospheric pressure covalent adduct chemical ionization tandem mass spectrometry for double bond localization in monoene- and diene-containing triacylglycerols. *Anal. Chem.* 79 (6): 2525–2536.

141 Polášek, M., Flenerová, Z., Žabka, J., and Cvačka, J. (2013). On the reaction mechanism behind the double-bond location technique utilizing acetonitrile-APCI MS. In: *14th European Symposium on Organic Reactivity, ESOR*, 47. Prague.

142 Vrkoslav, V., Háková, M., Pecková, K. et al. (2011). Localization of double bonds in wax esters by high-performance liquid chromatography/atmospheric pressure chemical ionization mass spectrometry utilizing the fragmentation of acetonitrile-related adducts. *Anal. Chem.* 83 (8): 2978–2986.

143 Vrkoslav, V. and Cvačka, J. (2012). Identification of the double-bond position in fatty acid methyl esters by liquid chromatography/atmospheric pressure chemical ionisation mass spectrometry. *J. Chromatogr. A* 1259: 244–250.

144 Barthelemy, M., Elie, N., Pellissier, L. et al. (2019). Structural identification of antibacterial lipids from Amazonian palm tree endophytes through the molecular network approach. *Int. J. Mol. Sci.* 20 (8).

145 Sorres, J., Hebra, T., Elie, N. et al. (2022). Antiparasitic ovalicin derivatives from *Pseudallescheria boydii*, a mutualistic fungus of French Guiana termites. *Molecules* 27 (4): 1182.

146 Kalužíková, A., Vrkoslav, V., Harazim, E. et al. (2017). Cholesteryl esters of omega-(*O*-acyl)-hydroxy fatty acids in vernix caseosa. *J. Lipid Res.* 58 (8): 1579–1590.

147 Šubčíková, L., Hoskovec, M., Vrkoslav, V. et al. (2015). Analysis of 1,2-diol diesters in vernix caseosa by high-performance liquid chromatography – atmospheric pressure chemical ionization mass spectrometry. *J. Chromatogr. A* 1378: 8–18.

148 Háková, E., Vrkoslav, V., Miková, R. et al. (2015). Localization of double bonds in triacylglycerols using high-performance liquid chromatography/atmospheric pressure chemical ionization ion-trap mass spectrometry. *Anal. Bioanal. Chem.* 407 (17): 5175–5188.

149 Vanderhart, W.J. (1989). Photodissociation of trapped ions. *Mass Spectrom. Rev.* 8 (4): 237–268.

150 Tecklenburg, R.E. and Russell, D.H. (1990). An evaluation of the analytical utility of the photodissociation of fast ion-beams. *Mass Spectrom. Rev.* 9 (4): 405–451.

151 Brodbelt, J.S., Morrison, L.J., and Santos, I. (2020). Ultraviolet photodissociation mass spectrometry for analysis of biological molecules. *Chem. Rev.* 120 (7): 3328–3380.

152 Ryan, E., Nguyen, C.Q.N., Shiea, C., and Reid, G.E. (2017). Detailed structural characterization of sphingolipids via 193 nm ultraviolet photodissociation and ultra high resolution tandem mass spectrometry. *J. Am. Soc. Mass Spectrom.* 28 (7): 1406–1419.

153 Pham, H.T., Ly, T., Trevitt, A.J. et al. (2012). Differentiation of complex lipid isomers by radical-directed dissociation mass spectrometry. *Anal. Chem.* 84 (17): 7525–7532.

154 Narreddula, V.R., McKinnon, B.I., Marlton, S.J.P. et al. (2021). Next-generation derivatization reagents optimized for enhanced product ion formation in photodissociation-mass spectrometry of fatty acids. *Analyst* 146 (1): 156–169.

155 Pham, H.T. and Julian, R.R. (2014). Radical delivery and fragmentation for structural analysis of glycerophospholipids. *Int. J. Mass Spectrom.* 370: 58–65.

156 Klein, D.R. and Brodbelt, J.S. (2017). Structural characterization of phosphatidylcholines using 193 nm ultraviolet photodissociation mass spectrometry. *Anal. Chem.* 89 (3): 1516–1522.

157 Fang, M.X., Rustam, Y., Palmieri, M. et al. (2020). Evaluation of ultraviolet photodissociation tandem mass spectrometry for the structural assignment of unsaturated fatty acid double bond positional isomers. *Anal. Bioanal. Chem.* 412 (10): 2339–2351.

158 Williams, P.E., Klein, D.R., Greer, S.M., and Brodbelt, J.S. (2017). Pinpointing double bond and *sn*-positions in glycerophospholipids via hybrid 193 nm ultraviolet Photodissociation (UVPD) mass spectrometry. *J. Am. Chem. Soc.* 139 (44): 15681–15690.

159 Macias, L.A., Feider, C.L., Eberlin, L.S., and Brodbelt, J.S. (2019). Hybrid 193 nm ultraviolet photodissociation mass spectrometry localizes cardiolipin unsaturations. *Anal. Chem.* 91 (19): 12509–12516.

160 Klein, D.R., Blevins, M.S., Macias, L.A. et al. (2020). Localization of double bonds in bacterial glycerophospholipids using 193 nm ultraviolet photodissociation in the negative mode. *Anal. Chem.* 92 (8): 5986–5993.

161 Blevins, M.S., James, V.K., Herrera, C.M. et al. (2020). Unsaturation elements and other modifications of phospholipids in bacteria: new insight from ultraviolet photodissociation mass spectrometry. *Anal. Chem.* 92 (13): 9146–9155.

162 Macias, L.A., Garza, K.Y., Feider, C.L. et al. (2021). Relative quantitation of unsaturated phosphatidylcholines using 193 nm ultraviolet photodissociation parallel reaction monitoring mass spectrometry. *J. Am. Chem. Soc.* 143 (36): 14622–14634.

163 Buenger, E.W. and Reid, G.E. (2020). Shedding light on isomeric FAHFA lipid structures using 213 nm ultraviolet photodissociation mass spectrometry. *Eur. J. Mass Spectrom.* 26 (5): 311–323.

164 Cody, R.B. and Freiser, B.S. (1979). Electron-impact excitation of ions from organics – alternative to collision-induced dissociation. *Anal. Chem.* 51 (4): 547–551.

165 Baba, T., Campbell, J.L., Le Blanc, J.C.Y. et al. (2015). Electron capture dissociation in a branched radio-frequency ion trap. *Anal. Chem.* 87 (1): 785–792.

166 Baba, T., Campbell, J.L., Le Blanc, J.C.Y. et al. (2017). Development of a branched radio-frequency ion trap for electron based dissociation and related applications. *Mass Spectrom.* 6 (1): A0058.

167 Campbell, J.L. and Baba, T. (2015). Near-complete structural characterization of phosphatidylcholines using Electron impact excitation of ions from organics. *Anal. Chem.* 87 (11): 5837–5845.

168 Jones, J.W., Thompson, C.J., Carter, C.L., and Kane, M.A. (2015). Electron-induced dissociation (EID) for structure characterization of glycerophosphatidylcholine: determination of double-bond positions and localization of acyl chains. *J. Mass Spectrom.* 50 (12): 1327–1339.

169 Baba, T., Campbell, J.L., Le Blanc, J.C.Y., and Baker, P.R.S. (2016). In-depth sphingomyelin characterization using electron impact excitation of ions from organics and mass spectrometry. *J. Lipid Res.* 57 (5): 858–867.

170 Baba, T., Campbell, J.L., Le Blanc, J.C.Y., and Baker, P.R.S. (2016). Structural identification of triacylglycerol isomers using electron impact excitation of ions from organics (EIEIO). *J. Lipid Res.* 57 (11): 2015–2027.

171 Baba, T., Campbell, J.L., Le Blanc, J.C.Y. et al. (2018). Quantitative structural multiclass lipidomics using differential mobility: electron impact excitation of ions from organics (EIEIO) mass spectrometry. *J. Lipid Res.* 59 (5): 910–919.

172 Baba, T., Ryumin, P., Duchoslav, E. et al. (2021). Dissociation of biomolecules by an intense low-energy Electron beam in a high sensitivity time-of-flight mass spectrometer. *J. Am. Soc. Mass Spectrom.* 32 (8): 1964–1975.

173 Li, P.F. and Jackson, G.P. (2017). Charge transfer dissociation of phosphocholines: gas-phase ion/ion reactions between helium cations and phospholipid cations. *J. Mass Spectrom.* 52 (5): 271–282.

174 Ran-Ressler, R.R., Devapatla, S., Lawrence, P., and Brenna, J.T. (2008). Branched chain fatty acids are constituents of the normal healthy newborn gastrointestinal tract. *Pediatr. Res.* 64 (6): 605–609.

175 Oku, H., Nakanishi, T., Kumamoto, K., and Chinen, I. (1990). Distribution of branched-chain fatty acid in the skin surface lipid of laboratory animals. *Comp. Biochem. Physiol. B* 96 (3): 475–482.

176 Ran-Ressler, R.R., Lawrence, P., and Brenna, J.T. (2012). Structural characterization of saturated branched chain fatty acid methyl esters by collisional dissociation of molecular ions generated by electron ionization [S]. *J. Lipid Res.* 53 (1): 195–203.

177 Lin, Q., Li, P., Jian, R., and Xia, Y. (2022). Localization of Intrachain modifications in bacterial lipids via radical-directed dissociation. *J. Am. Soc. Mass Spectrom.* 33 (4): 714–721.

178 Jian, R., Zhao, X., Lin, Q., and Xia, Y. (2022). Profiling of branched-chain fatty acids via nitroxide radical-directed dissociation integrated on an LC-MS/MS workflow. *Analyst* 147: 2115–2123.

179 Jensen, N.J. and Gross, M.L. (1986). Fast-atom-bombardment and tandem mass-spectrometry for determining Iso-fatty and anteiso-fatty acids. *Lipids* 21 (5): 362–365.

180 Contado, M.J. and Adams, J. (1991). Collision-induced dissociations and B/E linked scans for structural determination of modified fatty-acid esters. *Anal. Chim. Acta* 246 (1): 187–197.

181 Funk, C.D. (2001). Prostaglandins and leukotrienes: advances in eicosanoid biology. *Science* 294 (5548): 1871–1875.

182 Berglund, L. (2003). Lipid biochemistry: an introduction. *Am. J. Clin. Nutr.* 78 (2): 353–354.

183 Gladine, C., Ostermann, A.I., Newman, J.W., and Schebb, N.H. (2019). MS-based targeted metabolomics of eicosanoids and other oxylipins: analytical and inter-individual variabilities. *Free Radic. Biol. Med.* 144: 72–89.

184 Thakare, R., Chhonker, Y.S., Gautam, N. et al. (2018). Simultaneous LC-MS/MS analysis of eicosanoids and related metabolites in human serum, sputum and BALF. *Biomed. Chromatogr.* 32 (3).

185 Puppolo, M., Varma, D., and Jansen, S.A. (2014). A review of analytical methods for eicosanoids in brain tissue. *J. Chromatogr. B Analyt. Technol. Biomed. Life Sci.* 964: 50–64.

186 Mesaros, C. and Blair, I.A. (2012). Targeted chiral analysis of bioactive arachidonic acid metabolites using liquid-chromatography-mass spectrometry. *Metabolites* 2 (2): 337–365.

187 Murphy, R.C., Barkley, R.M., Zemski Berry, K. et al. (2005). Electrospray ionization and tandem mass spectrometry of eicosanoids. *Anal. Biochem.* 346 (1): 1–42.

188 Yang, J., Schmelzer, K., Georgi, K., and Hammock, B.D. (2009). Quantitative profiling method for oxylipin metabolome by liquid chromatography electrospray ionization tandem mass spectrometry. *Anal. Chem.* 81 (19): 8085–8093.

189 Chocholoušková, M., Jirásko, R., Vrána, D. et al. (2019). Reversed phase UHPLC/ESI-MS determination of oxylipins in human plasma: a case study of female breast cancer. *Anal. Bioanal. Chem.* 411 (6): 1239–1251.

190 Lee, S.H., Williams, M.V., DuBois, R.N., and Blair, I.A. (2003). Targeted lipidomics using electron capture atmospheric pressure chemical ionization mass spectrometry. *Rapid Commun. Mass Spectrom.* 17 (19): 2168–2176.

191 Di Giovanni, J.P., Barkley, R.M., Jones, D.N.M. et al. (2018). Tandem mass spectrometry and ion mobility reveals structural insight into eicosanoid product ion formation. *J. Am. Soc. Mass Spectrom.* 29 (6): 1231–1241.

192 Yuan, Z.X., Majchrzak-Hong, S., Keyes, G.S. et al. (2018). Lipidomic profiling of targeted oxylipins with ultra-performance liquid chromatography-tandem mass spectrometry. *Anal. Bioanal. Chem.* 410 (23): 6009–6029.

193 Sun, D., Meng, X., Ren, T. et al. (2018). Establishment of a charge reversal derivatization strategy to improve the ionization efficiency of Limaprost and investigation of the fragmentation patterns of Limaprost derivatives via exclusive neutral loss and survival yield method. *J. Am. Soc. Mass Spectrom.* 29 (7): 1365–1375.

194 Liu, X., Moon, S.H., Mancuso, D.J. et al. (2013). Oxidized fatty acid analysis by charge-switch derivatization, selected reaction monitoring, and accurate mass quantitation. *Anal. Biochem.* 442 (1): 40–50.

195 Narreddula, V.R., Sadowski, P., Boase, N.R.B. et al. (2020). Structural elucidation of hydroxy fatty acids by photodissociation mass spectrometry with photolabile derivatives. *Rapid Commun. Mass Spectrom.* 34 (9): e8741.

196 Hellhake, S., Meckelmann, S.W., Empl, M.T. et al. (2020). Non-targeted and targeted analysis of oxylipins in combination with charge-switch derivatization by ion mobility high-resolution mass spectrometry. *Anal. Bioanal. Chem.* 412 (23): 5743–5757.

197 Madsen, J.A., Cullen, T.W., Trent, M.S., and Brodbelt, J.S. (2011). IR and UV photodissociation as analytical tools for characterizing lipid a structures. *Anal. Chem.* 83 (13): 5107–5113.

198 Brejchová, K., Balas, L., Paluchová, V. et al. (2020). Understanding FAHFAs: from structure to metabolic regulation. *Prog. Lipid Res.* 79: 101053.

199 Butovich, I.A., Wojtowicz, J.C., and Molai, M. (2009). Human tear film and meibum. Very long chain wax esters and (*O*-acyl)-omega-hydroxy fatty acids of meibum. *J. Lipid Res.* 50 (12): 2471–2485.

200 Kuda, O., Brezinova, M., Rombaldova, M. et al. (2016). Docosahexaenoic acid-derived fatty acid esters of hydroxy fatty acids (FAHFAs) with anti-inflammatory properties. *Diabetes* 65 (9): 2580–2590.

201 Kolar, M.J., Nelson, A.T., Chang, T. et al. (2018). Faster protocol for endogenous fatty acid esters of hydroxy fatty acid (FAHFA) measurements. *Anal. Chem.* 90 (8): 5358–5365.

202 Ma, Y., Kind, T., Vaniya, A. et al. (2015). An in silico MS/MS library for automatic annotation of novel FAHFA lipids. *J. Cheminf.* 7 (1): 53.

203 Marshall, D.L., Saville, J.T., Maccarone, A.T. et al. (2016). Determination of ester position in isomeric (*O*-acyl)-hydroxy fatty acids by ion trap mass spectrometry. *Rapid Commun. Mass Spectrom.* 30 (21): 2351–2359.

204 Gowda, S.G.B., Liang, C., Gowda, D. et al. (2020). Identification of short-chain fatty acid esters of hydroxy fatty acids (SFAHFAs) in a murine model by nontargeted analysis using ultra-high-performance liquid chromatography/linear ion trap quadrupole-Orbitrap mass spectrometry. *Rapid Commun. Mass Spectrom.* 34 (17): e8831.

205 Hu, T., Lin, M., Zhang, D. et al. (2018). A UPLC/MS/MS method for comprehensive profiling and quantification of fatty acid esters of hydroxy fatty acids in white adipose tissue. *Anal. Bioanal. Chem.* 410 (28): 7415–7428.

206 Vavrušová, A., Vrkoslav, V., Plavka, R. et al. (2020). Analysis of (O-acyl) alpha- and omega-hydroxy fatty acids in vernix caseosa by high-performance liquid chromatography-Orbitrap mass spectrometry. *Anal. Bioanal. Chem.* 412 (10): 2291–2302.

207 Hu, C., Wang, M., Duan, Q., and Han, X. (2020). Sensitive analysis of fatty acid esters of hydroxy fatty acids in biological lipid extracts by shotgun lipidomics after one-step derivatization. *Anal. Chim. Acta* 1105: 105–111.

208 Zhu, Q.F., Yan, J.W., Gao, Y. et al. (2017). Highly sensitive determination of fatty acid esters of hydroxyl fatty acids by liquid chromatography-mass spectrometry. *J. Chromatogr. B Analyt. Technol. Biomed. Life Sci.* 1061-1062: 34–40.

209 Zhu, Q.F., Yan, J.W., Zhang, T.Y. et al. (2018). Comprehensive screening and identification of fatty acid esters of Hydroxy fatty acids in plant tissues by chemical isotope labeling-assisted liquid chromatography-mass spectrometry. *Anal. Chem.* 90 (16): 10056–10063.

210 Randolph, C.E., Marshall, D.L., Blanksby, S.J., and McLuckey, S.A. (2020). Charge-switch derivatization of fatty acid esters of hydroxy fatty acids via gas-phase ion/ion reactions. *Anal. Chim. Acta* 1129: 31–39.

211 Jiang, X., Duan, Y., Zhou, B. et al. (2019). The cyclopropane fatty acid synthase mediates antibiotic resistance and gastric colonization of *Helicobacter pylori*. *J. Bacteriol.* 201 (20).

212 Blevins, M.S., Klein, D.R., and Brodbelt, J.S. (2019). Localization of cyclopropane modifications in bacterial lipids via 213 nm ultraviolet photodissociation mass spectrometry. *Anal. Chem.* 91 (10): 6820–6828.

213 Randolph, C.E., Shenault, D.S.M., Blanksby, S.J., and McLuckey, S.A. (2021). Localization of carbon–carbon double bond and cyclopropane sites in cardiolipins via gas-phase charge inversion reactions. *J. Am. Soc. Mass Spectrom.* 32 (2): 455–464.

214 Mouchlis, V.D., Chen, Y., McCammon, J.A., and Dennis, E.A. (2018). Membrane allostery and unique hydrophobic sites promote enzyme substrate specificity. *J. Am. Chem. Soc.* 140 (9): 3285–3291.

215 Kawana, H., Kano, K., Shindou, H. et al. (2019). An accurate and versatile method for determining the acyl group-introducing position of lysophospholipid acyltransferases. *Biochim. Biophys. Acta, Mol. Cell. Biol. Lipids* 1864 (7): 1053–1060.

216 Groessl, M., Graf, S., and Knochenmuss, R. (2015). High resolution ion mobility-mass spectrometry for separation and identification of isomeric lipids. *Analyst* 140 (20): 6904–6911.

217 Bowman, A.P., Abzalimov, R.R., and Shvartsburg, A.A. (2017). Broad separation of isomeric lipids by high-resolution differential ion mobility spectrometry with tandem mass spectrometry. *J. Am. Soc. Mass Spectrom.* 28 (8): 1552–1561.

218 Maccarone, A.T., Duldig, J., Mitchell, T.W. et al. (2014). Characterization of acyl chain position in unsaturated phosphatidylcholines using differential mobility-mass spectrometry. *J. Lipid Res.* 55 (8): 1668–1677.

219 Laakso, P. (2002). Mass spectrometry of triacylglycerols. *Eur. J. Lipid Sci. Tech.* 104 (1): 43–49.

220 Becher, S., Esch, P., Heiles, S. et al. (2018). *Anal. Chem.* 90 (19): 11486–11494.

221 Hsu, F.F. and Turk, J. (2000). Characterization of phosphatidylethanolamine as a lithiated adduct by triple quadrupole tandem mass spectrometry with electrospray ionization. *J. Mass Spectrom.* 35 (5): 596–606.

222 Hsu, F.F. and Turk, J. (2003). Electrospray ionization/tandem quadrupole mass spectrometric studies on phosphatidylcholines: the fragmentation processes. *J. Am. Soc. Mass Spectrom.* 14 (4): 352–363.

223 Hsu, F.F. and Turk, J. (2005). Studies on phosphatidylserine by tandem quadrupole and multiple stage quadrupole ion-trap mass spectrometry with electrospray ionization: structural characterization and the fragmentation processes. *J. Am. Soc. Mass Spectrom.* 16 (9): 1510–1522.

224 Becher, S., Berden, G., Martens, J. et al. (2021). IRMPD spectroscopy of [PC (4:0/4:0) + M]$^+$ (M = H, Na, K) and corresponding CID fragment ions. *J. Am. Soc. Mass Spectrom.* 32: 2874–2884.

225 Zhao, X., Zhang, W., Zhang, D. et al. (2019). A lipidomic workflow capable of resolving *sn*- and C=C location isomers of phosphatidylcholines. *Chem. Sci. J.* 10 (46): 10740–10748.

8

Lipidomic Identification

Harald Köfeler

Medizinische Universität Graz, Center for Medical Research, Core Facility Mass Spectrometry, Stiftingtalstraße 24, 8010 Graz, Österreich

8.1 Overview

Identification of lipid entities by various bioanalytical methods is one of the most fundamental issues in lipidomics. This chapter will guide the reader through the different techniques for lipid identification and will illustrate not only their merits but also their limitations. After discussing these analytical techniques, an exemplified integrated workflow for automated data processing and data interpretation will be briefly introduced. The end of the chapter will focus on annotation issues and the conclusions, which can be drawn from data at various levels of analytical certainty.

When putting these different analytical and software modules together, there are several combinations, which have evolved and proven their robustness over the past three decades (Figure 8.1). From a historical perspective, the first lipidomics platforms in the 1990s were all direct infusion (shotgun) based, back then relying almost exclusively on triple-quadrupole technology [1–3]. About a decade later, high-resolution instruments – particularly quadrupole time of flight (QqTOF) and Orbitrap – gradually started to replace triple quadrupoles, adding the determination of elemental composition as an additional layer of identification certainty [4–6]. In parallel to these developments, chromatographic separation was introduced into lipidomic analysis from the beginning of the millennium [7]. In this category, reversed-phase high-performance liquid chromatography (HPLC) and hydrophilic interaction liquid chromatography (HILIC) are the most widely used systems (Figure 8.1). Although being a niche technology, chiral chromatography can nevertheless be invaluable for some specific scientific questions, where biological impact depends on specific enantiomers of a compound (e.g. 1,2-diacylglycerol (DG) versus 2,3-DG) [8]. Most recently, ion mobility spectrometry (IMS) started to contribute to lipid identification by its molecular shape-dependent separation approach [9–13]. At the moment, IMS is best realized in coupling with QqTOF mass spectrometers,

Mass Spectrometry for Lipidomics: Methods and Applications, First Edition.
Edited by Michal Holčapek and Kim Ekroos.
© 2023 WILEY-VCH GmbH. Published 2023 by WILEY-VCH GmbH.

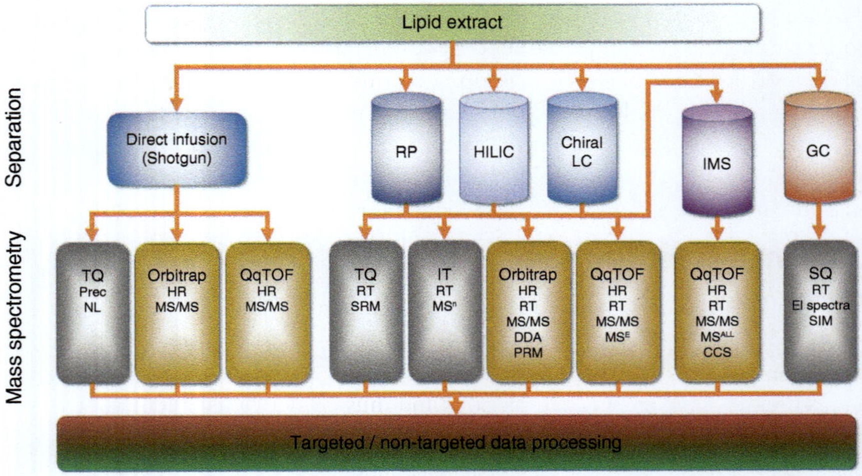

Figure 8.1 Overview about the lipidomics workflow including the most important combinations of direct infusion and separation techniques (LC, GC, and IMS) with various mass spectrometry equipment. Gray color indicates mass spectrometers' operation at nominal resolution and gold color indicates high-resolution mass spectrometers. Abbreviations: TQ: triple quadrupole; SQ: single quadrupole; IT: ion trap; RT: retention time; HR: high mass resolution; Prec: precursor ion scan; NL: neutral loss scan; DDA: data-dependent acquisition; PRM: parallel reaction monitoring; SIM: selected ion monitoring.

while liquid chromatographic separations are mostly coupled to triple-quadrupole, Orbitrap, QqTOF, and ion trap mass spectrometers (Figure 8.1). Among all these technological combinations, gas chromatography in combination with a quadrupole analyzer (gas chromatography–mass spectrometry) has by far the longest tradition in the analysis of lipids, going back to the late 1970s, and can still be regarded as a technology in its own right for small and volatile lipids.

8.2 Chromatography

Chromatographic separation serves two purposes: (i) separation of lipids by their physico-chemical properties and (ii) characterization of lipids by their retention time. While the first property alleviates identification issues arising from mixed spectra in complex biological samples, the second property may be used for identification itself. Depending on the chromatography chosen, the expected order of retention times for a given set of lipids will vary. The most widely used chromatography in lipidomics is reversed-phase HPLC because it separates lipids, which are by definition hydrophobic, according to their hydrophobicity. As the hydrophobicity of a lipid compound is predominantly constituted by its hydrocarbon content (fatty acyls, fatty alkyls, and isoprenoids), these moieties determine the order of elution. On the other hand, the accumulated hydrophilicity of functional groups constituting the headgroup also influences the elution behavior of a certain lipid species. Therefore, the specific retention time for a given lipid species depends on the size of the hydrocarbon content and the hydrophilicity of the headgroup. As a rule of thumb in many instances, the first bulk of eluting lipid classes is made up of fatty acids (FAs), lyso-phospholipids, monoacylglycerols, and cholesterol, the second bulk is made up of phospholipids, sphingolipids, and DG, while the last elution bulk is made up of triacylglycerols (TG) and cholesterol esters (CEs) [14, 15]. Furthermore, the retention behavior within a specific lipid class exclusively depends on the hydrophobic fatty acyl/alky tails, where an increasing carbon number results in later elution, while an increasing number of double bonds results in earlier elution [15]. The equivalent carbon number (ECN) model is the most commonly used model expressing the relationship between carbon and double-bond numbers [15]. The basic assumption of this model is that one double bond is roughly equivalent to two carbons and thus decreases the retention time of a certain lipid into the elution range of a lipid with two carbons less and without the corresponding double bond. For example, a phosphatidylcholine (PC) 34:1 would roughly overlap with PC 32:0. When plotting either the number of double bonds against retention time at a given carbon number or the number of carbons against retention time for a given double-bond number, this plot should result in a linear relationship. This kind of retention time analysis gives a substantial insight into the validity of lipid identifications because if this linear relationship is not at least roughly fulfilled for a lipid in comparison to other identified candidates from the same lipid class, chances are high that it is not the proposed compound. In this regard, Hartler et al. proposed an equation for calculating retention time predictions from empirical data [16]:

$$RT\left(x,y\right)=A*\left(1-B*x^{-C}\right)+D*e^{\left(-E*y+F*x\right)}+G$$

In this equation, x and y are the numbers of carbons and double bonds, while A through G are empirical coefficients. The determination of these coefficients needs at least seven independent mass chromatograms with known reference standards for retention time calculation of a certain lipid species, and with this fit, the algorithm is then primed to predict the retention time of this lipid as long as the chromatographic setting does not change. This can be a very convenient plausibility check for retention times in bigger sample batches.

Reversed-phase separations often just separate lipids at the species level according to their carbon and double-bond number, which would correspond to the TG 54:7 annotation. Nevertheless, some reversed-phase methods are even able to achieve baseline separation of individual molecular lipid species, which could further separate TG 54:7 into TG 18:2_18:2_18:3 and TG 18:1_18:3_18:3 [7]. Such kind of chromatography then provides even further identification certainty for lipids characterized by mass spectrometry. With such sophisticated chromatography, it was even possible to separately identify positional isomers of DG (e.g. 1,2-DG 18:1/18:1 versus 1,3-DG 18:1/18:1) [7].

In contrast to reversed-phase HPLC, HILIC separates lipids by their polar headgroups, rendering the factor of fatty acyl/fatty alkyl composition much less important for separation. This retention behavior results in an elution profile where the individual lipid species in each lipid class is almost co-eluting. While this alleviates quantitation of lipids [17], the overlap of lipid species also increases the chances for mixed spectra, which are more challenging in their interpretation. Nevertheless, retention times in HILIC separation clearly indicate to which lipid class a lipid species belongs, which is a useful property for identification [18]. The retention order is inverted in comparison to reversed-phase chromatography, starting with TG and CE and ending with lysophospholipids. Unlike in reversed-phase HPLC, separation of molecular species is not possible with HILIC, shifting this level of identification on mass spectrometry analysis.

For separation and subsequent identification of enantiomers, chiral HPLC is the method of choice. As a good example, Lisa et al. used cellulose-tris-(3,5-dimethylphenylcarbamate) as the stationary phase for chiral separation of a TG mixture [8]. This method enabled separate identification of enantiomeric TGs, e.g. TG 18:2/18:2/18:1 versus TG 18:1/18:2/18:2 or TG 20:4/18:1/18:1 versus TG 18:1/18:1/20:4. The drawback of such methodology is the very long run times of more than 130 minutes, which makes it rather unsuitable for high-throughput approaches, but when detailed information on enantiomeric lipids is required, it is the method of choice.

Gas chromatography (GC) is by its nature just applicable for small and volatile compounds such as fatty acids or oxylipins [19, 20]. As retention times are very stable for this kind of chromatography, it is possible to use the actual retention times within an elution range window of just a very few seconds for the identification of compounds. Because GC is most often coupled to a single quadrupole with electron ionization (EI), this enables identification of lipids by a combination of a database similarity search for EI spectra and the correct retention time of compounds. Additionally, chromatographic baseline separation of compounds is a prerequisite for unambiguous interpretation of EI spectra because mixed EI spectra will inherently lower the identification certainty scores of a database search, and their manual interpretation can become a very tedious task.

8.3 Mass Spectrometry

8.3.1 Exact Mass

Isomerism in lipidomics is caused by the natural wealth of fatty acids and the possibilities arising by their combination. This fact results in many potentially overlapping compounds for one molecular (adduct) ion. While separation of isomers can only be achieved by chromatography, mass spectral fragmentation, or IMS, isobaric lipids can be separated at the stage of molecular (adduct) ions when sufficient mass resolution is available. High-resolution mass spectrometers can provide this kind of resolution to various degrees and are therefore able to provide accurate mass measurements and elemental compositions of lipid species. Table 8.1 depicts some frequently encountered examples for isobaric overlaps of lipids. The resolution values provided can be regarded as approximations for the full width at half-height resolution needed to achieve baseline separation at the corresponding m/z values.

Table 8.1 Isobaric and isomeric mass overlaps frequently encountered in lipidomics.

Lipid species	Adduct	Isotope	Mass (*m/z*)	Elemental composition	Δ*m* (*m/z*)	R (FWHH)
PC 38:1	H^+	Monoisotopic	816.647637	$C_{44}H_{89}O_8N_1P_1$	0.0939	20000
PE 42:8	H^+	Monoisotopic	816.553737	$C_{45}H_{77}O_8N_1P_1$		
PC 34:0	H^+	Monoisotopic	762.600687	$C_{46}H_{85}O_8N_1P_1$	0.07278	25000
PS 34:1	H^+	Monoisotopic	762.527907	$C_{44}H_{77}O_{10}N_1P_1$		
SM 42:1;2	H^+	M+1	816.703367	$C_{38}{}^{13}C_1H_{80}O_6N_2P_1$	0.05573	35000
PC 38:1	H^+	Monoisotopic	816.647637	$C_{38}H_{75}O_8N_1P_1$		
PC 37:3	H^+	Monoisotopic	756.553737	$C_{41}H_{81}O_8N_1P_1$	0.03639	45000
PE a38:3	H^+	Monoisotopic	756.590127	$C_{42}H_{85}O_7N_1P_1$		
DG 36:0	$NH_4{}^+$	Monoisotopic	666.603071	$C_{39}H_{80}O_5N_1$	0.01527	100000
CE 16:0	$NH_4{}^+$	Monoisotopic	666.618341	$C_{43}H_{80}O_2N_1$		
PE 38:4	H^+	M+2	770.560447	$C_{40}{}^{13}C_2H_{83}O_8N_1P_1$	0.00894	200000
PE 38:3	H^+	Monoisotopic	770.569387	$C_{42}H_{85}O_8N_1P_1$		
PC 34:3	H^+	Monoisotopic	756.553737	$C_{44}H_{81}O_8N_1P_1$	0.00241	700000
PC 32:0	Na^+	Monoisotopic	756.551331	$C_{42}H_{82}O_8N_1P_1Na_1$		
PC 33:1	H^+	Monoisotopic	716.522437	$C_{41}H_{81}O_8N_1P_1$	0	–
PE 36:1	H^+	Monoisotopic	716.522437	$C_{41}H_{81}O_8N_1P_1$		

While for isobaric pairs of lipids the approximate full width at half-height mass resolution needed for their separation is depicted, for isomeric lipid pairs, the mass resolution needed is infinite by definition.

Baseline separation of isobars is particularly important when the compounds to be separated have huge differences in their peak height, usually reflecting their different concentrations, but becomes less important at roughly equivalent abundance. For the first four examples in Table 8.1, QqTOF instrumentation, which reaches up to 80 000 resolution in some instances, will provide sufficient mass resolution. The first two examples are often encountered in lipidomics, depicting an overlap of saturated PC with highly unsaturated phosphatidylethanolamine (PE) species and PC/phosphatidylserine (PS) isobaric twins. Separation of plasmalogens from diacyl phospholipids is a more demanding case and needs a resolution of 45 000. Furthermore, M+1 peaks of odd ions such as sphingomyelin (SM) could potentially overlap with the monoisotopic peak of an even mass peak, such as PC. This is prevented if a mass resolution of at least 35 000 is available. The following three examples would require Fourier transform-mass spectrometry (FT-MS) technology for isobaric separation, either Orbitrap or Fourier transform-ion cyclotrone resonance-mass spectrometry (FT-ICR-MS). While the exemplified DG and CE species require 100 000 resolution, overlapping sodiated and protonated PC species get only separated by a resolution of 700 000. The most widely encountered isobaric issue in lipidomics is the coalescence of a monoisotopic lipid mass and the M+2 peak of this same lipid with just one double bond less. At a resolution of approximately 180 000, this issue can be solved, but if this is not possible and also no chromatographic separation is available, an isotopic correction function has to be applied [21]. Briefly, such isotopic correction functions always factor in the known ^{13}C distribution of a certain lipid. Based on this knowledge, it is possible to calculate the size of M+1 and M+2 peaks of the lipid species under investigation and to subtract them from the overlapping monoisotopic mass with one double bond less. Although, as depicted in the last example in Table 8.1, lipid isomerism cannot be resolved by high mass resolution, exact mass and the resulting highly confident elemental compositions can vastly contribute to an increase in lipidomics identification certainty. This is very well demonstrated by the following example: Just for a PC with a nominal mass of 773, the number of possible structures will be 202 when just taking into account commonly encountered fatty acyl residues (12–24 carbons and a maximum of 6 double bonds) without any branches, rings, or other fatty acid modifications [22]. In this example, a mass resolution of 45 000 would be sufficient for cutting the number of candidates down to 58, mainly because alkyl and acyl species can be separated by their number of oxygens. However, when the original 202 structure proposals are cut down to 58, even higher mass resolution would be of no more benefit because they are all isomers. This illustrates very well the power but also the limitations of high mass resolution. For cutting down the number even further, either chromatography or mass spectral fragmentation will be needed.

8.3.2 Fragment Spectra

8.3.2.1 General Considerations

While EI as a hard gas-phase ionization technique is only used in coupling with GC and is not able to select any precursors, most lipidomics fragmentation techniques rely on collision-induced dissociation (CID) including precursor selection of ions previously generated by electrospray ionization (ESI). Precursor ion selection alleviates the challenge of mixed spectra, which is an inherent problem with EI spectra when chromatographic separation is not perfect. Nevertheless, when available, EI spectra are highly valuable because of their extremely information-rich nature. CID spectra can be roughly divided into high- and low-energy regimes, featuring collision energies of up to 20 000 eV and up to 500 eV, respectively. While low-energy CID predominantly induces charge-driven fragmentation (CDF) processes, high-energy CID additionally induces charge-remote fragmentations (CRFs), which allow deeper structural elucidation [23]. However, besides matrix-assisted laser desorption-time-of-flight/time-of-flight (MALDI TOF/TOF) and sector instruments, which are rarely used for lipidomics these days, most mass analyzers in lipidomics only allow for low-energy CID spectra, which generally rather provide information by breaking of heteropolar bonds (e.g. C=O and C=N) and not by breaking of C=C bonds. However, even low-energy CID spectra are dependent on the fragmentation mechanism. In this regard, quadrupole fragmentation and ion trap fragmentation can be divided, with the former depositing fragmentation energy by acceleration of ions on their flight trajectory, while the latter works by depositing radio-frequency (Rf)-induced resonance energy. The excitation mechanism of ion traps results in less energy-rich fragmentations and makes ion trap CID prone to either unspecific neutral losses (H_2O, NH_3) or low-energy fragmentation patterns. This can sometimes be compensated by the ability of MS^n, where unspecific but highly abundant fragments could be subjected to further fragmentation steps as long as sensitivity allows it. Quadrupole CID on the other hand can still be subdivided into a classical "Q2" setting and into higher collisional dissociation (HCD), which is provided by Orbitrap technology-based hybrid instrumentation. While in a typical "Q2" setting ions exit the CID cell on the opposite side of their entrance, ions in HCD enter and exit through the same orifice, but both fragmentation techniques result in similar fragment patterns. Another issue to be taken into consideration when talking about CID is the low mass cutoff encountered in ion trap CID, which does not exist with the other mentioned fragmentation methods. This can definitely be an advantage for non-ion trap CID because some characteristic fragment ions will get lost when they fall below the low mass cutoff of approximately 25% (depending slightly on the activation energy chosen). In sharp contrast to EI, all CID technologies are hard to standardize because, in addition to the type of CID, the resulting fragment spectra further depend on the collision energy chosen, the collision gas (Ar, N_2, and He), and the collision gas pressure. All of these factors need rigid control and often restrict the suitability of CID spectra for database searches.

8.3.2.2 Fatty Acids

The most widely used method for fatty acid identification is GC-EI/MS, including derivatization (e.g. methyl esters) before analysis [24]. As the National Institute of Standards and Technology (NIST) database has EI spectra deposited for the majority of commonly encountered fatty acids, a database similarity search coupled with the correct retention time usually delivers unambiguous results for fatty acid IDs. Another interesting option for in-depth structural elucidation of fatty acids would be high-energy CID with its associated CRF spectra, as depicted in Figure 8.2. This kind of analysis could, for instance, be performed by MALDI-TOF/TOF and results in fragmentation patterns made of homologous fragment series, interrupted by lower fragment intensities and reduced spacing at double-bond locations (Figure 8.2). For the same reason, it is also possible to locate branches by intensity interruptions of homologous fragment patterns [25].

8.3.2.3 Oxylipins

Oxylipins are hard to identify because at the one hand, they are often detected at trace concentrations, which complicates identification, and at the other hand, their identification suffers from a high degree of isomerism [26]. The bad news in this regard is that all these isomers do have distinct biological relevance and need to be separated for obtaining biologically meaningful data. The fragment spectra of isomeric oxylipins, particularly hydroxylated leukotrienes, hydroxy eicosatetraenoic acids (HETEs), resolvins, protectins, etc., often show the same fragments but at different intensities, individual for each compound [27]. An example for this would be resolvin D1 (RvD1) and RvD2, both of which show m/z 141 as a fragment [28].

Therefore, adequate chromatography for separation of isomers is mandatory, but also taking into account that multiple fragments could alleviate co-ionization issues of unseparated isomers. Consequently, targeted selected reaction monitoring (SRM) methods depending on just one mass transition used as a quantifier should be avoided, and addition of one or two further qualifiers to the SRM panel will vastly increase identification certainty.

8.3.2.4 Phospholipids

The unique structural feature of all phospholipids is their polar headgroup moiety. The headgroup is also the location of a phospholipids charge in ESI mass spectrometry. As in low-energy CID fragmentation processes are often charge driven, the headgroup is the initial source of fragmentation. Phospholipid fragments are basically divided into two categories: (i) headgroup fragments characteristic for the respective phospholipid class and (ii) fatty-acyl-/alkyl-chain-specific fragments indicative for the fatty acid/alkyl composition of an individual lipid species. While the first category aids in the identification of lipids according to their cumulative carbon and double-bond numbers (e.g. phosphatidylinositol [PI] 38:4), the second category will elucidate the molecular structures of lipid species down to the composition of fatty acids/alkyls. The latter fragmentations could result either in the fatty acyl/alky composition without known *sn*-position (e.g. PI 18:0_20:4) or with *sn*-positions determined by fatty acyl fragment intensity ratios (e.g. PI 18:0/20:4).

When sticking to PC as the most important phospholipid class, Figure 8.3a shows the fragmentation process of the abundant $[M+H]^+$ ion, leading to the choline headgroup fragment detected at m/z 184 [29]. This fragmentation results in charge retention at the headgroup and therefore offers the possibility for a class-specific

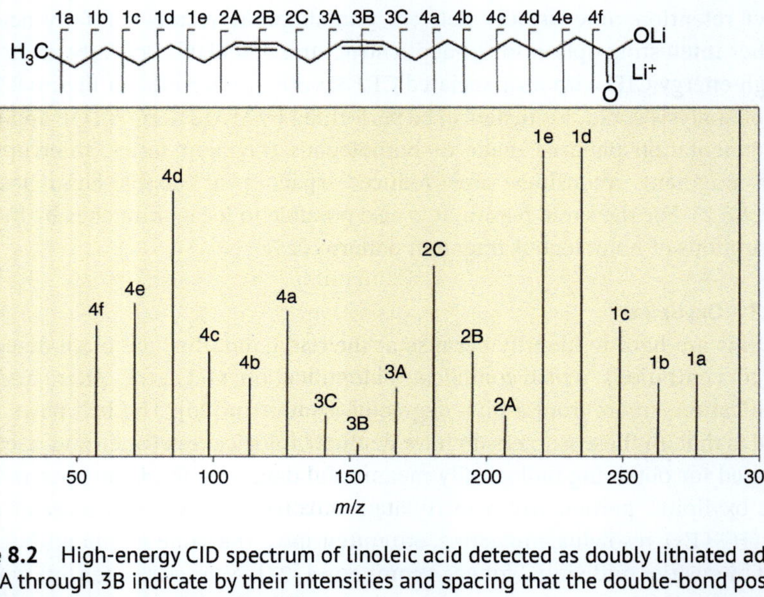

Figure 8.2 High-energy CID spectrum of linoleic acid detected as doubly lithiated adduct. Ions 2A through 3B indicate by their intensities and spacing that the double-bond positions are located at carbon 8 and carbon 11.

precursor ion scan for PC. The remaining neutral glycerol–fatty acyl moiety of the molecule forms a five-membered ring system by the formation of a bond between the carbonyl oxygen at the *sn*-2 ester and the C3 carbon of the glycerol backbone. Other $[M+H]^+$ fragmentation pathways of PC include neutral losses of both fatty acyls either as fatty acid loss $[M\text{-}RCOOH]^+$ or as ketene loss $[M\text{-}R'{\cdot}C{\cdot}O]^+$. Although of quite small intensity in comparison to the favored headgroup fragment, these four neutral losses can be used for the determination of the fatty acyl composition. In the negative-ion mode, PC ions are obtained as formate or acetate adducts, and in contrast to $[M+H]^+$ ions, they result in abundant $RCOO^-$ carboxylate fragments, which provide valuable pieces of complementary information when it comes to identification of PCs at the molecular species level. Nevertheless, the most widely used adduct ion for the analysis of PC is still the $[M+H]^+$ ion, just simply for the sheer ionization efficiency which the quaternary nitrogen in PC with its inherent positive charge offers in the positive ion mode. The most important fragments for PC and other major lipid classes are summarized in Table 8.2.

When moving to PE and PS, the imbalance between positive- and negative-ion formation efficiencies is not so drastic anymore. Thus, it is possible to either analyze these lipid classes as protonated or deprotonated species. Table 8.2 depicts the most widely used CID fragments to be expected from these both lipid classes in the positive- and negative-ion mode. While for PE the neutral loss of the headgroup (M.W. 141) from $[M+H]^+$ ions is very abundant, the headgroup fragment at m/z 196 from deprotonated PE is rather small. This makes the former by far more suitable for lipid-class-specific neutral loss scans than the latter. As the neutral loss 141 produces the dominant fragment ion in positive ESI, an ion trap with the possibility of MS^3 fragmentation on this neutral loss produced fragment could be a good way to dig for deeper information about the fatty acid constituents by producing the corresponding fatty acyl neutral losses as secondary fragment ions. PS shows abundant headgroup-specific fragments from both $[M+H]^+$ and $[M-H]^-$ ions [3]. In the positive-ion mode, it is a neutral loss of serine phosphate (M.W. 185), and in the negative-ion mode, it is the neutral loss of dehydrated serine (M.W. 87). When moving to the fatty acid moieties, the most valuable fragments in the positive-ion mode are acylium ions, which are observed for PE, PS, PI, phosphatidylglycerol (PG), and phosphatidic acid (PA) alike [29]. Figure 8.3b shows the proposed pathways for their formation as a two-step process. In the first step, a neutral loss of the polar headgroup either results in the formation of an intermediate ion containing a six-membered ring (1,3-dioxane) or a five-membered ring (1,3-dioxolane). Depending on these intermediate ring structures, either the *sn*-1 or the *sn*-2 fatty acyl is exposed to further cleavage, resulting in an $R\text{–}C{\cdot}O^+$ acylium ion. As in the first fragmentation step mainly the α-hydrogen at the *sn*-2 fatty acyl substituent is involved, the formation of the five-membered ring is favored, which further rather fosters the formation of a *sn*-1 acylium ion. Therefore, the ratios of acylium are indicative of the fatty acyls' *sn*-position, with the *sn*-1 substituent showing higher intensities than the *sn*-2 substituent. The most important acyl chain-related fragments arising from $[M-H]^-$ ions are the fatty acid carboxylates ($RCOO^-$), which allow unambiguous assignment of the fatty acyl substituents [29]. Depending on the fragmentation mechanism, *sn*-1 and *sn*-2

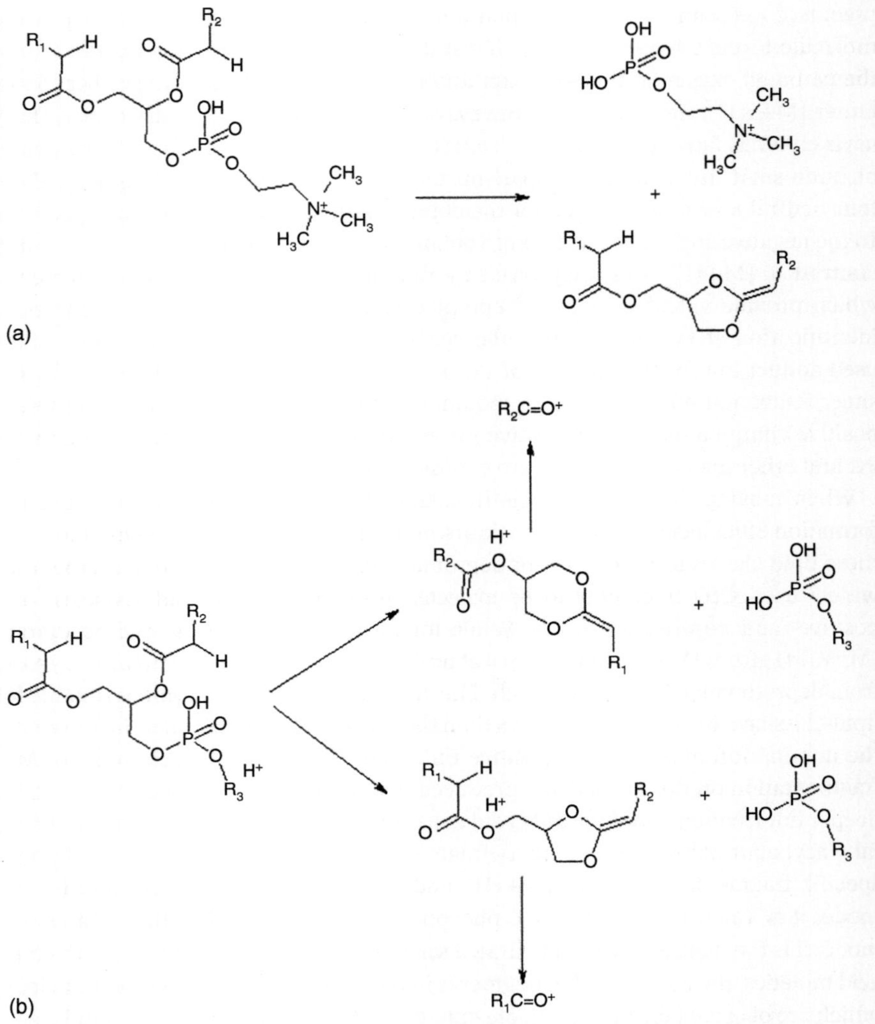

Figure 8.3 Proposed fragmentation mechanisms of PC as $[M+H]^+$. (a) Cleavage of the ester bond between the phosphate and the glycerol moiety results in the generation of the headgroup characteristic choline phosphate ion. (b) Fragmentation pattern leading to the generation of acylium ions from phospholipids in the positive-ion mode by sequential neutral loss of the headgroup and cleavage of the fatty acyl moiety as the R–C·O$^+$ ion. R_3 = PE, PS, PG, and PA.

carboxylates do not have the same likelihood of formation. This fact can be used for positional assignment of fatty acids in phospholipids. In the case of PE, the *sn*-2-derived carboxylate fragment is favored, while in the case of PS, the *sn*-1-derived carboxylate shows higher abundance. Another indication for a fatty acyl *sn*-position is the ratios of the *sn*-1-position and *sn*-2-position-derived fatty acyl neutral losses either as a fatty acid (RCOOH) or as a ketene (R–C·O·O). For PE and PS alike, both fragmentation pathways favor the *sn*-2 position-derived fragments.

Because of their nature, the anionic phospholipid classes PI, PG, and PA are mostly detected as $[M-H]^-$ ions [3]. While PI and PG do have unique headgroup fragments, PA lacks a lipid-class-specific headgroup fragment. The reason for this is that PA is a substructure of all other phospholipid classes. Thus, the fragments at *m/z* 79, 97, 153, and 171, which reflect the phosphate group and the phosphoglycerol moiety, do occur in the CID spectra of various phospholipid classes and are not specific for PA. While PI shows a wealth of characteristic headgroup fragments, PG still poses the challenge that its phosphoglycerol headgroup is a substructure of all other phospholipids as well. In this case, a combination of fragment *m/z* 171 (phosphoglycerol) and *m/z* 227 (glycero–phosphoglycerol) could be a good combination for identifying PG. In the case of PI, inositol–phosphate can be detected at *m/z* 259 and the subsequent dehydrations of this ion at *m/z* 241 and *m/z* 223, with *m/z* 241 being the most abundant of these three fragments. Furthermore, the diagnostic headgroup fragment at *m/z* 297 reflects the inositol–phosphate still containing the glycerol backbone moiety, arising from a subsequent neutral loss of both fatty acids. As PI, PG, and PA are best detected in negative polarity, fatty acid carboxylates are clearly the most abundant fragments arising from the fatty acyl moieties. For PI at lower CID energies (≤45 eV), formation of *sn*-2 carboxylates is favored over formation of *sn*-1 carboxylates. At higher energies, this process is reversed because more complex secondary and tertiary fragmentation processes start to slightly favor the formation of *sn*-1 carboxylates. The carboxylate anion ratio for PG is *sn*-2 > *sn*-1, while at PA, formation of *sn*-1 carboxylates is the sterically favorable fragmentation pathway. Similar to the above-described fragmentation processes for PE and PS, PI, PG, and PA also favor the neutral losses of the fatty acyl moiety at the *sn*-2 position either as fatty acid loss or as ketene loss.

8.3.2.5 Sphingolipids

Generally, most sphingolipid classes are very suitable for ionization as $[M+H]^+$ adduct ions because of the proton affinity of the secondary nitrogen at the amide bond, while in complex glycosylated sphingolipids (gangliosides), the carbohydrate moieties predominantly result in $[M-H]^-$ and $[M-2H]^{2-}$ ions. Thus, the preferred ionization polarity of ceramides, SM, and hexosyl ceramides is positive. As sphingolipids have only one fatty acyl moiety, they are devoid of any fatty-acyl-related combinatorial issues arising at lipids with two, three, or even four esterified fatty acids. In contrast to glycero(phospho)lipids, the fatty acyls are attached to the sphingoid backbone by an amide bond. In the case of ceramides, which do not even have a polar headgroup, the fatty-acyl-specific and the backbone-specific fragmentation collapses into one series of fragments, *m/z* 300, *m/z* 282, and *m/z* 264, which constitutes the sphingosine backbone less the fatty acid as a ketene neutral loss [30]. The two consecutive fragments at *m/z* 282 and *m/z* 264 arise from subsequent water losses at the two hydroxy groups (Table 8.2). Particularly, *m/z* 264 has because of its abundance good diagnostic potential for ceramides. Hexosyl ceramides (cerebrosides) on the other hand show an abundant neutral loss of M.W. 162, which corresponds to a dehydrated hexose ($C_6H_{10}O_5$) [30]. Additionally, *m/z* 264 is also useful for identification of hexosyl ceramides. Similar to PCs, the positive charge in SMs is

Table 8.2 List of the most important CID fragment ions of lipids arranged according to the building blocks they originate from (headgroup, fatty acyl *sn*-positions at the glycerol) and the ESI-generated pseudo-molecular ions most frequently encountered.

Lipid class	Adduct ions	Headgroup fragments			Acyl chain fragments						
					sn-1			*sn*-2			*sn*-3
TG	$[M+NH_4]^+$				$[M\text{-}R_1COOH]^+$	$[M\text{-}R_1'\text{-}C{\cdot}C{\cdot}O]^+$		$[M\text{-}R_2COOH]^+$	$[M\text{-}R_2'\text{-}C{\cdot}C{\cdot}O]^+$		$[M\text{-}R_3COOH]^+[M\text{-}R_3'\text{-}C{\cdot}C{\cdot}O]^+$
DG	$[M+NH_4]^+$				$[M\text{-}R_1COOH]^+$	$[M\text{-}R_1'\text{-}C{\cdot}C{\cdot}O]^+$		$[M\text{-}R_2COOH]^+$	$[M\text{-}R_2'\text{-}C{\cdot}C{\cdot}O]^+$		
PC	$[M+H]^+$	*m/z* 184			$[M\text{-}R_1COOH]^+$	$[M\text{-}R_2'\text{-}C{\cdot}C{\cdot}O]^+$		$[M\text{-}R_1'\text{-}C{\cdot}C{\cdot}O]^+$	$[M\text{-}R_2COOH]^+$		
	$[M+CH_3COO]^-$				R_1COOH^-			R_2COOH^-			
PE	$[M+H]^+$	NL 141			R_1CO^+	$[M\text{-}185\text{-}R_1'\text{-}C{\cdot}C{\cdot}O]^+$		R_2CO^+	$[M\text{-}185\text{-}R_2'\text{-}C{\cdot}C{\cdot}O]^+$		
	$[M-H]^-$	*m/z* 196			R_1COOH^-	$[M\text{-}R_1COOH]^-$	$[M\text{-}R_1'\text{-}C{\cdot}C{\cdot}O]^-$	R_2COOH^-	$[M\text{-}R_2COOH]-$	$[M\text{-}R_2'\text{-}C{\cdot}C{\cdot}O]^-$	
PS	$[M+H]^+$	NL 185			R_1CO^+	$[M\text{-}185\text{-}R_1'\text{-}C{\cdot}C{\cdot}O]^+$		R_2CO^+	$[M\text{-}185\text{-}R_2'\text{-}C{\cdot}C{\cdot}O]^+$		
	$[M-H]^-$	NL 87			R_1COOH^-	$[M\text{-}R_1COOH]^-$	$[M\text{-}R_1'\text{-}C{\cdot}C{\cdot}O]^-$	R_2COOH^-	$[M\text{-}R_2COOH]-$	$[M\text{-}R_2'\text{-}C{\cdot}C{\cdot}O]^-$	
PI	$[M-H]^-$	*m/z* 223	*m/z* 241	*m/z* 259	R_1COOH^-	$[M\text{-}R_1COOH]^-$	$[M\text{-}R_1'\text{-}C{\cdot}C{\cdot}O]^-$	R_2COOH^-	$[M\text{-}R_2COOH]^-$	$[M\text{-}R_2'\text{-}C{\cdot}C{=}O]^-$	
PG	$[M-H]^-$	*m/z* 171	*m/z* 227		R_1COOH^-	$[M\text{-}R_1COOH]^-$	$[M\text{-}R_1'\text{-}C{\cdot}C{\cdot}O]^-$	$\cdot R_2COOH^-$	$[M\text{-}R_2COOH]^-$	$[M\text{-}R_2'\text{-}C{\cdot}C{\cdot}O]^-$	

Lipid class	Adduct ions	Headgroup fragments		Acyl chain fragments						
				sn-1			*sn*-2			*sn*-3
PA	$[M-H]^-$	m/z 153		R_1COOH^-	$[M\text{-}R_1COOH]^-$	$[M\text{-}R_1'\text{-}C\cdot C\cdot O]^-$	$\cdot R_2COOH^-$	$[M\text{-}R_2COOH]^-$	$[M\text{-}R_2'\text{-}C\cdot C\cdot O]^-$	
Cer	$[M+H]^+$	m/z 264	m/z 282							
SM	$[M+H]^+$	m/z 184								
HexCer	$[M+H]^+$	NL 162	m/z 264							
CE	$[M+NH_4]^+$	m/z 369								

located at the nitrogen of the choline headgroup, and thus, SM results in the highly characteristic major fragment ion at *m/z* 184 [3]. As only one fatty acid is attached, further fatty-acyl-specific fragment ion scans are not needed. Despite this fact, which alleviates spectral interpretation, things get more tricky when other sphingoid bases than sphingosine (e.g. sphinganine, phytosphingosine, and 6-hydroxy sphingosine) are taken into account [30]. To complicate things further, fatty acyls can be modified by α- or ω-hydroxy groups or even by further esterified ω-hydroxy groups, which then gives rise to more complicated overlapping fragmentation patterns. Since a discussion of all these – from a mammalian perspective – exotic sphingolipids would justify an identification chapter at its own, the interested reader is referred to Hartler et al. for further reading [30].

Gangliosides with their extensive carbohydrate moieties are in terms of spectral interpretation among the most complex lipids. As the various carbohydrates (glucose, galactose, *N*-acyl-galactosamine, neuraminic acid, etc.) account for most of the molecular mass, the overwhelming part of characteristic fragments is attributed to carbohydrate building blocks. The fragmentation scheme of gangliosides is exemplified in Figure 8.4 for GQd1 (d18:1/18:0) with the corresponding fragment masses depicted in Table 8.3. In a nutshell, B, C, Y, and Z fragments arise from cleavage of

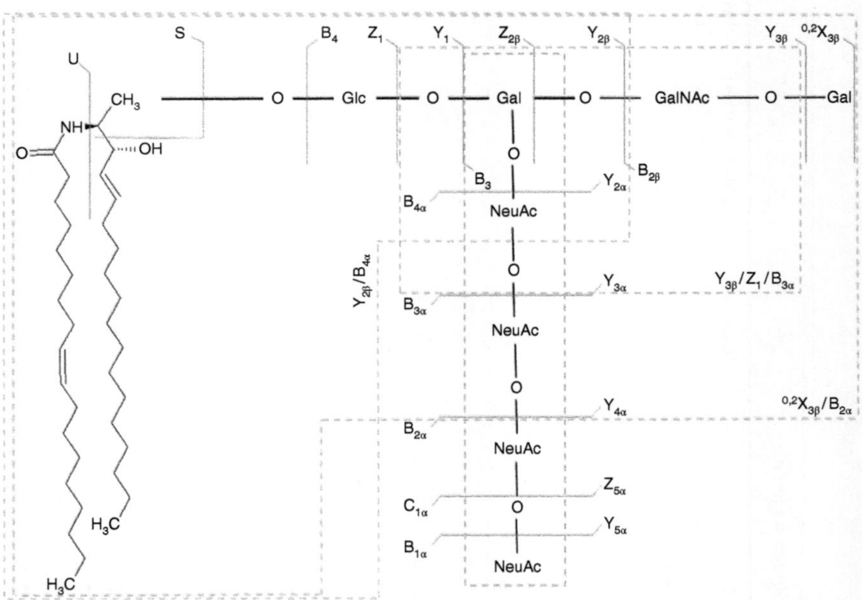

Figure 8.4 Fragmentation patterns of the ganglioside GQ1d(d18:1/18:1) by HCD in the negative-ion mode. The double cleavages $Z_2\beta/Y_1$ and ${}^{0,2}X_3\beta/B_2\alpha$ are essential for distinguishing this species from other GQ1 ganglioside structures. Fragments annotated by B, C, Y, and Z indicate cleavages of the glycosidic bond including their position, X indicates cross-ring cleavages at the sugar moieties, and S and U are indicative for the ceramide. Abbreviations: Glc: glucose; Gal: galactose; GalNAc: *N*-acetyl galactosamine; and NeuAc: neuraminic acid.

Table 8.3 Fragment ions arising from the ganglioside GQ1d(d18:1/18:0) by HCD fragmentation of the $[M-4H^{+}+Na^{+}]^{3-}$ ion including their corresponding *m/z* values.

Fragment	*m/z*	Charge (z)
U	283.263	1
$B_1\alpha$	290.0869	2
$C_1\alpha$	308.0974	1
S	325.183	1
$B_{2\beta}$	364.1233	1
$B_2\alpha$	581.181	1
$B_2\alpha$ (Na)	603.1629	1
$Y_{3\beta}/Z_1/sB_3\alpha$	673.2276	1
Y_1	726.5855	1
$[M-4H^{+}+Na^{+}]^{3-}$	812.7023	3
B_3 (Na)	855.7627	1
$Y_{2\beta}/B_4\alpha$	888.6374	1
$Y_4\alpha$	917.4742	2
B_4 (Na)	936.7887	2
$Y_5\alpha$ (Na)	1074.0119	2
$Y_2\alpha$	1253.7676	1
$Z_{2\beta}/Y_1$	1330.7238	1
$Y_3\alpha$	1544.8608	1
$^{0,2}X_{3\beta}/B_2\alpha$	1738.4412	1
$Y_{4\alpha}$ (Na)	1857.9373	1

the glycosidic bond on either side of the glycosidic oxygen while X fragments are cross-ring cleavages of hexosidic structures [31]. S and U are characteristic for the ceramide moiety. While Y and Z indicate that the charge resides on the fragment including the ceramide structure, B and C indicate that the charge is located on the fragment without the ceramide. The subscript numbers specify the exact bond, and α/β are used for the branches. Furthermore, the superscript numbers at the X indicate the two bonds cleaved within the ring structures. When coming back to our example, the HCD spectra of $[M-4H+Na]^{3-}$ show a wealth of fragments, with the α-series being indicative for four neuraminic acids. What discriminates this structure from other GQ1 isomers-, which do not have the four sialic acids in a row, but dispersed between the two galactoses – are the $Z_{2\beta}/Y_1$ and the $^{0,2}X_{3\beta}/B_2\alpha$ double-cleavage fragments [32]. While the former fragment supports four sialic acids in a row attached to a galactose, the latter indicates that this galactose is the one closer to the ceramide moiety. For further engulfing into the highly complex topic of ganglioside identification, the interested reader is referred to publications from the Zamfir group [31–34].

8.3.2.6 Glycerolipids

Glycerolipids do not show any polar headgroup, and therefore, no lipid-class-specific fragments are available. ESI in the positive-ion mode mostly results in abundant ($[M+NH_4]^+$) ions. Further fragmentation of these adduct ions results in neutral losses of the fatty acyls, which are indicative for the fatty acid composition of the molecular structure (Table 8.2). The fatty acyls are lost as either neutral fatty acids (RCOOH) or fatty acyl ketenes (RC·C·O) [14, 16, 35]. In the case of DGs, the fragment(s) of one fatty acid already allow inferring onto the identity of the second fatty acid, while for TGs, it is necessary to unambiguously identity two fatty acyl moieties for inferring on the identity of the third fatty acid. Particularly, for mixed spectra of isomeric TGs, identification can get complicated because all the fatty acid fragments need to be fitted together by a combinatorial approach for elucidating the underlying molecular species.

8.3.2.7 Sterols

Similar to glycerolipids, CEs are mostly analyzed in positive ESI as $[M+NH_4]^+$ adduct ions. The only abundant fragment in low-energy CID is found at m/z 369, which indicates the neutral loss of a fatty acid (M-RCOOH) from the cholesterol ring system, with the remaining fragment ion essentially being a dehydrated cholesterol structure (Table 8.2). Oxysterols occur at trace levels and are best analyzed by GC-EI/MS. While authentic standards provide the values for exact GC retention times, EI provides highly specific fragment patterns [36, 37]. These pieces of information are used for unambiguous identification of oxysterols. When using ESI, the method of choice for oxysterols is derivatization either by GirardP or by picolinic acid and analysis of $[M+H]^+$ adducts [37–39]. Since oxysterols show many isomeric structures, their identification is either possible by unambiguous chromatographic separation or by selective fragments, generated by MS^3 techniques in the low mass range.

8.3.3 Deep Structure Determination

Localization of double-bond positions in the fatty acyl chains require specific fragmentation techniques. One possibility would be the, mentioned above in the section Fatty Acids, fragmentation by high-energy CID, which results in highly specific CRF patterns [25]. As the instrumentation needed for employing such high acceleration voltages is rarely available, alternative methods have to be used. When ozone is used instead of conventional inert CID gases, fatty acyls are truncated at the location of their double bonds, similar to lipid peroxidation reactions [40]. The mechanism involves generation of a primary ozonide at the double-bond position. This labile structure immediately decomposes further into a secondary ozonide, an aldehyde, or a Criegee intermediate, which further rearranges into Criegee ions. The Criegee ions and the aldehyde are a characteristic pair of ions, indicative for the position of the double bond. By taking into consideration fragment ions in the lower mass region, it is even possible to infer the regioisomeric position of esterified fatty acyls. Although ozonolysis (OzID) of lipids is an efficient method for the determination of double-bond locations and regioisomers, it is nevertheless not very practical because instruments need to be customized for the introduction of ozone into the CID cell. Electron impact excitation of ions from organics (EIEIO) would be an alternative to OzID for localization of double bonds, determination of regioisomers, and even double-bond conformations [41]. At a kinetic energy of 10 eV, it was possible to pin down the aforementioned structural characteristics for glycerophospholipids, glycerolipids, and sphingolipids by providing specific fragments for unambiguous structure identification in a branched Rf ion trap. Paternò–Büchi reactions, a cycloaddition of acetone to double bonds catalyzed by UV light, enable localization of double bonds by generation of fatty acyls truncated at the Paternò–Büchi derivatization site [42]. When a UV-emitting online reactor is localized between the chromatographic column and the mass spectrometer, it is even possible to use this method online in a liquid chromatography-mass spectrometry (LC-MS) setting. Another elegant use of UV light for the generation of double-bond localization-specific fragments would be UV-induced photodissociation (UVPD) [43, 44]. UVPD is a very promising technique because by using a 193 nm laser, bonds between vinyl groups and their allylic methylene carbons are cleaved, resulting in fragments indicative of double-bond positions. In such a manner, it was possible to localize double bonds on acyl moieties of phospholipids [44], but also at the sphingoid backbone of sphingolipids and their attached fatty acyl chain [43]. Some vendors already offer instruments, which are regularly equipped with a UVPD fragmentation unit.

8.4 Ion Mobility Spectrometry

IMS is a most recent addition to the toolbox of lipidomics. When coupled to mass spectrometry, this technology enables separation of isomeric and isobaric molecular structures. While the latter can be resolved by high mass resolution, the former needs at least chromatography or fragmentation techniques. The strength of IMS is separation of isomers by their size and even more importantly by their shape. In this sense, IMS is able to provide valuable complementary information. Besides separation of molecular structures, the most beneficial property provided by IMS is a molecule's cross-collisional section (CCS). This is an invariable molecular property, just dependent on its size and shape. As IMS is a rather new analytical branch in lipidomics, generation of databases for CCS values is just in their infancy. Basically, IMS technologies are subdivided into drift tube ion mobility spectrometry (DTIMS) and differential ion mobility (DMS). Although the various vendors provide slightly different versions of DTIMS [13, 45], called traveling wave ion mobility spectrometry (TWIMS) [46] or trapped ion mobility spectrometry (TIMS) [47], they all readily provide CCS values for the identification of lipid species. DMS devices such as field asymmetric ion mobility spectrometry (FAIMS) on the other hand are just molecular filters (like a quadrupole), which sequentially filter molecule by molecule by its shape and size according to their compensation voltage (CV) [9, 48]. DMS does not provide any CCS values but rather a CV value associated with a particular structure.

This CV value is often specific for each lipid (class) on the target list and can therefore be used for transmitting only one lipid (class) at a time into the mass spectrometer. As all IMS devices are always located after the ion source, they are unlike chromatography not helpful in avoiding ion suppression effects.

8.5 Identification Workflows

There are two analytical workflows in lipidomics: shotgun lipidomics and chromatography-coupled approaches (LC-MS). While shotgun lipidomics relies just on mass spectrometry, LC-MS also includes the chromatographic dimension for lipid identification. Basically, both branches of analysis are available for IMS coupling. Figure 8.5 depicts a typical LC-MS-based workflow, exemplified for PE 18:0_22:6 acquired with an LTQ-Orbitrap mass spectrometer. From the technical point of view, the Orbitrap is generating one full-scan mass spectrum of intact molecular adduct ions per second, while the linear ion trap (LTQ) picks the 20 most intense ions of the full-scan spectrum via a low-resolution FT-MS preview scan after a few milliseconds. The LTQ then sequentially performs fragment spectra on each of these 20 ions, while the Orbitrap is still acquiring the full-scan spectrum up to full high resolution. This cycle results in a full set of MS and MS/MS spectra in one second and is repeated throughout the whole chromatographic runtime. The basic data derived from this LC-MS approach is a total ion current (TIC) spectrum, which sums up all full-scan ions for each spectrum (Figure 8.5, upper panel). When now the chromatographic peak at 25.27 minutes is scrutinized for its underlying masses, one of the observed masses fits to the elemental composition $C_{45}H_{77}N_1O_8P_1$ (Δm = 1.2 ppm), and one of the possibly matching molecular structures could be the $[M{-}H]^-$ ion of PE 40:6 (Figure 8.5, middle panel). Since e.g. the LIPID MAPS Structure Database (LMSD) shows 18 entries with this specific elemental composition, some of the entries being isomeric PCs containing an odd carbon numbered fatty acyl and some are isomeric PEs, just the exact mass of intact lipid species, leaves still open questions about a structures identity, although chromatography already diminishes the likelihood of co-elution. Nevertheless, unambiguous identification of such structures usually takes place at the MS/MS level (Figure 8.5, lower panel). In our example, the fragment ions at m/z 283, m/z 327, and m/z 480 unambiguously identify the lipid structure under investigation as a PE 40:6, containing fatty acid (FA) 18:0 (presumably stearic acid) and FA 22:6 (presumably docosahexaenoic acid), annotated as PE 18:0_22:6. The unlabeled mass peaks at m/z 281, 303, 307, and 329 indicate the existence of FA 18:1, FA 20:4, FA 20:2, and FA 22:5 as fatty acid carboxylate fragments. Thus, PE 18:1_22:5 and PE 20:2_20:4 are minor compositional constituents of PE 40:6. The here-exemplified workflow covers the most important aspects of lipidomic data interpretation. Additionally, the nitrogen rule is a fast way for a rough classification of lipid classes by manual review of spectra. According to the nitrogen rule, an ion with an even number of electrons and an even number of nitrogen atoms has an odd mass. As ions generated by ESI have an even number of electrons (closed shell ions), lipid classes with

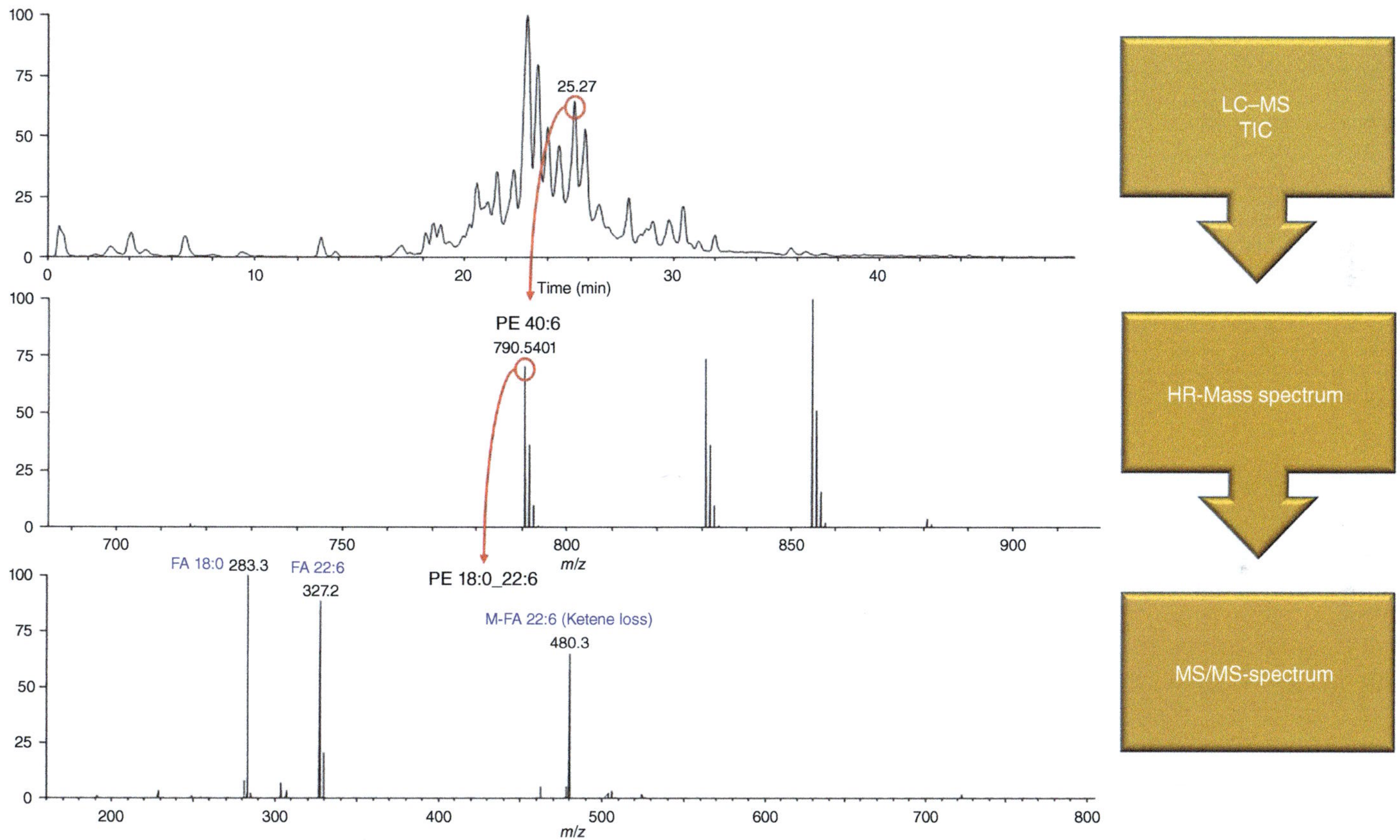

Figure 8.5 The upper panel shows a reversed-phase LC-MS total ion current (TIC) of a lipid extract. In the middle panel, the full-scan mass spectrum of the TIC peak at 25.27 minutes is depicted, showing a putative PE 40:6 identified as $[M-H]^-$ at *m/z* 790.5401. The lower panel confirms the identity of PE 40:6, and the fragment ions at *m/z* 283.3, *m/z* 327.2, and *m/z* 480.3 suggest a molecular structure of PE 18:0_22:6.

an odd number of nitrogen atoms (PC, PE, PS, ceramides, and hexosyl ceramides) do have even *m/z* values and lipid classes with even numbers of nitrogen atoms or no nitrogen atoms at all (FA, PI, PG, PA, cardiolipins [CL], and SM) have odd *m/z* values. Noteworthy, TG, DG, and CE are detected at even mass values when they generate $[M+NH_4]^+$ ions.

As manual data interpretation is tedious and time-consuming, in the past decade, many automated software solutions have been developed. Software packages are roughly divided into shotgun [49, 50, 51] and LC-MS applications [16, 52, 53] and into rule-based [16, 49, 50, 52] and similarity search applications [52, 53]. While shotgun applications do not include the chromatographic dimension into their scheme of analysis, similarity search applications have to rely on the existence of reference spectra, and decision rule-based applications work with predefined lists of target fragments. An example for a decision rule-based software, which includes chromatography, would be the Lipid Data Analyzer (LDA) [16]. As depicted in Figure 8.6, the LDA software checks the MS/MS spectra for fragment ions, including their intensities for verification or falsification of putative lipid species derived at the MS^1 level. The MS^1 hits are identified by exact mass of molecular adduct ions and the retention time. While exact mass results in elemental compositions, which correspond to certain lipid structures, the retention time can be correlated with the retention times of other putative lipid structures by the ECN model and thus corroborate the existence of the suggested MS^1 hit. When analyzing the corresponding MS/MS spectra, LDA takes into account two categories of fragment ions: headgroup-related fragments characteristic for the lipid class and fatty-acyl-related fragments characteristic for the molecular lipid species. In the first two steps, LDA checks if any mandatory headgroup fragments are found in the MS/MS spectrum and if their intensities are within the expected ratio range to each other (Figure 8.6). If these rules, which can be set by the user, are not fulfilled, the MS^1 hit is discarded, but if they are fulfilled, the algorithm then checks the spectrum for any possible fragments arising from the fatty acyls. For this reason, it calculates within a user-defined range the expected fragment ions for all possible fatty acyl combinations and inspects the MS/MS spectrum for them. If none of the expected fragments is detected, the search is finished and the existence of the proposed MS^1 hit is confirmed at the lipid species level, without exact knowledge of the fatty acyl identity (Figure 8.6). If fatty-acyl-related fragments are detected, but the combinatorial sum of the associated fatty acids does not fit with the proposed MS^1 hit, e.g. FA 16:0 and FA 18:2 for PC 34:1, the search is also ended and the MS^1 hit confirmed at the lipid species level. If any possible fatty acyl combinations are available, the algorithm then generates the intensity ratios of the calculated fatty acyl fragment pairs and compares them with the user-defined intensity ratio range for assigning the fatty acyl moieties to *sn*-positions. If the fragments are within the correct intensity ratio range, *sn*-positions of fatty acyls are assigned, and the lipid is reported at the *sn*-position level (Figure 8.6). If positional isomers are not successfully assigned, then the compound is reported at the molecular lipid species level, where only the identity of the esterified fatty acids is known.

Figure 8.7 sums up the correlation between identification certainty and the corresponding reporting suggestions. With an increasing level of analytical specificity,

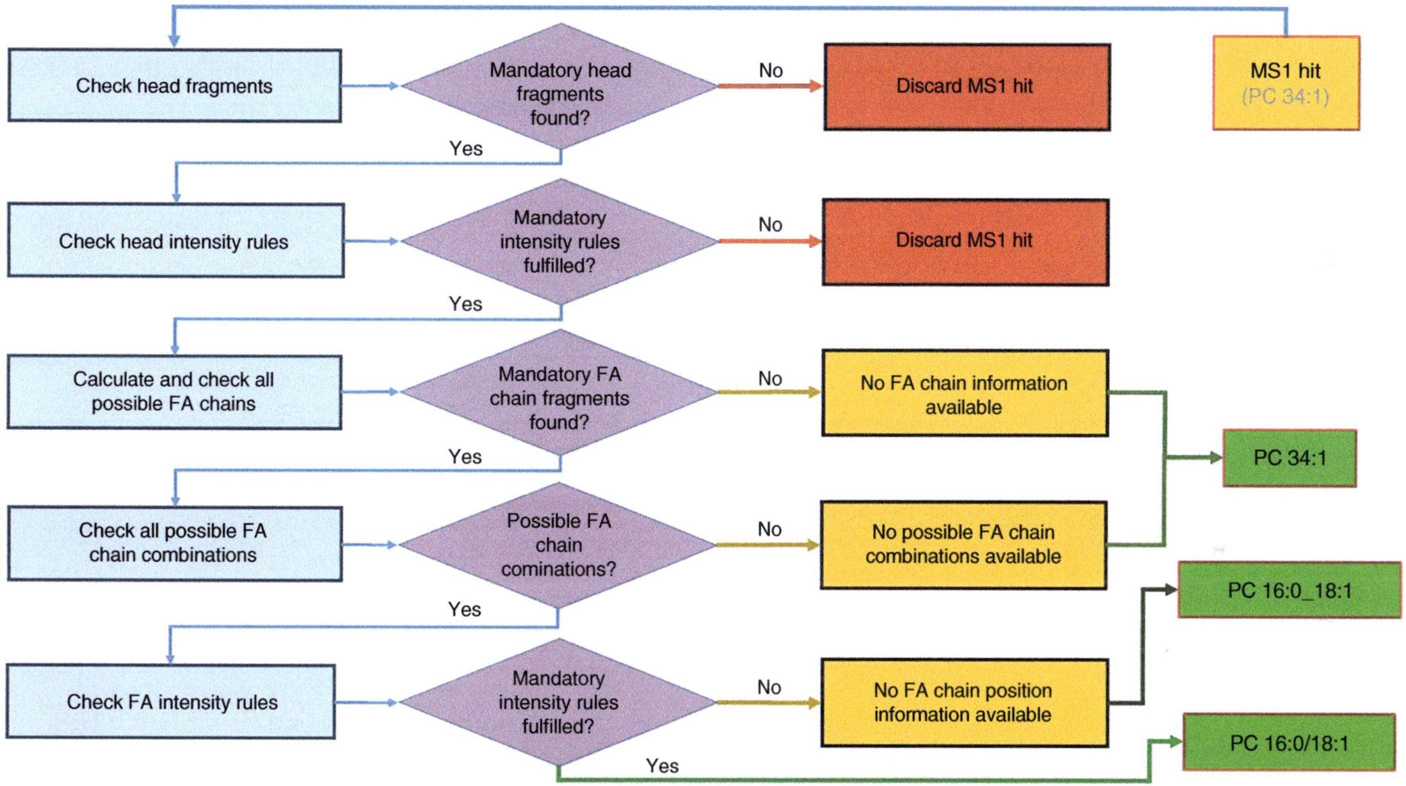

Figure 8.6 Decision tree of the identification workflow implemented in Lipid Data Analyzer. Blue boxes indicate tasks performed by the algorithm, purple diamonds indicate decisions, red boxes indicate end points without any annotated compound, and gold boxes indicate end points with the corresponding annotated compounds depicted in green boxes.

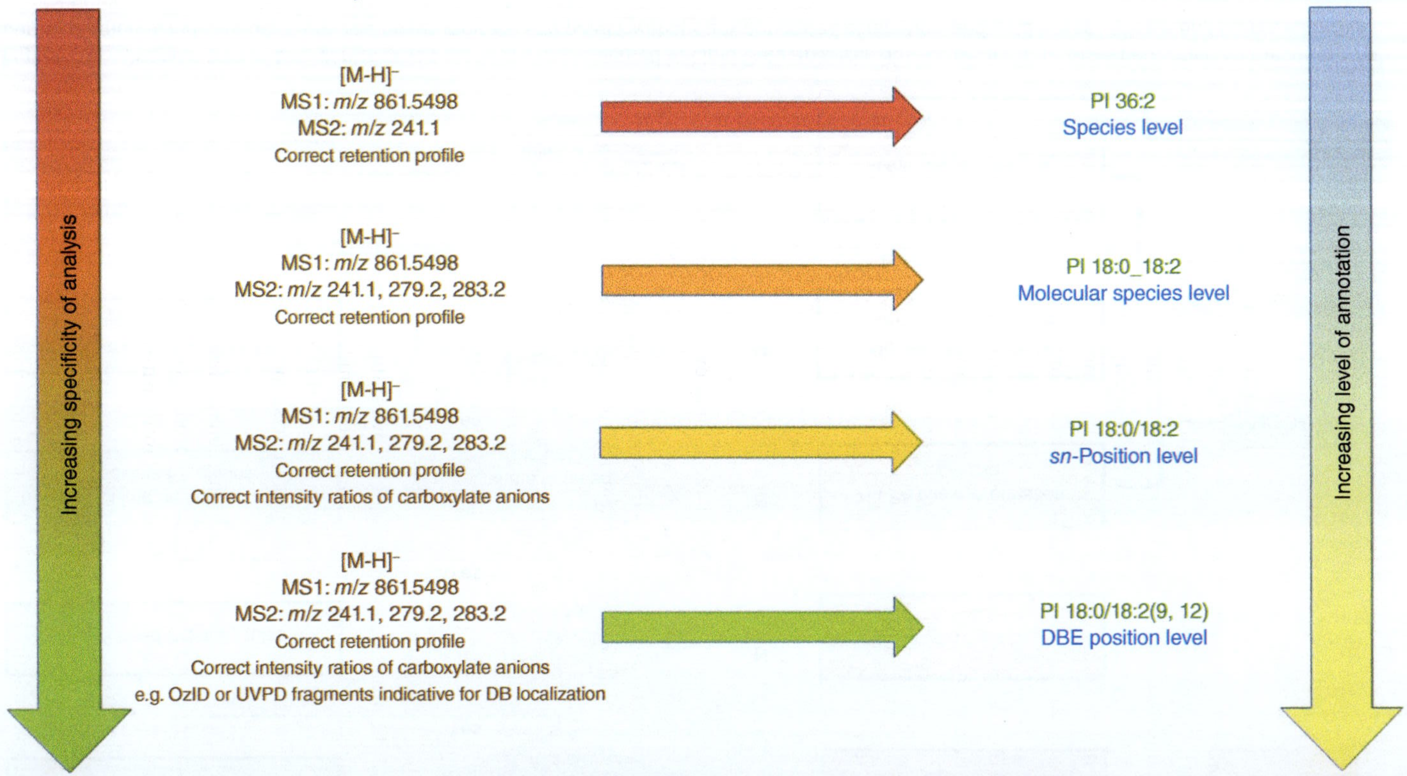

Figure 8.7 An increasing specificity in analysis results in an increased identification certainty, which is reflected in the corresponding annotation levels. This is exemplified by the stepwise uncovering of the identity of PI 18:0/18:2(9,12) as a result of various analytical techniques employed, including exact mass of deprotonated molecular ions, CID fragment spectra, retention time, and OzID or UVPD spectra.

identification certainty also increases and is reflected in annotations allowing to pinpoint more structural details [54, 55]. The lowest level is the species level, where the headgroup is confirmed, but in the fatty acyl chain region, only the sum of the esterified fatty acid residues is known. The proposed structure is corroborated by exact mass of the deprotonated molecular ion, one characteristic headgroup fragment, and the correct retention time, if chromatography is available. When moving up the ladder of certainty to the molecular species level, the additional fatty acid carboxylate fragments provide the specificity needed to infer about the fatty acid identity. If additionally the intensity ratios of the *sn*-1-position- and *sn*-2-position-derived carboxylate anions are also within their predicted range, it is possible to move further up to the *sn*-position level. The double-bond equivalent (DBE) position level is usually not obtained with conventional analytical measures (retention time, exact mass, and CID spectra) and requires specific fragmentation techniques such as OzID or UVPD to be employed. In conclusion, the take home message for lipid identification and the resulting annotation reflects a clear-cut position: "Report only what is experimentally proven and clearly indicate when assumptions are made."

References

1 Liebisch, G., Drobnik, W., Reil, M. et al. (1999). Quantitative measurement of different ceramide species from crude cellular extracts by electrospray ionization tandem mass spectrometry (ESI-MS/MS). *J. Lipid Res.* 40 (8): 1539–1546.

2 Han, X.L. and Gross, R.W. (1994). Electrospray-ionization mass spectroscopic analysis of human erythrocyte plasma-membrane phospholipids. *Proc. Natl. Acad. Sci. U.S.A.* 91 (22): 10635–10639.

3 Brugger, B., Erben, G., Sandhoff, R. et al. (1997). Quantitative analysis of biological membrane lipids at the low picomole level by nano-electrospray ionization tandem mass spectrometry. *Proc. Natl. Acad. Sci. U.S.A.* 94 (6): 2339–2344.

4 Ekroos, K., Chernushevich, I.V., Simons, K., and Shevchenko, A. (2002). Quantitative profiling of phospholipids by multiple precursor ion scanning on a hybrid quadrupole time-of-flight mass spectrometer. *Anal. Chem.* 74 (5): 941–949.

5 Ejsing, C.S., Sampaio, J.L., Surendranath, V. et al. (2009). Global analysis of the yeast lipidome by quantitative shotgun mass spectrometry. *Proc. Natl. Acad. Sci. U.S.A.* 106 (7): 2136–2141.

6 Davis, B., Koster, G., Douet, L.J. et al. (2008). Electrospray ionization mass spectrometry identifies substrates and products of lipoprotein-associated phospholipase A_2 in oxidized human low density lipoprotein. *J. Biol. Chem.* 283 (10): 6428–6437.

7 Holcapek, M., Jandera, P., Zderadicka, P., and Hruba, L. (2003). Characterization of triacylglycerol and diacylglycerol composition of plant oils using high-performance liquid chromatography-atmospheric pressure chemical ionization mass spectrometry. *J. Chromatogr. A* 1010 (2): 195–215.

8 Lisa, M. and Holcapek, M. (2013). Characterization of triacylglycerol enantiomers using chiral HPLC/APCI-MS and synthesis of enantiomeric triacylglycerols. *Anal. Chem.* 85 (3): 1852–1859.

9 Baker, P.R., Armando, A.M., Campbell, J.L. et al. (2014). Three-dimensional enhanced lipidomics analysis combining UPLC, differential ion mobility spectrometry, and mass spectrometric separation strategies. *J. Lipid Res.* 55 (11): 2432–2442.

10 Kyle, J.E., Zhang, X., Weitz, K.K. et al. (2016). Uncovering biologically significant lipid isomers with liquid chromatography, ion mobility spectrometry and mass spectrometry. *Analyst* 141 (5): 1649–1659.

11 Groessl, M., Graf, S., and Knochenmuss, R. (2015). High resolution ion mobility-mass spectrometry for separation and identification of isomeric lipids. *Analyst* 140 (20): 6904–6911.

12 Paglia, G., Kliman, M., Claude, E. et al. (2015). Applications of ion-mobility mass spectrometry for lipid analysis. *Anal. Bioanal. Chem.* 407 (17): 4995–5007.

13 Kliman, M., May, J.C., and McLean, J.A. (2011). Lipid analysis and lipidomics by structurally selective ion mobility-mass spectrometry. *Biochim. Biophys. Acta* 1811 (11): 935–945.

14 Fauland, A., Kofeler, H., Trotzmuller, M. et al. (2011). A comprehensive method for lipid profiling by liquid chromatography-ion cyclotron resonance mass spectrometry. *J. Lipid Res.* 52 (12): 2314–2322.

15 Ovcacikova, M., Lisa, M., Cifkova, E., and Holcapek, M. (2016). Retention behavior of lipids in reversed-phase ultrahigh-performance liquid chromatography-electrospray ionization mass spectrometry. *J. Chromatogr. A* 1450: 76–85.

16 Hartler, J., Triebl, A., Ziegl, A. et al. (2017). Deciphering lipid structures based on platform-independent decision rules. *Nat. Methods* 14 (12): 1171–1174.

17 Cifkova, E., Holcapek, M., Lisa, M. et al. (2012). Nontargeted quantitation of lipid classes using hydrophilic interaction liquid chromatography-electrospray ionization mass spectrometry with single internal standard and response factor approach. *Anal. Chem.* 84 (22): 10064–10070.

18 Leithner, K., Triebl, A., Trotzmuller, M. et al. (2018). The glycerol backbone of phospholipids derives from noncarbohydrate precursors in starved lung cancer cells. *Proc. Natl. Acad. Sci. U.S.A.* 115 (24): 6225–6230.

19 Gleispach, H., Moser, R., Mayer, B. et al. (1985). Qualitative and quantitative measurement of hydroxy fatty acids, thromboxanes and prostaglandins using stable isotope dilutions and detection by gas chromatography-mass spectrometry. *J. Chromatogr.* 344: 11–21.

20 Dommes, V., Wirtz-Peitz, F., and Kunau, W.H. (1976). Structure determination of polyunsaturated fatty acids by gas chromatography-mass spectrometry – a comparison of fragmentation patterns of various derivatives. *J. Chromatogr. Sci.* 14 (8): 360–366.

21 Han, X.L. and Gross, R.W. (2005). Shotgun lipidomics: electrospray ionization mass spectrometric analysis and quantitation of cellular lipidomes directly from crude extracts of biological samples. *Mass Spectrom. Rev.* 24 (3): 367–412.

22 Zullig, T. and Kofeler, H.C. (2021). High resolution mass spectrometry in lipidomics. *Mass Spectrom. Rev.* 40 (3): 162–176.

23 Cheng, C., Pittenauer, E., and Gross, M.L. (1998). Charge-remote fragmentations are energy-dependent processes. *J. Am. Soc. Mass Spectrom.* 9 (8): 840–844.

24 Mueller, M., Thorell, A., Claudel, T. et al. (2015). Ursodeoxycholic acid exerts farnesoid X receptor-antagonistic effects on bile acid and lipid metabolism in morbid obesity. *J. Hepatol.* 62 (6): 1398–1404.

25 Jensen, N.J. and Gross, M.L. (1987). Mass spectrometry methods for structural determination and analysis of fatty acids. *Mass Spectrom. Rev.* 6 (4): 497–536.

26 Serhan, C.N. and Savill, J. (2005). Resolution of inflammation: the beginning programs the end. *Nat. Immunol.* 6 (12): 1191–1197.

27 Norris, P.C. and Serhan, C.N. (2018). Metabololipidomic profiling of functional immunoresolvent clusters and eicosanoids in mammalian tissues. *Biochem. Biophys. Res. Commun.* 504 (3): 553–561.

28 Kutzner, L., Rund, K.M., Ostermann, A.I. et al. (2019). Development of an optimized LC–MS method for the detection of specialized pro-resolving mediators in biological samples. *Front. Pharmacol.* 10: 169.

29 Hsu, F.F. and Turk, J. (2009). Electrospray ionization with low-energy collisionally activated dissociation tandem mass spectrometry of glycerophospholipids: mechanisms of fragmentation and structural characterization. *J. Chromatogr. B, Analyt. Technol. Biomed. Life Sci.* 877 (26): 2673–2695.

30 Hartler, J., Armando, A.M., Trotzmuller, M. et al. (2020). Automated annotation of sphingolipids including accurate identification of hydroxylation sites using MS^n data. *Anal. Chem.* 92 (20): 14054–14062.

31 Zamfir, A.D., Serb, A., Vukelic, Z. et al. (2011). Assessment of the molecular expression and structure of gangliosides in brain metastasis of lung adenocarcinoma by an advanced approach based on fully automated chip-nanoelectrospray mass spectrometry. *J. Am. Soc. Mass Spectrom.* 22 (12): 2145–2159.

32 Ica, R., Petrut, A., Munteanu, C.V.A. et al. (2020). Orbitrap mass spectrometry for monitoring the ganglioside pattern in human cerebellum development and aging. *J. Mass Spectrom.* 55 (5): e4502.

33 Sisu, E., Flangea, C., Serb, A. et al. (2011). High-performance separation techniques hyphenated to mass spectrometry for ganglioside analysis. *Electrophoresis* 32 (13): 1591–1609.

34 Sarbu, M., Robu, A.C., Ghiulai, R.M. et al. (2016). Electrospray ionization ion mobility mass spectrometry of human brain gangliosides. *Anal. Chem.* 88 (10): 5166–5178.

35 Triebl, A., Hartler, J., Trotzmuller, M., and Harald, C.K. (2017). Lipidomics: prospects from a technological perspective. *Biochim. Biophys. Acta* 1862 (8): 740–746.

36 Bjorkhem, I., Diczfalusy, U., Olsson, T. et al. (2011). Detecting oxysterols in the human circulation. *Nat. Immunol.* 12 (7): 577.

37 Griffiths, W.J. and Wang, Y. (2017). Sterolomics: state of the art, developments, limitations and challenges. *Biochim. Biophys. Acta, Mol. Cell. Biol. Lipids* 1862 (8): 771–773.

38 Honda, A., Yamashita, K., Hara, T. et al. (2009). Highly sensitive quantification of key regulatory oxysterols in biological samples by LC-ESI-MS/MS. *J. Lipid Res.* 50 (2): 350–357.

39 Griffiths, W.J., Gilmore, I., Yutuc, E. et al. (2018). Identification of unusual oxysterols and bile acids with 7-oxo or 3β,5α,6β-trihydroxy functions in human plasma by charge-tagging mass spectrometry with multistage fragmentation. *J. Lipid Res.* 59 (6): 1058–1070.

40 Brown, S.H.J., Mitchell, T.W., and Blanksby, S.J. (2011). Analysis of unsaturated lipids by ozone-induced dissociation. *Biochim. Biophys. Acta* 1811 (11): 807–817.

41 Baba, T., Campbell, J.L., Le Blanc, J.C.Y. et al. (2018). Quantitative structural multiclass lipidomics using differential mobility: electron impact excitation of ions from organics (EIEIO) mass spectrometry. *J. Lipid Res.* 59 (5): 910–919.

42 Zhang, W., Zhang, D., Chen, Q. et al. (2019). Online photochemical derivatization enables comprehensive mass spectrometric analysis of unsaturated phospholipid isomers. *Nat. Commun.* 10 (1): 79.

43 Ryan, E., Nguyen, C.Q.N., Shiea, C., and Reid, G.E. (2017). Detailed structural characterization of sphingolipids via 193 nm ultraviolet photodissociation and ultra high resolution tandem mass spectrometry. *J. Am. Soc. Mass Spectrom.* 28 (7): 1406–1419.

44 Williams, P.E., Klein, D.R., Greer, S.M., and Brodbelt, J.S. (2017). Pinpointing double bond and *sn*-positions in glycerophospholipids via hybrid 193 nm ultraviolet photodissociation (UVPD) mass spectrometry. *J. Am. Chem. Soc.* 139 (44): 15681–15690.

45 Dodds, J.N. and Baker, E.S. (2019). Ion mobility spectrometry: fundamental concepts, instrumentation, applications, and the road ahead. *J. Am. Soc. Mass Spectrom.* 30 (11): 2185–2195.

46 Paglia, G. and Astarita, G. (2017). Metabolomics and lipidomics using traveling-wave ion mobility mass spectrometry. *Nat. Protoc.* 12 (4): 797–813.

47 Silveira, J.A., Ridgeway, M.E., and Park, M.A. (2014). High resolution trapped ion mobility spectrometry of peptides. *Anal. Chem.* 86 (12): 5624–5627.

48 Shvartsburg, A.A., Isaac, G., Leveque, N. et al. (2011). Separation and classification of lipids using differential ion mobility spectrometry. *J. Am. Soc. Mass Spectrom.* 22 (7): 1146–1155.

49 Herzog, R., Schwudke, D., Schuhmann, K. et al. (2011). A novel informatics concept for high-throughput shotgun lipidomics based on the molecular fragmentation query language. *Genome Biol.* 12 (1).

50 Husen, P., Tarasov, K., Katafiasz, M. et al. (2013). Analysis of lipid experiments (ALEX): a software framework for analysis of high-resolution shotgun lipidomics data. *PLoS One* 8 (11): e79736.

51 Yang, K., Cheng, H., Gross, R.W., and Han, X. (2009). Automated lipid identification and quantification by multidimensional mass spectrometry-based shotgun lipidomics. *Anal. Chem.* 81 (11): 4356–4368.

52 Tsugawa, H., Ikeda, K., Takahashi, M. et al. (2020). A lipidome atlas in MS-DIAL 4. *Nat. Biotechnol.* 38 (10): 1159–1163.

53 Kind, T., Liu, K.H., Lee, D.Y. et al. (2013). LipidBlast in silico tandem mass spectrometry database for lipid identification. *Nat. Methods* 10 (8): 755–758.

54 Liebisch, G., Vizcaino, J.A., Kofeler, H. et al. (2013). Shorthand notation for lipid structures derived from mass spectrometry. *J. Lipid Res.* 54 (6): 1523–1530.

55 Liebisch, G., Fahy, E., Aoki, J. et al. (2020). Update on LIPID MAPS classification, nomenclature, and shorthand notation for MS-derived lipid structures. *J. Lipid Res.* 61 (12): 1539–1555.

9

Lipidomics Quantitation

Michaela Chocholoušková, Denise Wolrab, Ondřej Peterka, Robert Jirásko, and Michal Holčapek

University of Pardubice, Faculty of Chemical Technology, Department of Analytical Chemistry, Studentská 573, 532 10 Pardubice, Czech Republic

9.1 Introduction to Lipidomics Quantitation

In general, the lipidomics analysis consists of two basic steps, qualitative (identification) and quantitative analysis. Concentrations determined in lipidomics mass spectrometry (MS)-based experiments can be expressed at different levels of information content and confidence. The highest level of confidence is achieved by the determination of molar concentrations (mol/l) using an isotopically labeled internal standard (IS) with a structure identical to that of the nonlabeled analyte (except for isotopically labeled atoms). The same matrix effect is guaranteed because of the coelution of the isotopically labeled IS and analytes. This rigorous approach provides the most reliable molar concentrations. However, this is applicable only for one or a few molecules with stable isotope standards available [1] and not for hundreds of compounds as common in lipidomics studies. Therefore, the compromise approach is often used with one or a few exogenous ISs (preferably labeled with stable isotopes) per each lipid class. This strategy is based on the simplified assumption that all lipid species within one class have very similar physicochemical properties, including ionization efficiency. This prerequisite could be slightly oversimplified in some cases. For polar lipids with comparable fatty acyl lengths and the number of double bonds, differences within one lipid class are small (typically less than 20–30%, at maximum up to 50% for larger structural differences), which is relatively acceptable for omics quantitation because this error is systematic and does not change too much from sample to sample. However, many serious problems are observed for nonpolar lipid classes with the absence of a polar head group with significant influence on the ionization efficiency. Therefore, the relative effect of double-bond

Mass Spectrometry for Lipidomics: Methods and Applications, First Edition.
Edited by Michal Holčapek and Kim Ekroos.
© 2023 WILEY-VCH GmbH. Published 2023 by WILEY-VCH GmbH.

number and fatty acyl length is much greater for nonpolar lipid classes and should be implemented in quantitative workflows. The quantitation of nonpolar lipid classes without the implementation of response factors may be strongly influenced, but the use of response factors calculated as the slope ratio of the calibration curves can compensate, as illustrated for cholesteryl ester (CE) [2] and triacylglycerol (TG) [3].

The simplest approach does not use IS and only expresses concentrations as a relative response (peak areas/intensities) in percentage (%) and compares differences between sample groups, which does not provide molar concentrations at all. This approach is common in metabolomics, where the availability of labeled IS is even worse compared to lipidomics. Moreover, the simplification with one IS per class cannot be routinely applied in metabolomics because metabolites do not usually belong to specific classes unlike lipids, which significantly complicates the quantitative metabolomic analysis. This approach is sometimes referred to as metabolic fingerprinting [4] and may be acceptable for starting experiments to provide quick information on trends between individual sample groups, but should be replaced as much as possible, by a more reliable quantitative approach for credible publication with at least one IS per lipid class according to the minimum requirements of the International Lipidomics Society [5]. A simplified approach could be used to detect differences within one lipid class, where the signal intensity of the individual lipid is related to the sum of all intensities for all lipid species within the class, which was applied, for example, to differentiate between case and control groups in matrix-assisted laser desorption/ionization MS measurement [6]. This approach does not require IS, but it cannot provide molar concentrations. The current chapter is focused on the explanation of how to obtain accurate molar concentrations for numerous lipid species; hence, the relative concentrations or measurements without IS will not be further discussed.

9.2 Principle of Quantitation

The basic principle of MS-based quantitation is that the concentrations of analytes are calculated as the relationship between the MS response and the response at a known concentration (ion intensity or peak area in the case of chromatography coupling) within a defined linear dynamic range. There are a few quantitation approaches, such as using external standards or IS. In general, a calibration curve is used to obtain a regression equation, which can be applied to calculate the amount of analyte in the sample of interest. In the case of the external standard approach, calibration is usually performed with the target compound, and it is assumed that the response behavior of the sample is identical to that of standard solutions. Unfortunately, such requirements cannot be guaranteed in MS analysis because several factors influence the signal response, such as different ionization efficiency caused by different sample matrices, the gradual contamination of the mass spectrometer, variations in spray stability, etc. This can lead to inaccurate quantitation results, and therefore, the external standard approach is generally discouraged for MS-based quantitation.

The use of IS is the best quantitation procedure in MS analysis, where IS has to be added before the first step in sample handling. Simultaneous processing and analysis of exogenous IS and endogenous analytes is achieved only in this way. Variations during the entire process should be negligible, assuming that IS and endogenous analytes are affected to the same extent by sample preparation or instrumental fluctuations. It is also suggested to perform a calibration curve with IS spiking before sample preparation and to prepare samples spiked with different concentrations of IS. This allows the determination of the linear range and the calculation of the accuracy by using the regression equation for quantitation. The simplified equation based on a single-point IS calibration can be used within the linear dynamic range. However, the IS concentration should be optimized to correspond to endogenous concentrations. The concentrations of analytes are then calculated using the modified Eq. (9.1):

$$c_{\mathrm{A}} = \frac{I_{\mathrm{A}}}{I_{\mathrm{IS}}} * c_{\mathrm{IS}} \tag{9.1}$$

where c_{A} and c_{IS} are the concentrations of the analyte and IS, respectively, and I_{A} and I_{IS} are the MS responses (intensity or area) of the analyte and IS, respectively [4]. Furthermore, the relationship expressed in Eq. (9.1) assumes that the analyte and IS have similar response factor (RF) under given experimental conditions. If the RF values are significantly different, then the analyte concentration should be calculated using Eq. (9.2):

$$c_{\mathrm{A}} = \frac{I_{\mathrm{A}}}{I_{\mathrm{IS}}} * \frac{\mathrm{RF_A}}{\mathrm{RF_{IS}}} * c_{\mathrm{IS}} \tag{9.2}$$

where $\mathrm{RF_A}$ and $\mathrm{RF_{IS}}$ are the RF of the analyte and IS, respectively. The identical RF can be achieved only for the isotopically labeled IS with the same ionization and fragmentation behavior as for the analyte. Unfortunately, it is impossible to use one IS for each lipid species because of the substantial complexity of the cellular lipidome, which includes hundreds or thousands of lipids. Type I isotopic correction and the selection of universal IS or more IS per lipid class may be applied to minimize the effect of different RF of IS and endogenous compounds. The applicability of simple Eq. (9.1) to determine the molar concentrations after careful optimization of the method was shown by various studies [2, 3, 7].

9.3 Internal Standards

ISs are essential for accurate quantitation [5, 8, 9], and Table 9.1 shows the common IS used for human lipidome. The MS response can be affected by several factors, including sample preparation and measurement conditions. Variations occur over time because of various reasons, such as different configurations of mass spectrometers, different extraction and measurement protocols, different operators, used consumables, gradual contamination of the mass spectrometer during the sample

Table 9.1 Typical internal standards (IS) used in the lipidomic quantitation for human samples.

Lipid category	Lipid (sub)class	Internal standards: Exogenous	Internal standards: Deuterated
Fatty acyls	FA		FA 18:1-D9; FA 20:4-D11
	Oxylipins		(9-HODE; 9,10-DiHOME; LTB_4; PGF2a)-D4; 20-HETE-D6; (5-HETE)-D8; 5(6)-EET-D11
	Endocannabinoids		20:4-D11 anandamide; 2-arachidonoyl-D11 glycerol
	Acyl carnitine (CAR)		CAR (14:0-D3; 12:0-D3; 24:0-D4); *CAR-D3 (10:0; 12:0; 14:0; 16:0; 18:0; 18:1); CAR-D9 (14:0; 26:0)*
Glycerolipids	MG	19:1	MG 18:1-D7
	DG	12:1/12:1; 14:0/14:0; 20:0/20:0	DG 15:0/18:1-D7; DG-D5 18:1/18:1
	TG	12:0/12:0/12:0; 19:0/19:0/19:0; 19:1/19:1/19:1	TG 15:0/18:1-D7/15:0; TG-D5 16:0/19:2/16:0
Phospholipids	PC	13:0/13:0; 14:0/14:0; 22:0/22:0; 22:1/22:1	PC 15:0/18:1-D7; PC-D5 17:0/22:4; PC P-18:0/18:1-D9
	LPC	13:0	LPC 18:1-D7; LPC-D5 19:0
	PE	14:0/14:0; 20:0/20:0	PE 15:0/18:1-D7; PE-D5 17:0/22:4; PE P-18:0/18:1-D9
	LPE	13:0; 14:0	LPE 18:1-D7; LPE-D5 19:0
	PI	12:0/13:0; 17:0/14:1; 15:0/18:1	PI 15:0/18:1-D7; PI-D5 17:0/22:4
	Phosphatidylinositol-monophosphate (PIP)		PI(5′)P-5D 16:0/16:0
	PIP2		PI(3′,5′)P2-5D 16:0/16:0
	Lysophosphatidylinositol (LPI)	13:0; 17:1	LPI-D5 15:0

Table 9.1 (Continued)

Lipid category	Lipid (sub)class	Internal standards	
		Exogenous	**Deuterated**
	PG	14:0/14:0; 20:0/20:0	PG 15:0/18:1-D7; *PG-D5 16:0/18:1;* PG-D5 17:0/22:4
	Lysophosphatidylglycerol (LPG)	14:0; 17:0	LPG-D5 15:0
	PS	14:0/14:0; 20:0/20:0	PS 15:0/18:1-D7; PS-D5 17:0/22:4
	Lysophosphatidylserine (LPS)	13:0; 14:0; 17:1	LPS-D5 15:0
	PA	14:0/14:0	PA 15:0/18:1-D7
	LPA	14:0; 17:0	LPA 16:0-D9
	Bis[monoacylglycero] phosphate (BMP)	14:0/14:0	
	Cardiolipin (CL)	14:0/14:0/14:0/14:0	CL-D5 18:2/18:2/18:2/18:2
Sphingolipids	Cer	18:1/12:0; 18:1/17:0	*Cer 18:1-D7/18:0*
	SM	18:1/12:0	SM 18:1/18:1-D9; *SM-D9 18:1/15:0*
	GlcCer	18:1/12:0; 18:1/17:0	*GlcCer 18:1-D5/18:0; GlcCer 18:1-D7/15:0*
	GalCer	18:1/12:0	*GalCer 18:1-D7/13:0; GalCer 18:1-D7/24:1*
	LacCer	18:1/12:0; 18:1/17:0	*LacCer 18:1-D7/15:0; LacCer 18:1-D7/24:1*
	GM3		GM3 18:1/18:0-D5; GM3 18:1/16:0-D9
	GM2		GM2 18:1/16:0-D9
	GM1		GM1 18:1/18:0-D5; GM1 18:1/16:0-D9
	Gb3	18:1/17:0	Gb3 18:1/16:0-D9
	SGalCer	18:1/12:0; 18:1/17:0	*SGalCer 18:1-D7/13:0; SGalCer 18:1-D7/24:1*
	Sphingoid base (SPB)	17:1	*SPB-D7*
	S1P	17:1	*S1P-D7*
	Ceramide-phosphate (CERP)	18:1/12:0	*CERP 18:1-D7/15:0*
Sterols	Chol		*Chol-D7*
	CE	19:0	*CE-D7 16:0*; CE 18:1-D7

IS providing different fragments than endogenous lipids are written in italics.
Source: Adapted from [9–15].

sequence, stability of spray, etc. These selected examples may lead to fluctuations in signal response, which highlights the urgent need for appropriate IS in lipidomics analysis. The addition of the IS in the earliest possible step before any sample handling allows to monitor, minimize, and compensate for signal response fluctuations. IS must be selected more carefully for the shotgun approach because IS with the same fatty acid (FA) composition (especially glycerolipids and phospholipids) can generate fragments identical to other IS by in-source fragmentation, such as TG to diacylglycerol (DG) to monoacylglycerol (MG), phospholipids (PL) to phosphatidic acid (PA), phosphatidylcholine (PC) to phosphatidylethanolamine (PE), etc.

There are generic rules for selecting the appropriate IS. IS should have the same structure, chemical properties, and MS/MS fragmentation patterns, or at least similar to the endogenous lipids to be quantified. The best approach is the use of labeled IS with stable isotopes (D or ^{13}C) for each endogenous lipid species. However, this is not feasible in lipidomics because of two principal reasons: the high complexity of the lipidome and the limited number and high costs of commercially available stable isotope-labeled standards. Therefore, it is necessary to make a certain compromise when choosing IS in lipidomics. The number, structure, and concentration of IS per lipid class depend on the applied method and conditions and must be optimized during the validation of the analytical method. The number of deuterium atoms in individual compounds influences the retention behavior; therefore, the IS with five to nine deuterium atoms are most often used unlike IS containing (almost) completely deuterated fatty acyls. The use of ^{13}C-labeled standards has the advantage that the retention shifts are negligible and no migration of ^{13}C is possible, but the price is significantly higher in comparison to deuterated standards. IS with less than four deuterium atoms interferes with the isotope pattern that may lead to incorrect quantitation, which is especially observed for high-mass lipids, such as gangliosides, but whose IS for more glycosylated sphingolipids is still limited. Moreover, it is also important to consider the position of deuterium for methods based on MS/MS, especially for the shotgun approach with low-resolution MS and methods using MRM, for example, deuterated FA in sphingomyelin (SM) 18:1/18:1-D9 (precursor ion scan [PIS] 184) versus deuterated choline in SM-D9 18:1/15:0 (PIS 193) or deuterated sterol skeleton in CE-D7 16:0 (PIS 376) versus deuterated FA in CE 18:1-D7 (PIS 369). Nowadays, there are many possibilities of fatty acyl composition of IS including deuterium; therefore, it is recommended to select the composition closest to the analyte.

If isotopically labeled ISs are not available, then cheaper exogenous lipid standards with shorter, longer, or odd carbon fatty acyl chains may be considered. Their absence in real biological samples must be carefully verified; otherwise, the quantitation can be seriously compromised. However, especially deuterated ISs for TG are recommended because TG is a highly diverse lipid class, and therefore, the selection of a suitable exogenous IS is complicated. The number of ISs depends on the lipidomics approach. In the case of lipid class, separation and shotgun MS are recommended for at least one IS per lipid class but more ISs per lipid class for lipid species separation that elutes over a longer elution window with possible different matrix effects. However, recent publications demonstrate the advantages of using more IS per lipid class also for lipid class-based lipidomics approaches, which allows the calculation of the error of quantification [16, 17]. The concentration of IS should be close to the physiological values for the corresponding lipid species, but in the case of one IS per lipid class, the range two-thirds to one-half of the most abundant analyte is recommended.

IS mixtures can be either purchased as premixed sets or they can be self-prepared. Commercially available IS mixtures can be selected according to your lipid preferences or lipid interests, such as oxysterols, sphingolipids (SL), PC, PE, phosphatidylglycerol (PG), phosphatidylinositol (PI), phosphatidylserine (PS), and their lyso forms, SM, Cer, TG, CE, or IS mixtures for quantitation of more lipid classes, which includes representative standards within the lipid class (UltimateSplash™ or Lipidyzer™). The main advantage of commercially available IS mixtures is that they are ready for immediate use without any preparation. However, concentrations are defined without the possibility of change, which may be a disadvantage for certain sample matrices, sample preparation protocols, or methods. Self-prepared IS mixtures allow optimization and adjustment of the composition and concentrations of IS mixtures, which can eventually be modified for customized applications and methods. The main manufacturers of IS for lipidomics are Avanti Polar Lipids, Cayman Chemical, Nu-Chek Prep, and Cambridge Isotope Laboratories.

9.4 Isotopic Correction

The main isotopic contributions for the lipid species are carbon (^{12}C) and hydrogen (^{1}H), which are present together with their isotopologs, i.e. ^{13}C and deuterium (D). The natural isotopic abundance of D is low (0.0115%) compared to ^{13}C (1.09%). Therefore, the carbon atom has the greatest influence on the isotopic distribution of lipid species, taking into account the total number of carbon atoms in the lipid structure. Other atoms, such as oxygen and nitrogen, present in lipid molecules also have their own isotopic contribution, but their distribution is equal because of their same numbers for a given lipid class. Therefore, only carbon isotopes must be considered for type I isotopic correction to achieve accurate quantitation within individual lipid classes [8].

9.4.1 Isotopic Correction Type I

The response of lipid species within the lipid class differs according to the length of fatty acyl chains. Lipid species with shorter fatty acyl chains have higher monoisotopic intensities than those with longer fatty acyl chains because of their different isotopic distribution (Figure 9.1). Therefore, the isotopic contribution of lipid

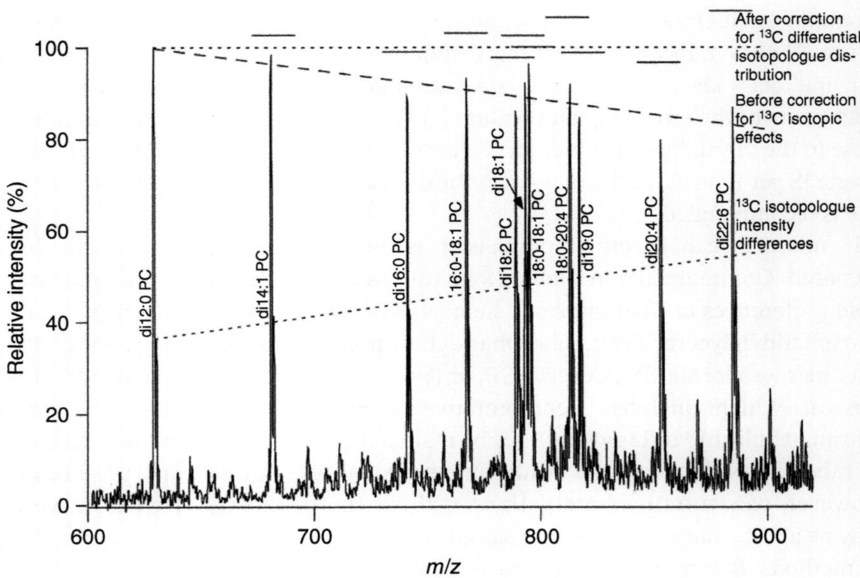

Figure 9.1 Type I ^{13}C isotopic correction. *Source:* Reproduced with permission from Wang et al. [8]/John wiley & Sons.

species and IS should be considered for the calculation of lipid concentrations. The following Eqs. (9.3) and (9.4) include the calculation with Type I correction:

$$c_A = Z_I * \frac{I_A}{I_{IS}} * c_{IS} \tag{9.3}$$

$$Z_I = \frac{1 + 0.0109 n_A + \frac{0.0109^2 n_A (n_A - 1)}{2} + \ldots}{1 + 0.0109 n_{IS} + \frac{0.0109^2 n_{IS} (n_{IS} - 1)}{2} + \ldots} \tag{9.4}$$

where c_A and c_{IS} are the concentrations of analyte and IS, respectively, and I_A and I_{IS} are MS responses (intensity or area) of the analyte and IS, respectively. Z_I is defined as the Type I ^{13}C isotopic correction factor expressed as the ratio between the sum of isotopic peak clusters (M, M+1, M+2, etc.) of the lipid species with n_A carbon atoms and the sum of isotopic peak clusters (M, M+1, M+2, etc.) of IS with n_{IS} carbon atoms. This type of correction should be applied to all lipidomics quantitation approaches [8].

9.4.2 Isotopic Correction Type II

This type of isotopic correction is needed only in the event that there is no differentiation of lipid species differing by one double bond (lipid class separation and low-resolution shotgun MS), as illustrated in Figure 9.2.

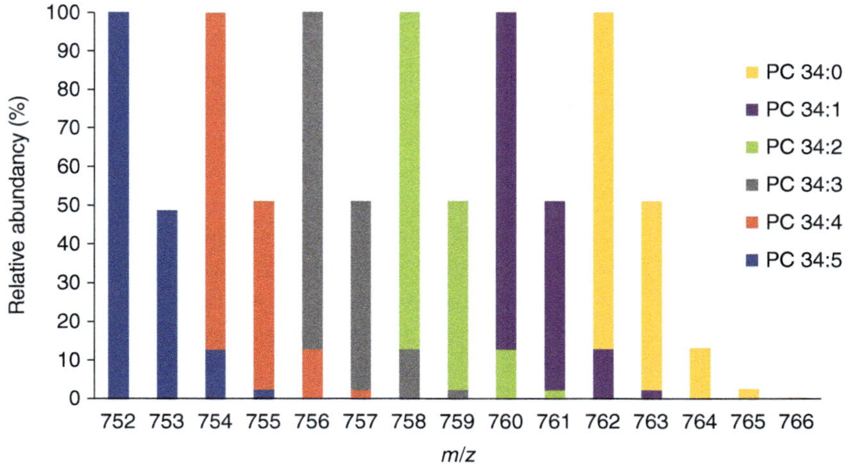

Figure 9.2 Type II isotopic correction.

When the Type II isotopic correction is included, the concentrations are calculated using Eqs. (9.5) and (9.6):

$$c_A = Z_{II} * \frac{I_A}{I_{IS}} * c_{IS} \tag{9.5}$$

$$Z_{II} = 1 - F_{M+2}(\%)/100 \tag{9.6}$$

where c_A and c_{IS} are the concentrations of the analyte and IS, respectively, and I_A and I_{IS} are MS responses (intensity or area) of the analyte and IS, respectively. Z_{II} is defined as the Type II ^{13}C isotopic correction factor calculated using the contribution of M+2 isotope of the lipid species with one more double bond than the lipid species of interest (F_{M+2}).

9.5 Common Approaches for Lipidomics Quantitation

As discussed above, different lipidomics quantitation approaches require slightly different quantitation postulates. MS-based methods are strongly influenced by the following factors, such as ionization efficiency and ion suppression/enhancement, matrix effects, or ion source fragmentation. All these factors must be taken into account, investigated, and normalized to obtain reliable quantitative data during the establishment of new quantitative methods.

9.5.1 Shotgun MS

The basic definition of shotgun MS is that the sample extract is infused into the MS without any chromatographic separation and analyzed only by MS-based scan events. Low-resolution shotgun MS lipidomics analysis (QqQ or Q-LIT) is based on the characteristic MS/MS fragmentation behavior of lipid classes (precursor ion scanning and neutral loss scanning) [18–20]. The high-resolution shotgun MS lipidomics analysis is based on full MS spectra typically measured by an ultrahigh-resolution Orbitrap mass analyzer and eventually with the support of product ion mass spectra for selected mass windows [21–23]. The diluted lipidomics extract is infused into the MS using constant flow, which warrants the same ionization conditions and the same matrix effects for all lipids. However, low abundant lipid species or less ionizable lipid species are usually ion suppressed by colonization of high abundant lipids. A good quantitation practice is the use of at least one IS within one lipid class but published references also recommend using at least two IS within the lipid class of different concentrations to cover low- and high-abundance lipids and to compensate for their different RF.

For reliable quantitation using the shotgun MS lipidomics approach, the effect of in-source fragmentation and isotopic overlap should be considered because several lipid classes are easily fragmented. The ion source fragmentation can cause various artifacts, such as the loss of serine from PS leading to PA, TG can be fragmented to DG, lysophosphatidylcholine (LPC) may fragment to lysophosphatidic acid (LPA), etc. The ion source fragmentation under given instrumental and experimental conditions should be carefully investigated and minimized during the method development and validation. In the case of low-resolution shotgun MS, the isotopic correction Type II has to be always applied. On the other hand, if two isobaric peaks are resolved using high-resolution shotgun MS analysis, the Type II isotopic correction is not needed. The Type I isotopic correction should be applied in all cases.

9.5.2 Chromatography – MS

Methods based on MS with prior chromatography are separated into two groups: lipid class separation and lipid species separation [24]. Generally, liquid chromatography – mass spectrometry (LC/MS) methods usually work with gradient elution, leading to different ionization efficiencies, ion suppression, and matrix effects within a chromatographic run. The advantage of lipid class separation is a coelution of lipid species belonging to the same lipid class; therefore, the use of at least one IS per lipid class is recommended [10, 25]. On the other hand, the lipid species separation approach separates individual lipid species within the lipid class, requiring the use of more IS per lipid class (at least three to four for complex classes, such as TG). Figure 9.3 shows the separation of oxylipins using reversed-phase (RP) ultrahigh-performance liquid chromatography (UHPLC)/MS, where 14 deuterated IS were used for their quantitation. Because of the separation of lipid classes and species, the ion source fragmentation leading to misinterpretation of the quantitative data is suppressed. In the case of lipid class separation, isotopic correction Type II must be applied, and isotopic correction Type I should be used for all approaches [8].

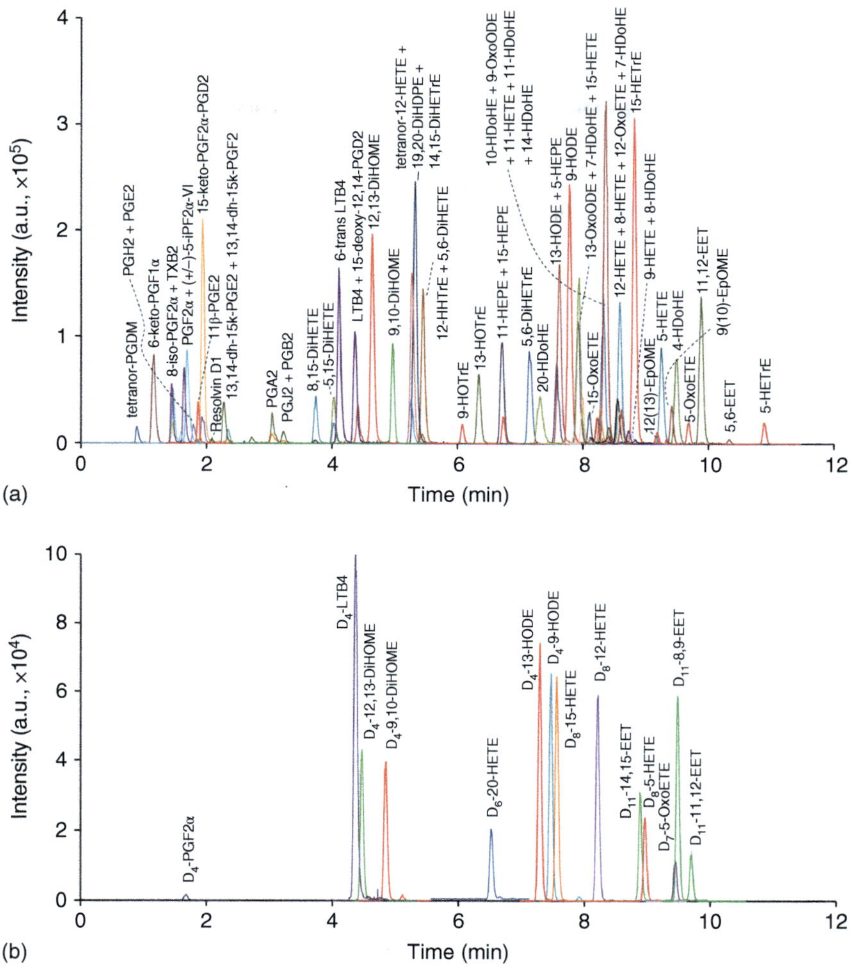

Figure 9.3 RP-UHPLC/MS analysis of oxylipins in the negative-ion mode with extracted ion chromatograms of (a) human plasma and (b) deuterated IS. Source: Reproduced with permission from Chocholoušková et al. [11]/Springer Nature.

9.6 Validation

All developed methods aimed at quantitative lipidomics analysis should be subjected to method validation [16]. The validation is a set of tests that should verify the suitability and reliability of these quantitative methods for the accurate and precise quantitation of lipids in biological samples of interest, such as blood, serum, plasma, urine, saliva, cells, tissues, etc. The validation is performed using quality control

(QC) samples (e.g. pooled samples) and individual samples (for matrix effect and selectivity only) with the same matrix as the study samples, and generally, the full validation should be performed for each sample type. There are numerous validation parameters, for example, the calibration curve, (lower) limit of quantitation, carryover, repeatability, precision, accuracy, selectivity, extraction recovery, matrix effect, dilution integrity, and stability. Until now, the official validation guidelines for lipidomics analysis have not been established, but the guidelines of the European Medicine Agency (EMA) [26] and the Food and Drug Administration (FDA) [27] for bioanalytical validation for lipidomics analysis have been adopted [16]. The validation parameters criteria are described in Table 9.2. The lipidomics analysis does not have official guidelines for bioanalytical validation unlike pharmaceutical analysis, but it is useful to adopt recommendations from this field with eventual modifications for the improvement of robustness of lipidomics data.

The calibration curve should be prepared in the real matrix to determine the instrument response with respect to the concentration of the analyte and to establish a quantitation range. The calibration curve range should be defined by the lower limit of quantitation (LLOQ) and the upper limit of quantitation (ULOQ), and one calibration curve for each IS must be prepared. The LLOQ is the lowest concentration of analyte that can be reliably quantified with acceptable accuracy and precision. During the development of the quantitative method, the carryover effect should be minimized and evaluated using the blank sample injected after the high-concentration sample or ULOQ.

The accuracy describes the closeness of the concentration determined to the nominal (theoretical) value and is expressed as the percentage of the nominal value obtained from the calibration curve. The precision describes the closeness of repeated measures and is expressed by the relative standard deviation (RSD), also known as the coefficient of variation (CV). Both accuracy and precision should be measured at multiple concentration levels within a single run (within-run accuracy and precision) and in different runs (between-run accuracy and precision).

The selectivity verifies the suitability of IS by ensuring the absence of interferences of the same *m/z* from endogenous components in biological samples or system impurities. This validation parameter must be carefully optimized, especially in the case of the use of exogenous IS with short, longer, or odd fatty acyl chains, which could be naturally present in biological samples. The selectivity is demonstrated using the blank matrix sample (without IS) and individual samples of interest. The pooled sample should not be used for the evaluation of this validation parameter.

The matrix effect is a validation parameter that reflects the influence of the biological matrix on the MS response of the analytes, leading to either ion suppression or ion enhancement. The pooled sample should not be used in a way similar to the selectivity. The matrix effect is calculated as the CV of at least six matrix factors, which are determined by comparing individual samples of interest spiked with IS after extraction and a diluted neat IS mixture (without matrix). Any value of the matrix effect is acceptable as long as the variance of the matrix effect (matrix factor) is reproducible.

Table 9.2 Validation criteria based on EMA [26] and FDA [27] authorities.

	Validation parameter	Description	Authority
Pooled sample	Calibration curve range	• LLOQ, ULOQ	EMA, FDA
	Calibration curve	• min 6 calibration levels	EMA, FDA
	Acceptance criteria	• ±15% of nominal (theoretical) value, except at LLOQ (±20%) for back-calculated values • 75% and a minimum of 6 calibration levels have to fulfill this criteria	
	Carry over	• Analyzing of blank sample after the calibration standard at the ULOQ	EMA, FDA
	Acceptance criteria	• ≤20% of LLOQ	
	Lower limit of quantitation (LLOQ)	• The lowest concentration which can be quantified reliably	EMA, FDA
	Acceptance criteria	• ≤20% for precision and ±20% for accuracy	
	Accuracy and precision	• Five samples per level at a minimum of four concentration levels • Within-run and between-run (at least three independent runs during at least two different days)	EMA, FDA
	Acceptance criteria	• ≤15% for precision and ±15% for accuracy	
	Extraction recovery	• For three concentration levels in at least duplicates in each run	FDA
	Acceptance criteria	• Not defined	
	Stability	• For two concentration levels • For three concentration levels in at least duplicates in each run	EMA FDA
	Acceptance criteria	• ±15%	EMA, FDA
	Dilution integrity	• At least five replicates per dilution factor	EMA, FDA
	Acceptance criteria	• ≤15% CV for precision and ± 15% for accuracy	
Individual samples	Selectivity	• Analyzing of blank matrix (no IS) from at least six individual sources	EMA, FDA
	Acceptance criteria	• ≤5% of LLOQ for IS	
	Matrix effect	• Analyzing of three replicates of two concentration levels from at least six individual sources • Analyzing of at least six individual sources	EMA FDA
	Acceptance criteria	• ≤15% CV • No defined	EMA FDA

Source: Adapted from [26, 27].

The extraction recovery of the sample preparation should also be known and calculated as the ratio of the IS intensities in samples, where IS was added before and after extraction. Any value of extraction efficiency is acceptable as long as the variance in extraction recovery is reproducible.

The dilution integrity is the validation parameter to ensure that the dilution does not affect the precision and accuracy. The stability should be known to ensure that individual steps of the lipidomics analysis and storage conditions do not affect the analyte concentration. The stability study should investigate the stability of the stock solution of IS, freezing and thawing cycles, autosampler stability, storage stability, etc.

9.7 Quality Control (QC)

Regular QC measurements are of great importance for quantitative approaches to ensure and verify the quality of quantitative results. There are different types of QC samples, such as blanks, calibration samples, reference material samples, system standard samples, and representative samples for the matrix studied. QC samples should be prepared from the same source (e.g. pooled sample of a representative subset of the study) and submitted to the same procedures as samples of interest [16]. All types of QC samples should be regularly measured and monitored to ensure high data quality, whereby the total number of QC samples depends on the size of the sample study. The NIST SRM 1950 plasma is widely used and accepted as a standard reference plasma material prepared from 100 healthy donors. The inclusion of this reference material in lipidomics studies as QC sample is strongly recommended because it can be used to compare the quantitative performance with other methods [28, 29] and for normalization to compensate method-specific differences in quantitation caused by the instrument, platform, or software [12, 17]. Another important part of good quantitation practice is the sample randomization. The sample randomization guarantees that quantitative data are not influenced by measurement artifacts as a result of grouping of the same sample type within the sequence.

References

1 Laaksonen, R., Ekroos, K., Sysi-Aho, M. et al. (2016). Plasma ceramides predict cardiovascular death in patients with stable coronary artery disease and acute coronary syndromes beyond LDL-cholesterol. *Eur. Heart J.* 37 (25): 1967–1976.

2 Höring, M., Ejsing, C.S., Hermansson, M., and Liebisch, G. (2019). Quantification of cholesterol and cholesteryl ester by direct flow injection high-resolution Fourier transform mass spectrometry utilizing species-specific response factors. *Anal. Chem.* 91 (5): 3459–3466.

3 Holčapek, M., Lísa, M., Jandera, P., and Kabátová, N. (2005). Quantitation of triacylglycerols in plant oils using HPLC with APCI-MS, evaporative light-scattering, and UV detection. *J. Sep. Sci.* 28 (12): 1315–1333.

4 Carrasco-Pancorbo, A., Navas-Iglesias, N., and Cuadros-Rodriguez, L. (2009). From lipid analysis towards lipidomics, a new challenge for the analytical chemistry of the 21st century. Part 1: modern lipid analysis. *TrAC, Trends Anal. Chem.* 28 (3): 263–278.

5 Liebisch, G., Ahrends, R., Arita, M. et al. (2019). Lipidomics needs more standardization. *Nat. Metabolism* 1 (8): 745–747.

6 Jirásko, R., Holčapek, M., Khalikova, M. et al. (2017). MALDI orbitrap mass spectrometry profiling of dysregulated sulfoglycosphingolipids in renal cell carcinoma tissues. *J. Am. Mass Spectrom. Soc.* 28: 1562–1574.

7 Weir, J.M., Wong, G., Barlow, C.K. et al. (2013). Plasma lipid profiling in a large population-based cohort. *J. Lipid Res.* 54 (10): 2898–2908.

8 Wang, M., Wang, C.Y., and Han, X.L. (2017). Selection of internal standards for accurate quantification of complex lipid species in biological extracts by electrospray ionization mass spectrometry–what, how and why? *Mass Spectrom. Rev.* 36 (6): 693–714.

9 Holčapek, M., Liebisch, G., and Ekroos, K. (2018). Lipidomic analysis. *Anal. Chem.* 90 (7): 4249–4257.

10 Wolrab, D., Jirásko, R., Cífková, E. et al. (2022). Lipidomic profiling of human serum enables detection of pancreatic cancer. *Nat. Commun.* 13 (124): 1–16.

11 Chocholoušková, M., Jirásko, R., Vrána, D. et al. (2019). Reversed phase UHPLC/ESI-MS determination of oxylipins in human plasma: a case study of female breast cancer. *Anal. Bioanal. Chem.* 411 (6): 1239–1251.

12 Triebl, A., Burla, B., Selvalatchmanan, J. et al. (2020). Shared reference materials harmonize lipidomics across MS-based detection platforms and laboratories. *J. Lipid Res.* 61 (1): 105–115.

13 Saigusa, D., Hishinuma, E., Matsukawa, N. et al. (2021). Comparison of kit-based metabolomics with other methodologies in a large cohort, towards establishing reference values. *Metabolites* 11 (10): 652.

14 Huynh, K., Barlow, C.K., Jayawardana, K.S. et al. (2019). High-throughput plasma lipidomics: detailed mapping of the associations with cardiometabolic risk factors. *Cell Chem. Biol.* 26 (1): 71–84.

15 Hořejší, K., Jirásko, R., Chocholoušková, M. et al. (2021). Comprehensive identification of glycosphingolipids in human plasma using hydrophilic interaction liquid chromatography–electrospray ionization mass spectrometry. *Metabolites* 11 (3): 140.

16 Wolrab, D., Chocholoušková, M., Jirásko, R. et al. (2020). Validation of lipidomic analysis of human plasma and serum by supercritical fluid chromatography–mass spectrometry and hydrophilic interaction liquid chromatography–mass spectrometry. *Anal. Bioanal. Chem.* 412 (10): 2375–2388.

17 Chocholoušková, M., Wolrab, D., Jirásko, R. et al. (2021). Intra-laboratory comparison of four analytical platforms for lipidomic quantitation using hydrophilic interaction liquid chromatography or supercritical fluid chromatography coupled to quadrupole – time-of-flight mass spectrometry. *Talanta* 231 (15): 122367.

18 Yang, K., Zhao, Z.D., Gross, R.W., and Han, X.L. (2009). Systematic analysis of choline-containing phospholipids using multi-dimensional mass spectrometry-based shotgun lipidomics. *J. Chromatogr. B Analyt. Technol. Biomed. Life Sci.* 877 (26): 2924–2936.

19 Han, X.L., Yang, K., and Gross, R.W. (2012). Multi-dimensional mass spectrometry-based shotgun lipidomics and novel strategies for lipidomic analyses. *Mass Spectrom. Rev.* 31 (1): 134–178.

20 Wang, M., Wang, C.Y., Han, R.H., and Han, X.L. (2016). Novel advances in shotgun lipidomics for biology and medicine. *Prog. Lipid Res.* 61: 83–108.

21 Almeida, R., Pauling, J.K., Sokol, E. et al. (2015). Comprehensive lipidome analysis by shotgun lipidomics on a hybrid quadrupole-orbitrap-linear ion trap mass spectrometer. *J. Am. Soc. Mass Spectrom.* 26 (1): 133–148.

22 Herzog, R., Schwudke, D., Schuhmann, K. et al. (2011). A novel informatics concept for high-throughput shotgun lipidomics based on the molecular fragmentation query language. *Genome Biol.* 12 (1): 1–25.

23 Eggers, L.F. and Schwudke, D. (2018). Shotgun lipidomics approaches for clinical samples. *Methods Mol. Biol.* 1730: 163–174.

24 Wolrab, D., Jirásko, R., Chocholoušková, M. et al. (2019). Oncolipidomics: mass spectrometric quantitation of lipids in cancer research. *TrAC, Trends Anal. Chem.* 120: 115480.

25 Wolrab, D., Jirásko, R., Peterka, O. et al. (2021). Plasma lipidomic profiles of kidney, breast and prostate cancer patients differ from healthy controls. *Sci. Rep.* 11 (1): 20322.

26 European Medicines Agency (2015). Guidelines on bioanalytical method validation. https://www.ema.europa.eu/en/documents/scientific-guideline/guideline-bioanalytical-method-validation_en.pdf (accessed 23 July 2022).

27 U.S. Department of Health and Human Services Food and Drug Administration (2018). Draft guidance for industry: bioanalytical method validation. https://www.fda.gov/files/drugs/published/Bioanalytical-Method-Validation-Guidance-for-Industry.pdf (accessed 1 July 2022).

28 Quehenberger, O., Armando, A.M., Brown, A.H. et al. (2010). Lipidomics reveals a remarkable diversity of lipids in human plasma. *J. Lipid Res.* 51 (11): 3299–3305.

29 Bowden, J.A., Heckert, A., Ulmer, C.Z. et al. (2017). Harmonizing lipidomics: NIST interlaboratory comparison exercise for lipidomics using SRM 1950-metabolites in frozen human plasma. *J. Lipid Res.* 58 (12): 2275–2288.

10

The Past and Future of Lipidomics Bioinformatics

Dominik Kopczynski[1], Daniel Krause[2], Fadi Al Machot[3], Dominik Schwudke[2,4,5], Nils Hoffmann[6], and Robert Ahrends[1]

[1] *University of Vienna, Department of Analytical Chemistry, Währinger Straße 38, A-1090 Vienna, Austria*
[2] *Bioanalytical Chemistry, Forschungszentrum Borstel, Leibniz Lung Center, Parkallee 1-40, 23845 Borstel, Germany*
[3] *Faculty of Science and Technology, Norwegian University for Life Science (NMBU), 1433 Ås, Norway*
[4] *Airway Research Center North, German Center for Lung Research (DZL), 23845 Borstel, Germany*
[5] *German Center for Infection Research (DZIF), TTU Tuberculosis, 23845 Borstel, Germany*
[6] *Institute for Bio- and Geosciences (IBG-5), Forschungszentrum Jülich GmbH, Wilhelm-Johnen-Straße, 52425 Jülich, Germany*

10.1 Introduction

Computational lipidomics [1] is a subdiscipline of lipidomics [2] that covers all computational aspects to support lipid metabolism research. This includes all computational processes for identification and quantification of lipids from biological samples and data integration – when driven by a biological question – and data modeling to gain insights into metabolic networks behavior and to predict system behavior. This field is rapidly growing, intending to provide robust and reliable tools for performing several steps in data analysis for lipidomics studies. The analytical method of choice for high-throughput lipid analysis is mass spectrometry (MS). MS technology has gained speed and sensitivity over the past decade, laying the necessary foundation for identifying lipids and determining reliable quantities for hundreds of lipids. If a more specific hypothesis can be formulated, a more targeted analysis approach is suitable for validating the results, e.g. by using calibration lines, internal standards, and an increased sample number. Appropriate data visualization and multivariate analysis tools are crucial for a sound data interpretation and may help answer biological questions. Each step in such computational workflows poses challenges in complexity, data storage, and handling, as well as visualization of results. One group working intensively on software solutions is the "Lipidomics Informatics for Life-Science" (LIFS) [3] initiative. The LIFS partners are developing

Mass Spectrometry for Lipidomics: Methods and Applications, First Edition.
Edited by Michal Holčapek and Kim Ekroos.
© 2023 WILEY-VCH GmbH. Published 2023 by WILEY-VCH GmbH.

search engines, quantification algorithms, visualization tools, and databases to provide the essential components for comprehensive lipidomics analysis workflows. Their interest is to bridge the gap between analytical chemistry, computer and data science, and the end users, e.g. biochemists, biologists, and clinicians, by developing tools that are easy to use, yet powerful, fast, and reliable. LIFS collaborates with the Lipidomics Standards Initiative (LSI) on standardization efforts concerning lipid identification, quantification, naming, and reporting [4, 5].

Here, we present our workflow and how we suggest to perform lipidomics experiments. The overall objective is to have comprehensive and modular computational workflows for several lipidomics approaches. We describe the current state of single modules and what remains to be done to fully achieve this goal. This book chapter is not intended to give an extensive overview of the field nor judge other existing workflows or platforms. Our vision of a comprehensive computational workflow contains five stages, which are (i) assay design, (ii) raw data analysis, (iii) standardization of results, (iv) visualization and integration, and (v) data storage and data organization as foundations for knowledge gain and reusability (see Figure 10.1). We focus on two major acquisition strategies: targeted and untargeted lipidomics. Depending on the prior knowledge of the system to be analyzed, different strategies may be chosen. Analyzing a defined set of specific lipids, we denote as *targeted lipidomics*. Acquisition techniques such as selective or parallel reaction monitoring are ideally suited for this task. For *untargeted lipidomics* approaches, the number of lipids of interest may vary, and the constraints (e.g. lipid class, range of double bonds, and carbon chain length) are typically less restrictive. With a vast search space of up to 10^{12} [6] unique lipid structures, approaches like shotgun lipidomics or liquid chromatography-mass spectrometry (LC-MS^n) should be chosen. Here, we will not cover the analysis with a fully open lipidomics search space where no constraints are provided.

First, we give a general overview of formats for storing lipidomics data such as raw MS files, identification/quantification results, or spectral libraries. Well-designed formats are essential for the interoperability between individual stages. Tools within the stages should provide results in standard formats that follow-up

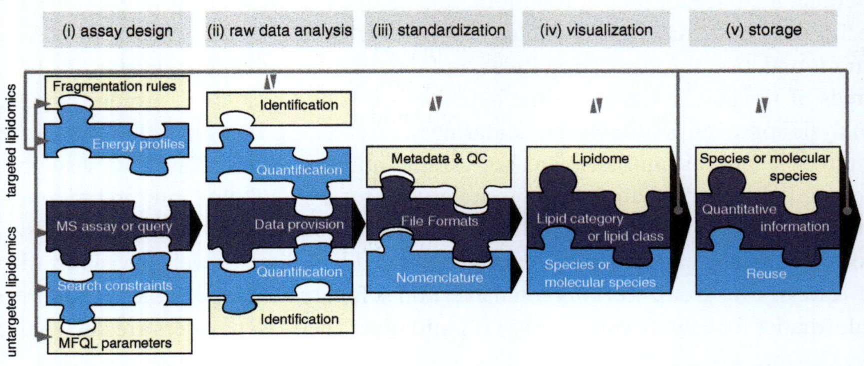

Figure 10.1 Envisioned lipidomics workflow for assay design, analysis, standardization, visualization, and storage.

tools can read in the consecutive stages without the need to interpret data, forming the basis for streamlined analysis.

Concerning assay design, two major acquisition strategies can be distinguished, namely, untargeted and targeted lipidomics. Whereas a targeted approach requires prior knowledge of lipids involved in the studied biological process, i.e. the precursor and fragment masses [6–12], an untargeted approach focuses on the unbiased discovery of lipids, which should be carried out first to understand the lipid sample content. The targeted approach is more sensitive in the detection and quantification of lipids. However, only the specified lipids within a target, inclusion, or transition list can be detected and quantified. Untargeted approaches may provide insight into unknown lipids, but this is often not well established and lacks sophisticated workflows with proper identification error estimation. It is important to note that often untargeted approaches are not fully untargeted because databases containing only a subset of lipid classes or only certain chain lengths and number of double bonds are allowed within the search space. Here, we present our tools of choice for untargeted lipidomics and targeted lipidomics, namely, LipidXplorer, a shotgun lipidomics search engine for the unbiased investigation of lipidomes [13, 14], and LipidCreator, a knowledge-based and targeted assay generator [6, 8] designed to work together with Skyline [15].

After describing both tools and their specific applications, we discuss the necessity of sufficient standardization conventions for lipid names. Therefore, we introduce our lipid normalization and name standardization tools lxPostman and Goslin, of which the latter was recently released in version 2.0. The reader should keep in mind that for a comprehensive understanding of the lipidome within the current limits of structural identification using MS, the experimenter should use the hierarchical order of lipid naming [16–18] (shorthand notation) when reporting lipid identifications.

The fourth workflow module in Section 10.6 deals with the visualization of the acquired lipid data. Lipidome jUXtaposition (LUX) Score is a tool for the qualitative comparison of different lipidomes exploring differences and commonalities in the lipid structural or *chemical space* of the individual lipidomes. It visualizes both the lipid composition of the individual lipidomes and their relations to each other, based on a measure of structural distance. In the last module-describing Section 10.7, we discuss data provision and availability. Here, we introduce our vision of current state-of-the-art databases for quick browsing and exploration of acquired and generated lipidomics data. In Section 10.8, we discuss the future development of our tools and vision. The current state of our tools establishes a solid base for a seamless modular lipidomics workflow. However, we will start to address three significant issues that have to be satisfied to achieve our vision:

(1) Design of interfaces and exchange formats for lipidomics tools.
(2) Quality control mechanisms and structures for the analysis and reanalysis of lipidomics data.
(3) Framework for ontology-driven data sharing of lipidomics studies.

10.2 A Modular Lipidomics Workflow

10.2.1 Data Formats

Many vendors use proprietary data formats to provide output from mass spectrometers. Therefore, challenges arise for follow-up analyses such as reusability of data or interoperability since these data formats may require licensed tools and libraries for reading and interpretation. Additionally, licenses may expire or new software versions may not offer backward compatibility, complicating data handling in this field. Thus, an inherent necessity exists for standardized data formats with open specifications and defined controlled vocabularies (CVs). The FAIR guiding principles for scientific data state that data must be findable, accessible, interoperable, and reusable [19]. Many scientific data repositories for natural sciences, such as proteomics identification database (PRIDE) [20] or MetaboLights [21], already provide research data following these guidelines and demand that users submit and deposit their raw data together with sufficient metadata and results from data processing to reuse, reprocess, and reinvestigate the data. The benefit is easier access to the public data for all participating and interested communities, allowing reanalysis and data aggregation for reuse in other contexts, such as the competitive evaluation of novel algorithms for lipid identification.

Automated analysis within a computational workflow of lipidomics experiments requires that data are processed by several algorithms that serve different purposes such as filtering, peak picking, identification, quantification, quality control, and data integration. Many of these algorithms require specific formats for storing the gained and extracted information. The Human Proteome Organization–Proteomics Standards Initiative (HUPO–PSI) [22] has defined standard formats, a CV, and ontologies, especially for computational proteomics based on MS with the proteomics standards initiative controlled vocabulary for mass spectrometry (PSI-MS). One of these formats is the open and human-readable XML-based format mzML for vendor-independent MS raw data [23], supporting different modes of (chromatographic) separation and levels of MS fragmentation. The mzML format is not specific to an omics discipline but contains all necessary information to be used in lipidomic informatics workflows without the need for further adaptation. The HUPO–PSI developed two additional formats to store identification and quantification results. Again, XML-based file formats were used since they are both human- and machine-readable, mzIdentML for protein and peptide identification [24], and mzQuantML for quantification data for proteins and peptides [25]. However, due to the tree-structured nature of the XML-based format along with the massive overhead introduced by opening and closing tags to enclose data (e.g. <information type>content</information type>), this format was not practical for browsing with standard text processing software. Hence, scientists demanded a more compact file format that was table structured. The result was the tabulator-separated mzTab format, initially designed for computational proteomics [26] and only with minimal support for small molecules. This format was specially designed to

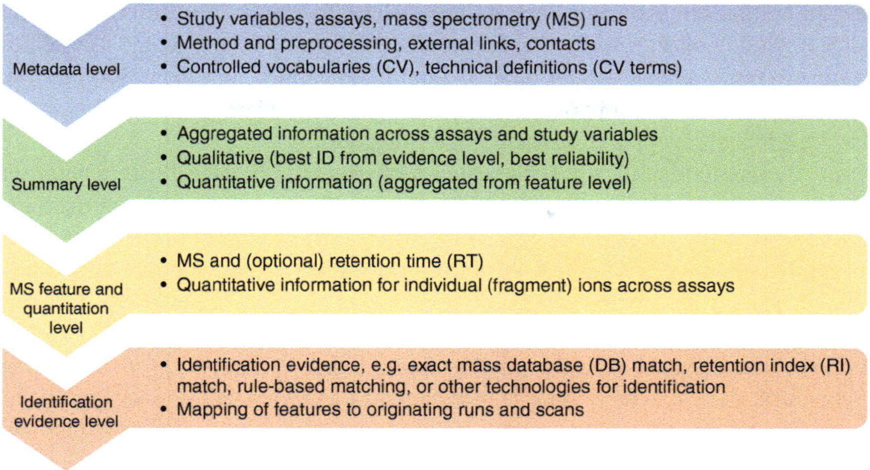

Figure 10.2 Here, mzTab-M is hierarchically organized, from metadata to summary information to mass spectrometry (MS) features and evidence. It captures quantitative and qualitative information about reported molecules for individual MS runs and aggregates across study variables, follows minimum recommended reporting guidelines for omics experiments, and provides structural and logical validation and semantic validation based on controlled vocabulary (CV) terms via its validator implementation.

be comprehensive and intuitive for reviewing by humans and accessible for automated parsing by software. Its structure follows a relational paradigm where several tables are stored sequentially in one file, connected via unique primary keys that identify records in one table, which can then be referenced from other tables by foreign keys to realize a *1-to-n* relation. Spreadsheet tools like LibreOffice Calc or Microsoft Office Excel are compatible to open this file format for reviewing and editing, and since it is not stored in binary format but as plain text, the file handling is highly simplified (Figure 10.2).

The file format specification allows a software developer to interpret the data correctly, check for a valid structure (e.g. missing information), and correctly edit the file, e.g. adding further information such as identification or quantification data.

To adapt the PSI-based mzTab format, the Metabolomics Standards Initiative (MSI) [27] and LSI [28] defined guidelines for the provision of minimum information [4]. Based on the standards set by the PSI, the MSI/LSI devised a standardization process resulting in crucial extensions for the proteomics data formats. This includes, for instance, supporting gas chromatography–mass spectrometry (GC-MS) information in the mzML format or an extended set of CV terms tailored for metabolomics and lipidomics. One of these efforts was to adapt the mzTab format to fully support both lipidomics and metabolomics requirements, resulting in the mzTab-M 2.0 file format [29]. This format follows a strict structure to be both computer-readable and automatically validatable. As depicted in Figure 10.2, an mzTab-M file contains four sections (Metadata, Summary, Features, Evidence), each of which holds elements that report bits of information, e.g. on MS run details, small molecule-related details, such as quantified values, sum formulas, or structures, where available, supported by evidence, e.g. from mass spectral fragments or database hits that support a particular identification.

Another subfield of data handling deals with spectral libraries. Especially for targeted approaches, it is essential to provide the specific precursor reference mass and their corresponding fragments mass over charge (*m/z*) information (transition) for the analysis of the biomolecules. With this information, a mass spectrometer can be programmed to select and record only certain target signals. Usually, this information can be extracted from formats either containing complete measured spectra with annotated fragments assigned to a certain biomolecule (.blib) or a list of fragments with their corresponding *m/z* assigned to a biomolecule (.msp, .sptxt). All these formats are open formats with public specifications. Formats like .msp and .sptxt contain sequential information for each biomolecule with a meta-information preamble, followed by a mass-to-intensity and annotation table. These formats are human-readable and can be opened and manipulated with spreadsheet software. On the other hand, binary formats such as .splib and .blib need to be opened with special tools capable of correctly reading these formats. The .blib format, for instance, is an SQLite database file that can be opened with regular SQLite browser tools. These spectral library formats can be interconverted (e.g. using the Proteowizard tools [30]), with possible information loss.

10.3 Targeted Lipidomics: Assay Design and Raw Data Analysis with LipidCreator and Skyline

The identification and quantification of lipids is a crucial step in analytical lipidomics. In a targeted approach, we most often aim for quantitative information. Here, a small set of lipids of interest is defined; typically, up to 10^2 lipid species and subspecies can be targeted with all their properties, like lipid class and fatty acyl (FA) chain lengths. The advantage is that providing the mass spectrometer with the precise precursor and fragment mass information results in much higher sensitivity during a measurement over an untargeted approach while at the same time decreasing data complexity and thus total data analysis time.

A so-called *transition* or *inclusion list* has to be set up in the first preparation step for targeted lipidomics. This list includes precursor and corresponding fragment *m/z* pairs. It is then directly transferred to the mass spectrometer with the MS platform-specific parameters such as polarity, collision energy, declustering potential, and time of MS/MS acquisition. The manual creation of such lists poses several challenges. First and foremost, each lipid class (head group) has a characteristic fragmentation pattern. Fragment intensities further depend on the number of double bonds, hydroxy groups, and carbon chain lengths. For some lipid classes, the presence of a fatty ether bond instead of a fatty ester bond changes the fragmentation pattern entirely. In addition, lipids can form adducts with several different positive or negative ions, such as ammonia (NH_4^+), sodium (Na^+), or lithium (Li^+) in positive ionization mode and with acetate (CH_3COO^-), formate ($COOH^-$), or chloride (Cl^-) in negative ionization mode. On top of that, varying collision energies change the formation rate of each fragment so that for a given collision energy, some lipids may form many different fragments. In contrast, others may only form a few or just a single fragment. Fragmentation depends on a multitude of properties, but mainly on the gas-phase structure of the analyte ion, its internal bond energy distribution, and thus its stability after activation. To oversee such a vast number of parameters makes method development a challenging and time-consuming task that is prone to mistakes in calculating target masses (m/z) manually.

To address the challenges mentioned earlier, we developed the building block concept for fast lipid structure creation [8] and implemented it in LipidCreator [6] for the quick and reliable generation of targeted lipidomics MS assays (Figure 10.3). Assay generation can be conducted with a graphical user interface (GUI) or by using command-line functionality, covering lipids of the following categories:

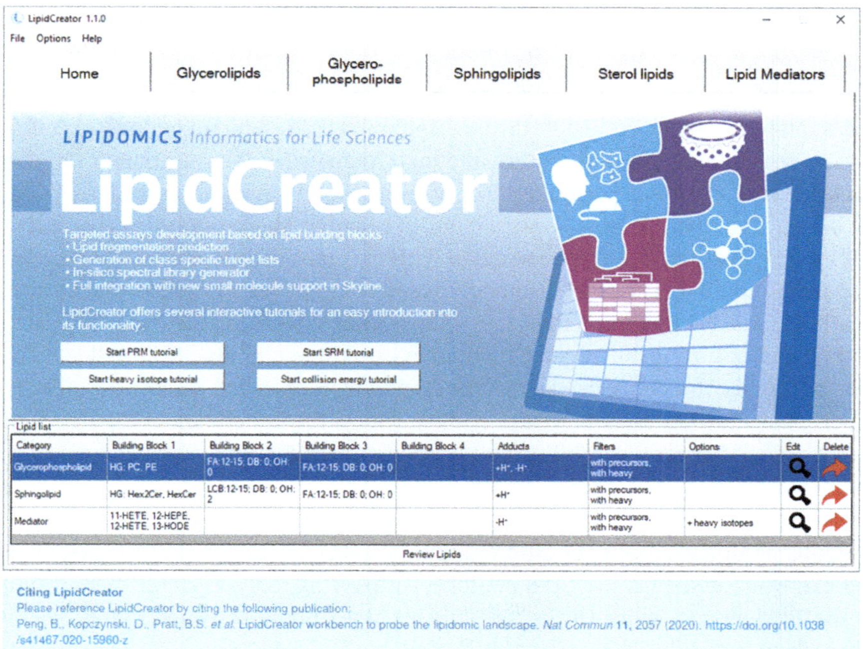

Figure 10.3 LipidCreator provides a user-friendly graphical interface for the five most common lipid categories: glycerolipids, glycerophospholipids, sphingolipids, sterol lipids, and lipid mediators. From the start page, the user has immediate access to four interactive tutorials. LipidCreator can run either stand-alone or as an external tool with bidirectional integration and communication with Skyline.

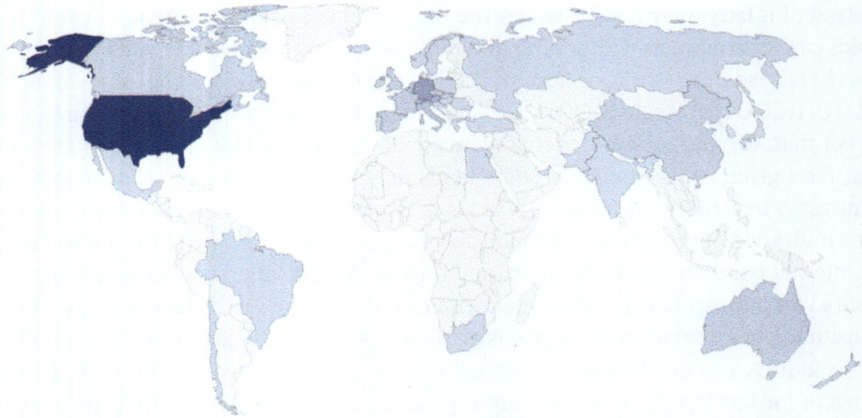

Figure 10.4 Geographic location of LipidCreator users. Data displayed includes unique users from January 2020 to February 2022, with 2662 users in total (light blue less than 200 user, dark blue more than 200).

sphingolipids (SP), glycerolipids (GL), glycerophospholipids (GP), sterol lipids (ST), and fatty acyls including lipid mediators (LM). LipidCreator can calculate mass-to-charge ratios (m/z) for lipid species and their derived fragment ions, including many common adducts and even isotopically labeled lipids, covering over 61 lipid classes and a total number of up to 10^{12} distinct lipid molecules. The fragmentation information was obtained from literature and own fragmentation experiments. On this basis, the computational permutation of precursors and fragments considering double bonds and chain lengths is carried out to calculate the present lipid list. From this list, the lipids of interest are selected with the consensus nomenclature recommended by the LSI. The stable isotope feature of LipidCreator enables the custom creation of labeled lipids and their transitions. After submitting the transition list to Skyline and executing the targeted lipidomics experiment, lipids can be validated by spectral library matching or via their coeluting isotope-coded internal standards, which can be further used for quantification. Due to the integration of LipidCreator with Skyline, different possibilities for absolute quantification, statistical analysis, and downstream quality control systems, such as Panorama (a web-based database for storing targeted assays) [31], are available.

LipidCreator is used in many different countries on all five continents (Figure 10.4) and can be accessed via the LIFS platform (https://lifs-tools.org/lipidcreator.html) or the Skyline tool store (https://skyline.ms/skyts/home/software/Skyline/tools/begin.view). Extensive documentation is available for LipidCreator, such as comprehensive user guides, interactive tutorials, and a quick wizard for simple assay creation. The source code of LipidCreator is openly available under a permissive OpenSource license (https://github.com/lifs-tools/lipidcreator, MIT license), and we are updating it regularly with new features and supported lipids.

10.4 Untargeted Lipidomics: Assay Design and Raw Data Analysis with LipidXplorer

In shotgun lipidomics, lipid extracts are directly infused into mass spectrometers without any prior pre-separation [14, 32]. Two strategies are common in lipidomics analyses: (i) top-down lipidomics is an approach for the identification and quantification of lipids and their variances over a set of samples on intact lipid molecules [33], and (ii) In bottom-up lipidomics, single molecular species or subspecies are characterized by utilizing the ability of mass spectrometers to identify lipids in MS/MS experiments [34]. Breaking a lipid into fragments gives the possibility to measure the individual fragment masses and infer their probable precursor depending on their characteristic fragment pattern. LipidXplorer [13, 14] is designed to support the quantitative characterization of complex lipid mixture samples by interpreting big data sets of mass spectra in shotgun experiments. LipidXplorer can process MS spectra from all types of tandem mass spectrometers, preferably with high mass resolution. The characterization of any ionizable lipid class is possible. Both bottom-up and especially top-down (e.g. for shotgun lipidomics screens) strategies are supported by LipidXplorer. The user defines queries written in the Molecular Fragmentation Query Language (MFQL) by determining lipid class or even lipid species features, e.g. head group mass, the number of fatty acyl chains (FA), ranges for the carbon chain length, and double bond number of FAs, other functional modifications, fragment ion intensity ratios, etc. MS data files are then analyzed according to these queries. Identified lipids are reported along with their measured abundance. Isotopic pattern overlaps are corrected for both MS and MS/MS scans. The MFQL engine compiles a final report of identified and annotated lipid species across multiple samples, along with intensities of user-defined fragment or precursor ions in a tabular comma separated values (CSV) format.

To show the interpretation capabilities of LipidXplorer, we demonstrate its function on total lipid extracts of different platelet sample types using a standard methyl *tert*-butyl ether (MTBE) extraction protocol [35]. The samples are analyzed by top-down or bottom-up shotgun MS experiments performed in different polarity modes. With LipidXplorer, we can generally detect 400 lipid species derived from 21 different lipid classes. Using class-specific internal standards, absolute quantities of lipids in a sample can be calculated. Depending on the MS acquisition mode, LipidXplorer can then conduct the data analysis in either top-down or bottom-up mode. To interpret all raw data, mzML files are generated from vendor raw data using msConvert [36]. These files are then processed by LipidXplorer, which then summarizes the data across samples within the MasterScan file. This MasterScan is composed of the aligned and transformed spectra and evaluated by class specific MFQL queries. To quantify the lipid species, isotopic correction of precursors and fragment intensities is applied (Figure 10.5). We experimentally validated that the quantitative profiles obtained in the independent experiments were consistent across different MS platforms.

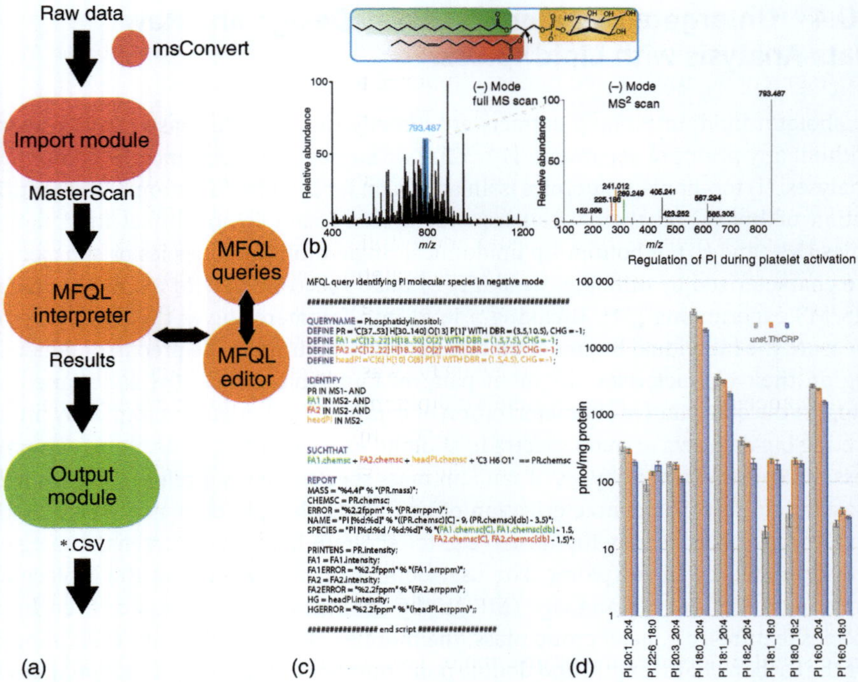

Figure 10.5 General LipidXplorer workflow with MFQL editor and application. (a) Displays the LipidXplorer [13, 14] architecture with its functional modules (boxes) and the internal data flow (arrows). The import module converts technical replicates into a flat-file database, the MasterScan. The interpretation module analyzes the MasterScan with interpretation queries written in MFQL. In the end, the output module exports the results. (b) Full scan of a platelet lipidome and the subsequent data-dependent acquisition of a selected phosphatidylinositols (PI) with its corresponding collision-induced dissociation (CID) fragment spectrum. (c) An MFQL example as it can be designed with the MFQL Editor. (d) PIs are reported in pmol/mg protein at the molecular lipid level after platelet activation with thrombin (Thr) or through the collagen-related peptide (CRP).

10.5 Standardization of Lipidomics Data with Goslin and LxPostman

Data processing includes all intermediate steps from the beginning of data acquisition to the end of data analysis and visualization. For the end user, a predictable and trustworthy processing operation that leads to consistent results every time depends on a reproducible and structured workflow. A clear, standardized structure and proper reporting of all applied steps and mathematical operations are the foundation of this. The standardized approach starts with the lipid identification in LipidXplorer and the detailed reporting with information and data from the identified molecules, as described in the previous section. The identified molecule is reported with details regarding the shorthand nomenclature [17], the lipid class and category, adduct ions, applied derivatizations, level of identification in MS and MS/MS, fragment naming [18], and mass difference to theoretical mass.

Lipid names (or identifiers) that are reported by these tools are designed to encode the chemical structure of lipids to correctly describe and distinguish them from each other. Several lipid nomenclatures have been proposed in the different scientific communities for fatty acyls and lipids. The old, established nomenclature follows the International Union of Pure and Applied Chemistry (IUPAC) standards, e.g. 1-heptadecanoyl-2-(5*Z*,8*Z*,11*Z*,14*Z*-eicosatetraenoyl)-*sn*-glycero-3-phosphoserine. However, more modern nomenclatures were developed to improve adoption of standardized nomenclature by human end users. The shorthand nomenclature [16] introduced in 2013 and updated in 2020 [17] was especially designed to unify existing nomenclatures developed by the MS lipidomics community. It encodes the different levels of descriptive information on lipids by defining a lipid-naming hierarchy, or taxonomy, based on the available resolution of the chemical structure provided in MS analyses. Lipid names are structured according to their lipid class, followed by a description of their fatty acyl chains, e.g. *PS 17:0/20:4(5Z,8Z,11Z,14Z)* on the highest level of structural resolution, corresponding to the lowest level of the taxonomy. Other databases, such as LIPID MAPS, use a derivative of this nomenclature with a slightly different formatting pattern, e.g. *PS(17:0_20:4)* or *PS(37:4)*. These slight differences may cause major issues during a computational analysis, especially when comparing/merging data sets from different origins such as labs or databases. The effect may be that lipid species from different sets are not mapped together because an exact match between *PS(17:0_20:4)* and *PS 17:0/20:4* will fail. To tackle this issue, Goslin [37] was developed for providing standardized lipid names following the most recent lipid nomenclature and common dialects. To satisfy the recent nomenclature, a new version of Goslin [38] was released. Goslin provides both a web application for automatic parsing and normalization based on context-free grammars and libraries for several programming languages (including C++, C#, Java, Python, and R). These libraries provide the main normalization functions and can easily be included in other lipidomics analysis tools. For each of the multiple lipid name dialects, a custom grammar was designed to parse the names, including LIPID MAPS [39], SwissLipids [40], Human Metabolome Database (HMDB) [41], and Shorthand 2020 nomenclature. Providing a simple list of lipid names, the user obtains for each lipid name the normalized lipid name with all its variations along the structural hierarchy, detailed information about the properties (number of carbon atoms, number of double bonds for each fatty acyl chain or long-chain base), sum formula composition, and mass. With Goslin, developers and users of lipidomics tools can easily replenish old data sets, update common databases such as LIPID MAPS or SwissLipids, and provide quality control concerning valid lipid names when adding annotations into a database or identification list or connect different data sets via the normalized name.

One of our tools is also dedicated to satisfying our standardization claims. Once LipidXplorer reports the identified lipids, this information is further enriched in the next step with additional metadata about the study and the individual samples in lxPostman. The application is available upon request at https://apps.lifs-tools.org/shiny as a browser-based web service based on R and Shiny. Group information and quantification of internal standards and normalization on outside variables are part of the standard repertoire of data processing. Applied filtering steps remove invalid identifications, either by eliminating background noise or infrequent identifications across the whole sample group. The used lipid nomenclature is checked, parsed, and converted to the latest shorthand nomenclature by using the Goslin parser. Each software working with processed data expects a slightly different data formatting and extent of information as input. Proper coordination between various tools is necessary by the provision of acceptable data formats. In lxPostman, the data is transformed to the standard formats for LIFS-Tools applications such as Clover and LUX Score and plain *.csv and *.xlsx files for data analysis and visualization in Microsoft Office Excel, Python, R, or other statistical software tools. All intermediate steps, as well as user inputs and changes, are available in a downloadable report file.

10.6 Visualization and Lipidome Comparison with LUX Score and Beyond

Depending on the biological question or the generic exploration of the biological system in different conditions, lipids must be identified and quantified within a sample or measurement and need to be compared as a complete composition, the so-called lipidome, against the other samples within an experiment. Differences in the presence and concentration of lipids across conditions can hint at certain conditions' properties or behavior, which ultimately can lead to the discovery of biomarkers or phenotypic features. In time-series experiments, similar changes in lipid concentrations hint at common biological mechanisms and dynamic behavior and adaptation of a biological system before, during, and after perturbation. From a systems biology point of view, comparing lipidomes of different organisms or mutants can lead to differences in lipid quantities but ultimately also to a loss or gain of lipid species. While analyses within a certain biological system often can be performed with all multivariate data analysis tools applied in other *omics* disciplines, principal differences in lipidome composition cannot be addressed. A metric for the similarity between two lipidomes in terms of such qualitative changes is a challenging task. A simple match or mismatch is insufficient when lipids differ on a structural level. Such qualitative differences can start with deviating numbers or positions of double bonds in lipids or might concern the presence of a complete lipid classes. These compositional changes of a lipidome can be inferred with a proper model for evolutionary and functional adaptation of a biological system by providing a homology metric, which can be in general interpreted like in genomics. The first approach to solve this problem was the introduction of the "Lipidome jUXtaposition – LUX Score" [42] to quantify systematic differences in the composition of lipidomes. To compare whole lipidomes with each other, lipids must first be compared pairwisely. LUX Score calculates a quantitative distance by first converting all chemical lipid structures into a linear sequence representation called the simplified molecular-input line-entry system (SMILES) format [43]. To ensure comparable results between any two SMILES, Template SMILES were introduced where the variable parts of lipid species, e.g. fatty acyl chains or long-chain bases, are dynamically generated and incorporated into well-defined and structured SMILES. Template SMILES are designed to share features of canonical SMILES to reduce artifacts in the pairwise distance calculation. To determine the distance of any two lipid Template SMILES, the Levenshtein distance metric is applied. The outcome is a square distance matrix, with each dimension equal to the number of lipids in the lipidome. A principal component analysis (PCA) then projects the high-dimensional structural space onto a lower-dimensional subspace that better captures the largest variances within a lipidome's species or subspecies composition. The result is either a two- or three-dimensional distance space of lipids (Figure 10.6c).

To compare two lipidome spaces with each other, the Hausdorff distance is applied next, which determines how far two subsets of a metric space are apart. With this method, two or more lipidomes can be compared. By applying a pairwise comparison, again, a distance matrix is generated. Hierarchical clustering is used on this distance matrix, resulting in a dendrogram connecting all lipidomes (Figure 10.6a) to put all lipidomes into relation with each other.

Here, we used the LUX Score to investigate complex platelet lipidomes of mice and humans in the resting, unstimulated state (Figure 10.6a). This experiment determined the lipidome composition of six human individuals and four mice. Our analysis included 360 lipid species from 22 classes, which covers the reported lipidomes [10]. Of these, 174 structures were shared, 127 were specific for human platelets and 59 for the mouse platelet lipidome (Figure 10.6c). Overall, we observed a greater lipid diversity for human platelets. For visualization, a two-dimensional representation was chosen; we here preferred the LUX Score based on the original high-dimensional distances for biological interpretation (Figure 10.6a,b). As displayed in Figure 10.6b, the human and mouse lipidomes have an overall high level of similarity, even under a 50-fold error modeling. Bipartitions in the tree indicate the number of times this partition was present after randomly removing lipids under a predefined abundance threshold. There are differences within the human samples, which could be a hint for sample-specific abundance deviations. However, although the lipidomes between human and mouse samples are overall quite similar concerning the shared lipid species, they are very distinct from each other when it comes to their glycosphingolipids (Figure 10.6c,d). The mouse lipidome only shows some very low abundant *DiHexCer* and *HexCer* species, whereas multiple species can be found in human platelets, pointing likely toward a more polar outer plasma membrane for human platelets. Besides, other interesting properties of these lipidomes are the complexity of triacylglycerols and cholesteryl esters, which seem more diverse for human platelets.

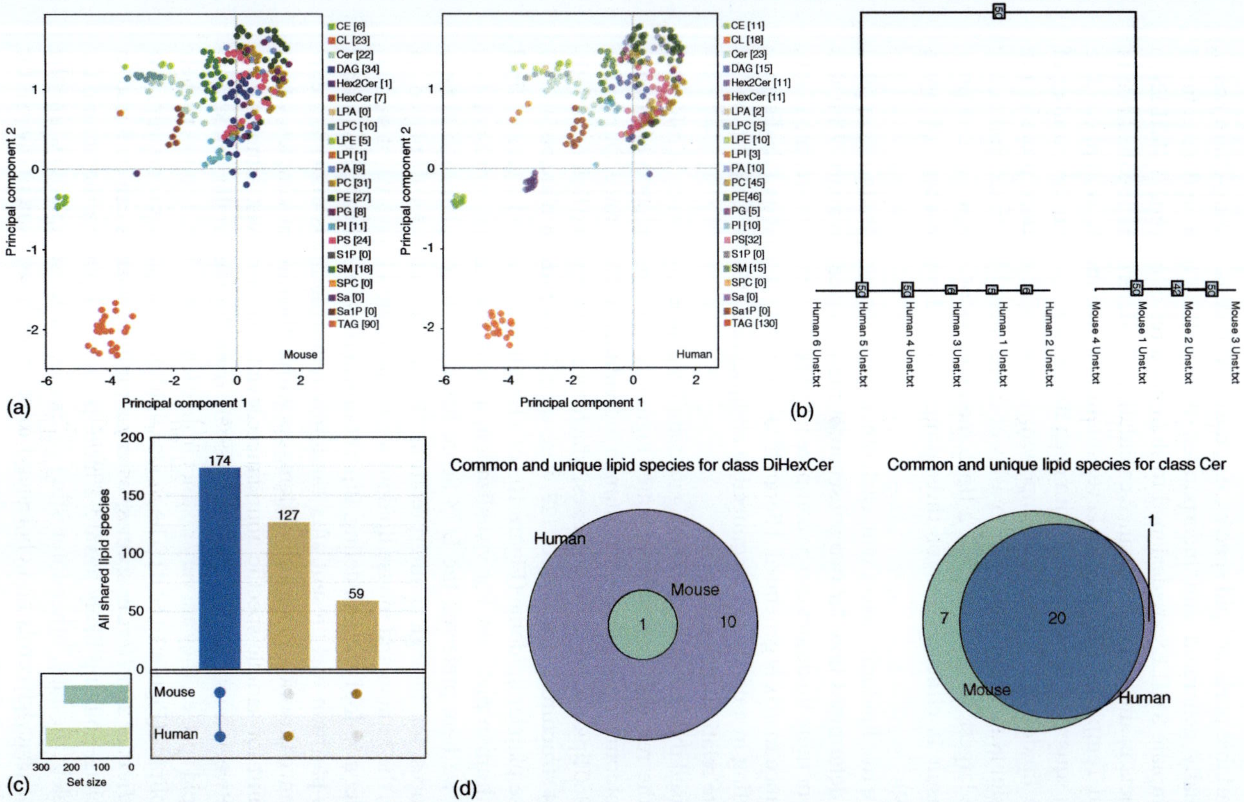

Figure 10.6 LUX Score is the first metric for comparing lipidomes. It measures homology between lipidomes similar to genetic analyses. The LUX Score Browser provides all processing steps for computing the LUX Score from your lipidome data within one software. (a) 2D lipidome maps of the human and mouse platelet lipidome each colored circle corresponds to a unique lipid species. (b) Dendrogram of calculated similarity of human and mouse platelet lipidomes using error modeling. (c) Shared and distinct species within these lipidomes. (d) Venn diagrams of *DiHexCer* and *Cer* lipid species for both lipidomes. The original version is available at http://luxold.fz-borstel.de/. The LUX Score Browser now provides all processing steps for computing the LUX Score from your lipidome data within one software (https://lifs-tools.org/lux-score.html). Source: Adapted from Marella et al. [42].

10.7 Storage in Lipid Databases: What Is Currently There and What Should Be There

Lipid science currently suffers from a lack of suitable tools to report, compare, and visualize lipidomics data sets and to mine the available published knowledge. Until now, no database allows the qualitative or quantitative comparison of experimental data sets with specific attention to the hierarchical nature of lipids. So far, even in the LIPID MAPS [39] structural database, the origin of the reported lipid species is not included, making it very laborious to compare lipidomics data sets vertically (different origins) or horizontally (same origin). Due to this shortcoming, promising results from small-scale studies can often not be compared and validated with more extensive clinical trials or with other model systems, thereby hampering the progress of clinical lipid research.

To foster comparative lipidomics and facilitate the quantitative exploration of lipidomes, we need to develop a data resource for the comprehensive navigation of the quantitative lipidomics landscape (Figure 10.7). The envisioned exploration and

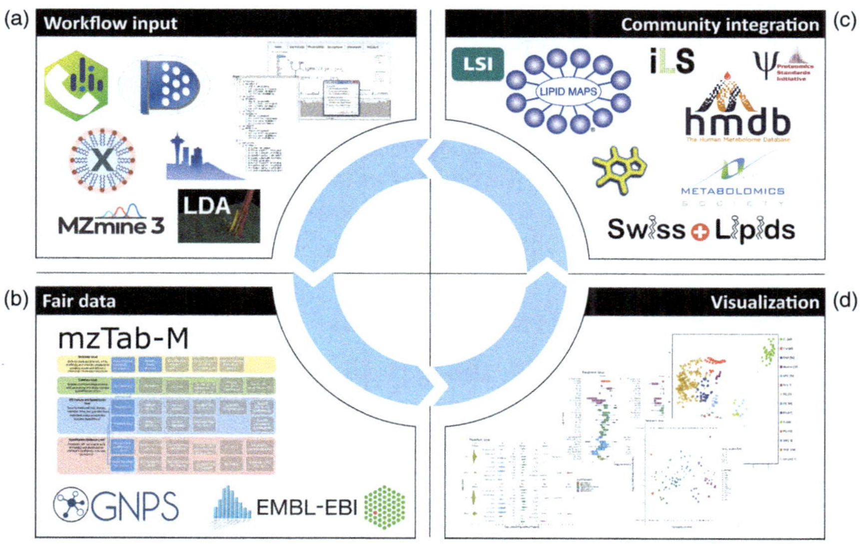

Figure 10.7 Envisioned quantitative lipidomics integration and connectivity to external tools and databases. (a) (top-left) Data for submission can be created with different tools, such as LipidXplorer, LipidDataAnalyzer, or Skyline, covering targeted and untargeted LC-MS or shotgun lipidomics workflows from arbitrary vendor MS instruments. (b) (bottom-left) Data are provided in the mzTab-M 2.0 format with additional requirements for metadata and semantic validation of the data reported. It is also planned to support submission of the data to the MetaboLights repository and then to import it into the envisioned database (which will require mzML and mzTab-M data). (c) (top-right) Lipid names in the database will follow a hierarchical taxonomy that follows the levels of the latest shorthand nomenclature, cross-linking to SwissLipids and LIPID MAPS levels and entries, where appropriate. Cross-links to ChEBI and HMDB provide additional context information. (d) (bottom-right) The quantitative database will provide comparative, comprehensive visualizations that display interactive quantitative and qualitative lipid profiles for compatible studies on user-definable levels of structural resolution.

navigation platform should (i) follow the FAIR guidelines; (ii) provide curated knowledge of measured lipids at different levels of certainty, including their quantitative information; and (iii) follow a hierarchical classification linking the analytical outputs to the appropriate lipid structure levels. Therefore, a first quantitative lipidomics database should provide evidence-supported whole lipidome results. It should allow custom comparisons and visualizations of absolute lipid quantities within and between curated studies. The knowledge about evidence-based species and tissue-specific lipidomes should be transferable across different lipidomics tools to facilitate further assay development or reuse already available data sets. This first comprehensive and comparative platform for post-acquisition, MS-based quantitative lipid analysis should be established in a community-based effort with quantitative database core. This platform will give an overview of lipidomes and will provide a consensus for lipid populations over different tissues, individuals, cohorts, or species.

10.8 Outlook

A solid foundation for a modular workflow for computational lipidomics (Figure 10.1) based on the tools we described in this chapter exists, spanning the processing of lipidomics data sets from raw files all the way to providing quantitative results ready for human interpretation (https://lifs-tools.org). Nevertheless, much effort still must be applied in this field to provide a comprehensive, reliable, and efficient pipeline capable of processing different types of analyses. A truly comprehensive pipeline that covers all mentioned points is not yet fully introduced to our best knowledge. Therefore, we determined the following three major goals for our venture.

10.8.1 Compatible Interfaces Between Modules

Although the lipidomics community already possesses powerful data formats suited to follow the FAIR guideline principles, some information can so far not be stored properly. For example, data formats cannot store information containing experimental designs or the utilized pipeline. Standardizing data storage and processing must gain a much higher awareness within the community. Tools such as LipidXplorer or LipidCreator, or other lipid identification/quantification tools, should update their output concerning the recent updates in the lipid shorthand nomenclature, e.g. by including Goslin. They also should provide more metadata, both from input file formats and from user input. Many ideas for these challenges may be adapted from the proteomics area, which has successfully solved some of these issues [44]. However, not all of them can be transferred immediately due to the different chemical nature of lipids and proteins/peptides in the MS environment. Therefore, good communication and collaboration with developers between both the lipidomics, metabolomics, and proteomics disciplines should be established, too.

10.8.2 Quality Control

A still open and "hot" topic within both analytical and computational lipidomics is the introduction of sophisticated quality control mechanisms. The field cannot compute false discovery rates (FDRs) for their identified and quantified lipid sets. Various state-of-the-art lipid identification tools still have a high rate of false identifications of an MS signal as a lipid. Strategies as they exist, e.g. in the field of proteomics, cannot be easily adopted into the lipidomics domain due to the more complex nature of lipids and their structure compared to proteins and their rather easy digestible (linear) composition. Even without an FDR, the proper use of retention time indices or correlation cross-section within one lipid class should improve the reliability of reported lipid identification with the reported precursor and fragment masses.

10.8.3 Reusability

The interoperability and reusage aspects of public data sets remain open issues within the lipidomics domain. Advanced web-based databases should offer annotated data following standardized formats, offering well-documented interfaces for both human access and application programming interfaces (APIs) for automated, programmatic access. Accessibility and reusage of data should be further established, refined, and simplified. Comprehensive submissions should contain the required information in data formats provided, curated, and continuously evolved by the community. Results of the data sets/experiments should be accessible and visualized properly for quick investigation with cross-links to further information sources that also simplify integration into enriched, semantic web information hubs.

References

1 Pauling, J. and Klipp, E. (2016). Computational lipidomics and lipid bioinformatics: filling in the blanks. *J. Int. Bioinform.* 13 (1): 299.

2 Yang, K. and Han, X. (2016). Lipidomics: techniques, applications, and outcomes related to biomedical sciences. *Trends Biochem. Sci.* 41 (11): 954–969.

3 Schwudke, D., Shevchenko, A., Hoffmann, N., and Ahrends, R. (2017). Lipidomics informatics for life-science. *J. Biotechnol.* 261: 131–136.

4 Köfeler, H.C., Ahrends, R., Baker, E.S. et al. (2021). Recommendations for good practice in MS-based lipidomics. *J. Lipid Res.* 62: 100138.

5 Köfeler, H.C., Eichmann, T.O., Ahrends, R. et al. (2021). Quality control requirements for the correct annotation of lipidomics data. *Nat. Commun.* 12 (1): 4771.

6 Peng, B., Kopczynski, D., Pratt, B.S. et al. (2020). LipidCreator workbench to probe the lipidomic landscape. *Nat. Commun.* 11 (1): 2057.

7 Manke, M.C., Geue, S., Coman, C. et al. (2021). ANXA7 regulates platelet lipid metabolism and Ca^{2+} release in arterial thrombosis. *Circ. Res.* 129 (4): 494–507.

8 Peng, B. and Ahrends, R. (2016). Adaptation of skyline for targeted lipidomics. *J. Proteome Res.* 15 (1): 291–301.

9 Peng, B., Weintraub, S.T., Coman, C. et al. (2017). A comprehensive high-resolution targeted workflow for the deep profiling of sphingolipids. *Anal. Chem.* 89 (22): 12480–12487.

10 Peng, B., Geue, S., Coman, C. et al. (2018). Identification of key lipids critical for platelet activation by comprehensive analysis of the platelet lipidome. *Blood* 132 (5): e1–e12.

11 Scheller, I., Stritt, S., Beck, S. et al. (2020). Coactosin-like 1 integrates signaling critical for shear-dependent thrombus formation in mouse platelets. *Haematologica* 105 (6): 1667–1676.

12 Wegner, M.S., Schömel, N., Gruber, L. et al. (2018). UDP-glucose ceramide glucosyltransferase activates AKT, promoted proliferation, and doxorubicin resistance in breast cancer cells. *Cell. Mol. Life Sci.* 75 (18): 3393–3410.

13 Herzog, R., Schwudke, D., Schuhmann, K. et al. (2011). A novel informatics concept for high-throughput shotgun lipidomics based on the molecular fragmentation query language. *Genome Biol.* 12 (1): R8.

14 Herzog, R., Schuhmann, K., Schwudke, D. et al. (2012). LipidXplorer: a software for consensual cross-platform lipidomics. *PLoS One* 7 (1): e29851.

15 MacLean, B., Tomazela, D.M., Shulman, N. et al. (2010). Skyline: an open-source document editor for creating and analyzing targeted proteomics experiments. *Bioinformatics* 26 (7): 966–968.

16 Liebisch, G., Vizcaíno, J.A., Köfeler, H. et al. (2013). Shorthand notation for lipid structures derived from mass spectrometry. *J. Lipid Res.* 54 (6): 1523–1530.

17 Liebisch, G., Fahy, E., Aoki, J. et al. (2020). Update on LIPID MAPS classification, nomenclature, and shorthand notation for MS-derived lipid structures. *J. Lipid Res.* 61 (12): 1539–1555.

18 Pauling, J.K., Hermansson, M., Hartler, J. et al. (2017). Proposal for a common nomenclature for fragment ions in mass spectra of lipids. *PLoS One* 12 (11): e0188394.

19 Wilkinson, M.D. et al. (2016). The FAIR Guiding Principles for scientific data management and stewardship. *Sci. Data* 15 (3): 160018.

20 Perez-Riverol, Y., Csordas, A., Bai, J. et al. (2019). The PRIDE database and related tools and resources in 2019: improving support for quantification data. *Nucleic Acids Res.* 47 (D1): D442–D450.

21 Haug, K., Cochrane, K., Nainala, V.C. et al. (2020). MetaboLights: a resource evolving in response to the needs of its scientific community. *Nucleic Acids Res.* 48 (D1): D440–D444.

22 Deutsch, E.W., Orchard, S., Binz, P.A. et al. (2017). Proteomics Standards Initiative: fifteen years of progress and future work. *J. Proteome Res.* 16 (12): 4288–4298.

23 Martens, L., Chambers, M., Sturm, M. et al. (2011). mzML – a community standard for mass spectrometry data. *Mol. Cell. Proteomics* 10 (1): R110.000133.

24 Jones, A.R., Eisenacher, M., Mayer, G. et al. (2012). The mzIdentML data standard for mass spectrometry-based proteomics results. *Mol. Cell. Proteomics* 11 (7): M111.014381.

25 Walzer, M., Qi, D., Mayer, G. et al. (2013). The mzQuantML data standard for mass spectrometry-based quantitative studies in proteomics. *Mol. Cell. Proteomics* 12 (8): 2332–2340.

26 Griss, J., Jones, A.R., Sachsenberg, T. et al. (2014). The mzTab data exchange format: communicating mass-spectrometry-based proteomics and metabolomics experimental results to a wider audience. *Mol. Cell. Proteomics* 13 (10): 2765–2775.

27 MSI Board Members (2007). The metabolomics standards initiative. *Nat. Biotechnol.* 25 (8): 846–848.

28 Lipidomics Standards Initiative Consortium (2019). Lipidomics needs more standardization. *Nat. Metab.* 1 (8): 745–747.

29 Hoffmann, N., Rein, J., Sachsenberg, T. et al. (2019). mzTab-M: a data standard for sharing quantitative results in mass spectrometry metabolomics. *Anal. Chem.* 91 (5): 3302–3310.

30 Adusumilli, R. and Mallick, P. (2017). Data conversion with ProteoWizard msConvert. *Methods Mol. Biol.* 1550: 339–368.

31 Sharma, V., Eckels, J., Taylor, G.K. et al. (2014). Panorama: a targeted proteomics knowledge base. *J. Proteome Res.* 13 (9): 4205–4210.

32 Han, X. and Gross, R.W. (2005). Shotgun lipidomics: electrospray ionization mass spectrometric analysis and quantitation of cellular lipidomes directly from crude extracts of biological samples. *Mass Spectrom. Rev.* 24 (3): 367–412.

33 Schuhmann, K., Almeida, R., Baumert, M. et al. (2012). Shotgun lipidomics on a LTQ Orbitrap mass spectrometer by successive switching between acquisition polarity modes. *J. Mass Spectrom.* 47 (1): 96–104.

34 Schuhmann, K., Herzog, R., Schwudke, D. et al. (2011). Bottom-up shotgun lipidomics by higher energy collisional dissociation on LTQ Orbitrap mass spectrometers. *Anal. Chem.* 83 (14): 5480–5487.

35 Matyash, V., Liebisch, G., Kurzchalia, T.V. et al. (2008). Lipid extraction by methyl-*tert*-butyl ether for high-throughput lipidomics. *J. Lipid Res.* 49 (5): 1137–1146.

36 Chambers, M.C. et al. (2012). A cross-platform toolkit for mass spectrometry and proteomics. *Nat. Biotechnol.* 30 (10): 918–920.

37 Kopczynski, D., Hoffmann, N., Peng, B., and Ahrends, R. (2020). Goslin: a grammar of succinct lipid nomenclature. *Anal. Chem.* 92 (16): 10957–10960.

38 Kopczynski, D., Hoffmann, N., Peng, B. et al. (2022). Goslin 2.0 implements the recent lipid shorthand nomenclature for MS-derived lipid structures. *Anal. Chem.* 94 (16): 6097–6101.

39 Sud, M., Fahy, E., Cotter, D. et al. (2007). LMSD: LIPID MAPS structure database. *Nucleic Acids Res.* 35: D527–D532.

40 Aimo, L., Liechti, R., Hyka-Nouspikel, N. et al. (2015). The SwissLipids knowledgebase for lipid biology. *Bioinformatics* 31 (17): 2860–2866.

41 Wishart, D.S. et al. (2009). HMDB: a knowledgebase for the human metabolome. *Nucleic Acids Res.* 37: D603–D610.
42 Marella, C., Torda, A.E., and Schwudke, D. (2015). The LUX score: a metric for lipidome homology. *PLoS Comput. Biol.* 11 (9): e1004511.
43 Weininger, D. (1988). SMILES, a chemical language and information system. *J. Chem. Inf. Comput. Sci* 28 (1): 31–36.
44 Dai, C., Füllgrabe, A., Pfeuffer, J. et al. (2021). A proteomics sample metadata representation for multiomics integration and big data analysis. *Nat. Commun.* 12 (1): 5854.